THIRD EDITION

BUSINESS MATH

Using Percents

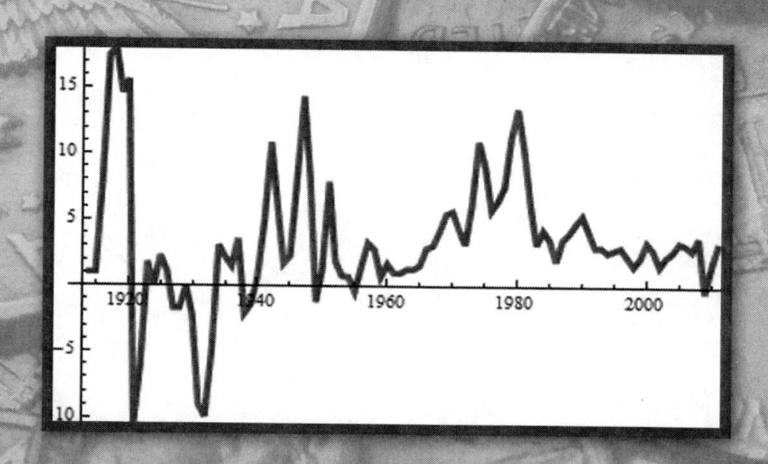

Steven J. Wilson

Johnson County Community College

Backgound cover image © Shutterstock, Inc.

Kendall Hunt
publishing company

www.kendallhunt.com
Send all inquiries to:
4050 Westmark Drive
Dubuque, IA 52004-1840

Copyright © 2001, 2006, 2012 by Steven J. Wilson

ISBN 978-1-4652-0377-9

Kendall Hunt Publishing Company has the exclusive rights to reproduce this work, to prepare derivative works from this work, to publicly distribute this work, to publicly perform this work and to publicly display this work.

All rights reserved. No part of this publication may be reproduced, stored in a retrieval system, or transmitted, in any form or by any means, electronic, mechanical, photocopying, recording, or otherwise, without the prior written permission of Kendall Hunt Publishing Company.

Printed in the United States of America
10 9 8 7 6 5 4 3 2

Table of Contents

Preface

This third edition of *Business Math: Using Percents* is designed for a one-semester post-arithmetic college level course in Business Mathematics. Major features of the text include:

- ▲ emphasis on the use of percentages in business
- ▲ the use of non-algebraic methods throughout the text
- ▲ the use of financial calculators for compound interest and annuity problems
- ▲ graded exercise sets
- ▲ a web site containing additional calculator and current tax information

This course emphasizes the use of percentages in business. After an introduction to percents, topics include payroll, retailing, the value of assets, simple and compound interest, and the time value of money.

This textbook assumes that a student is proficient in the operations of elementary arithmetic (fractions and decimals). Chapter 1 is provided as a review of some of those operations needed in this course. Algebra is neither required as a prerequisite, nor are algebraic concepts taught in this text. Non-algebraic methods are used throughout. This text is not designed to be an applied pre-algebra course.

Upon completion of a Business Mathematics course using this textbook, the student should be able to:

- ▲ understand both the business concepts and the mathematics concepts presented
- ▲ apply knowledge of business math concepts in problem solving situations
- ▲ accurately compute values of business math quantities
- ▲ interpret the results in the specific application, and recognize the implications of the results
- ▲ interpret the results in a historical context

This text endeavors to present business mathematics as an application of a very few mathematical topics, used in many different situations. Most business mathematics topics are applications of percents. Basic techniques in the use of percentages are presented in chapter 2. Business math topics presented in the later chapters will use these basic techniques. We encourage students to recognize the similarities in the different business math topics, rather than offering a plethora of recipes for many different contexts. Therefore, only a minimal number of broadly applicable formulas are used throughout.

There are several major changes in the third edition. Tax rates and information (sections 3.3-3.5) are once again more current. The material on depreciation (sections 5.3 and 5.4) has been rearranged, so that the commonalities and differences in the types of depreciation method are emphasized. The Actuarial Method for applying loan payments has been included (section 6.6) and compared with the U.S. Rule. The material on compound interest and annuities (chapters 7 and 8) has been completely reorganized, in the recognition that the distinctions made for the existence of payments is rather artificial when financial calculators are employed. This has allowed us to present the basic instruction of the different TVM types in chapter 7, and discuss some more advanced topics in finance in a unified fashion in chapter 8. And there have been a host of smaller changes as well.

Technology is prevalent in business settings, and it is our desire that students be able to use the available technology. For problems involving the time value of money (chapters 7 and 8), we recommend the use of a financial calculator. Current prices are less than $30 for the simplest models, which are completely adequate for this course. No particular brand or model of financial calculator is necessary. The focus of the text is on setting up the problems and identifying the variables, not on the keystrokes of the calculator.

It is possible to use this text without a financial calculator, though we do not recommend that approach. The variables still need to be identified if algebraic formulas or tables are used. We do provide the algebraic formulas in the appendix, but those who wish to use tables will have to obtain them from another source. Tables are very limiting, in that each interest rate requires a different table, so a set of tables can never be complete. Algebraic methods are certainly superior to tables, in that every problem can be turned into an algebraic equation. However, solving the algebraic equation for the interest rate presents obstacles which most students at this level find insurmountable. The financial calculator avoids these difficulties.

The exercises of each section are graded by difficulty. One-star exercises provide routine practice of the basic mathematical computations needed. Two-star exercises generally provide routine applications of business math. Three-star exercises may combine multiple ideas, be at a more difficult level, require a fair amount of time to complete, or ask the student to discuss implications of various situations. We believe every business math student should become proficient in solving two-star problems.

One of the most annoying features of any business mathematics book is the speed at which business math material becomes dated. To partially alleviate this problem, we have made available a web site where current payroll tax information can be found. We have also provided some information about specific financial calculators on this web site. Point your browser to http://www.milefoot.com/math/businessmath/.

The author has taught business math at Johnson County Community College for over 20 years, and has long felt the need for a textbook in line with the goals of the course as taught at JCCC. Encouraged by other colleagues in the same situation, he availed himself of a sabbatical opportunity offered by the college to write such a textbook. The author would like to express his sincere appreciation to the Board of Trustees of JCCC for granting sabbatical leave during the spring of 1999 which made this textbook possible. Special thanks for their comments and suggestions also go to Jeff Frost and Libby Holmgren, my colleagues in the JCCC mathematics department, and to the students from spring 2000, fall 2000, and spring 2001, who tested the preliminary edition. Additional thanks are due to colleagues and students too numerous to mention for their comments, corrections, and suggestions over the succeeding years. Their input has helped make the previous second edition (which appeared in 2006) and this current edition a substantial improvement over the first.

1 Fundamentals

1.1 Numbers

Numbers pervade our life. Looking through a newspaper, virtually every article will provide some numerical information. We use numbers to identify items, locate places, compare objects, measure amounts, and assign values. Business transactions are based on exchanges of goods and services of equal value, measured numerically.

There are many different ways by which numbers are expressed. From your previous study of math, you are undoubtedly familiar with whole numbers, fractions, and decimals. In this chapter, we shall be reviewing some of the concepts regarding these three types of numbers. Percents are also frequently used in business settings, and they will receive much of our attention in the rest of this textbook.

Many years ago, you learned how to count. The numbers which we use to count are called **counting numbers** or **natural numbers.** The smallest counting number is 1. You undoubtedly know how to produce the rest, although it would be very difficult to write them all down. When a retail store performs an inventory, part of the process includes counting the items on the shelf.

• • • • • •
1 2 3 4 etc.

The diagram above is a picture of the natural numbers. It ought to remind you a little bit of a number line. We've just left out any number that was not a counting number.

How many calculators does Pete's Stationery have in stock? We would expect the answer to be 11, or 27, or 4, or some other counting number. After all, we could count them. But there is a possible answer which is not a counting number. (No, $2\frac{1}{2}$ is not a possible answer. How could Pete have $2\frac{1}{2}$ calculators in stock?) What if Pete has run out of calculators, and has none in stock? Zero is a possible answer, but it is not a counting number.

The **whole numbers** consist of all of the counting numbers together with zero. Often, the answer to the question "how many?" will be a whole number. The smallest whole number is zero. We can't count zero, since counting always starts with one. But we could give zero a place at the beginning of our number line, and describe zero as the answer if we couldn't get started counting.

• • • • • • •
0 1 2 3 4 etc.

There is an infinite quantity of counting numbers (and whole numbers). If you start counting at one, you can keep going, and going, and going . . . There is no stopping. But after a short while, we have to reuse the same old symbols, called **digits,** since there are only ten symbols in our decimal system. The number *twelve,* for instance, does not have its own unique symbol, but is made up of a 1 and a 2. By themselves, 1 and 2 are pretty small numbers. But in the number 12, the 1 is not worth 1, but 10. We say that the place value of the digit 1 in the number 12 is 10. The **place value** of a digit is the value that the digit takes on because of the place it holds in a number.

To read and understand numbers properly (especially those big numbers like the price of a new car, or the profit General Motors made last year), we must know the values of the different places in a number. Here are the details for a number whose size is approximately equal to the national debt of our country.

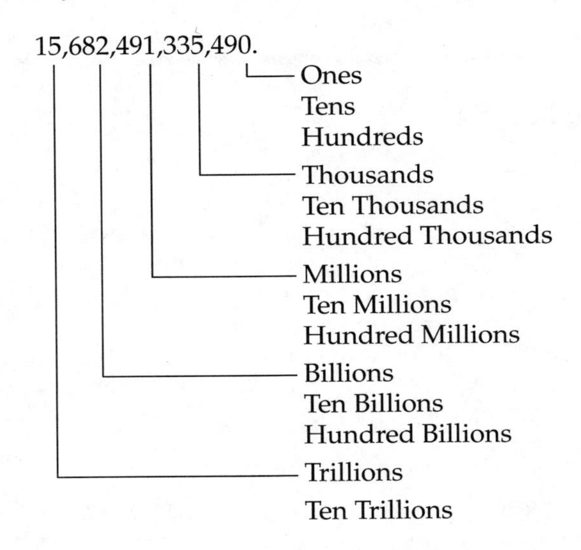

Hopefully, you recognize a pattern in the names of the different places. The word *ten* repeats every three places, as does *hundred*. In fact, that is why the number uses commas every three places, to help us read the number. In the number above, the digit 8 has the value 80,000,000,000, or 80 billion.

Do you remember negative numbers? Somehow, they always seem illusive, since we never count negative quantities. But on a really cold day, the local bank may report that the temperature is –5 degrees. Some people would call this "minus 5", and some people would say "negative 5". Either way, we see "–5" and think "5 degrees below zero". What does this mean? Why didn't Mr. Fahrenheit (or Mr. Celsius) create a temperature scale that would have avoided negative numbers? In any case, negative numbers are here to stay, and we can also place them on our scale.

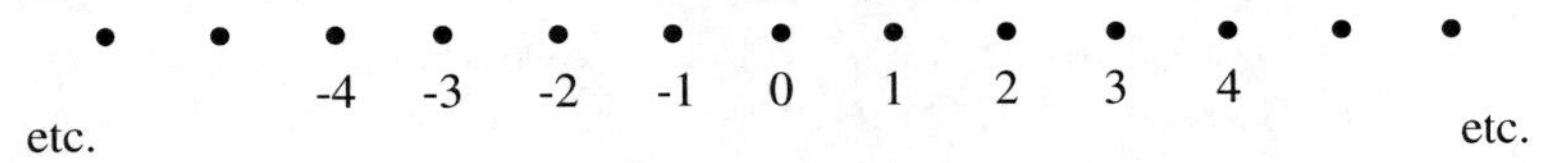

And to allow the inclusion of fractions and decimals, we can connect all of the dots (which are now tick marks) with a line.

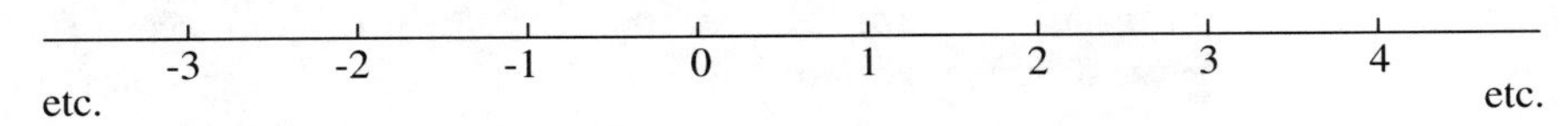

A basic understanding of negative numbers is made easier by the number line above. **Positive numbers** are the numbers to the right of zero on the number line. All of our "normal" numbers are positive numbers. Sometimes we will accentuate that fact by using a positive sign with the number, as in writing +2 for 2. **Negative numbers** are the numbers to the left of zero on the number line. Zero is neither a positive nor a negative number. But zero is still a number.

Negative numbers are the **opposites** of positive numbers, and vice versa. On the number line, –3 is opposite +3, in that –3 is in the opposite direction from zero as the number +3 is from zero. When we use numbers to describe situations in real life, we can use their opposites, negative numbers, to describe the opposite situation. For example, the opposite of increase is decrease, the opposite of profit is loss, and the opposite of "I owe you $5" is "you owe me $5".

"Two out of every five students recommend Acme pencils." Sounds like an interesting advertising slogan, and it certainly contains a pair of whole numbers. But those numbers are not only being used individually, they are being compared with each other. A **ratio** is a comparison of two numbers. Often the ratio will be written as a **fraction,** where one number is placed above another. "Two out of every five students recommend Acme pencils" would become "$\frac{2}{5}$ of all students recommend Acme pencils".

The two parts of the fraction each have their own name. The **numerator** of a fraction is found on top of the fraction bar, and the **denominator** is found on the bottom. In the fraction $\frac{2}{5}$, the 2 is the numerator and the 5 is the denominator.

How many watermelons do you have at home? Chances are good that the answer is either one or zero, unless you have a garden. Or maybe there is a half-eaten melon in the back of your refrigerator. Maybe the answer is somewhere between zero and one, like $\frac{1}{2}$. If so, the question "how many?" was not answered by a whole number, but by a fraction. To see the comparison of the two numbers 1 and 2, you need to think in halves. When the original watermelon was cut into two halves, one of those halves was placed in the back of the refrigerator, and is still there. (Hopefully, you made good use of the other half!)

Suppose you cut your watermelon into quarters instead of halves. If you stored two quarters in the back of your refrigerator, you would have saved the same amount of watermelon, but as a fraction it would be written as $\frac{2}{4}$. It would be easier to think in terms of halves rather than quarters of watermelon, and so most people feel it is easier to use the fraction $\frac{1}{2}$ rather than $\frac{2}{4}$, even though they are equal. The **simplest form** of a fraction is a fraction of equal value that uses the smallest possible whole number values for the numerator and denominator.

To reduce a fraction to simplest form, examine the numerator and denominator to see if they have any common factors (other than 1). If they do, divide the numerator and denominator by those factors.

EXAMPLE 1

Simplify the fraction $\frac{24}{44}$.

SOLUTION

Both 24 and 44 have a factor of 2. Dividing both by 2, we get the result $\frac{12}{22}$. But this is not in simplest form, since both 12 and 22 also have a common factor. We divide both of these by 2 again, and get $\frac{6}{11}$.

FASTER SOLUTION

Both 24 and 44 have a factor of 4. In fact, 4 is the greatest (i.e. largest) common factor of 24 and 44. Dividing both the numerator and denominator by the greatest common factor will always produce simplest form in one step. So we divide and get $\frac{6}{11}$.

Answers expressed in fraction form should normally be expressed in simplest form. However, there are some situations in which fractions should not be reduced. We shall mention these as they occur.

Fractions can also be combined with whole numbers to create **mixed numbers.** For example, suppose you have $2\frac{1}{2}$ watermelons tucked away in anticipation of a party. If you cut each of the whole watermelons in half, then you would have 5 halves, or $\frac{5}{2}$ watermelons. In other words, mixed numbers are equal to fractions whose numerator is larger than the denominator.

In addition to fractions, we can also use decimals to describe numbers which are not whole numbers. Today, with the frequent use of calculators, decimals are probably more commonly used than fractions. A decimal is simply a mixed number, where the place values of the digits after the decimal point are fractions. Here is an example.

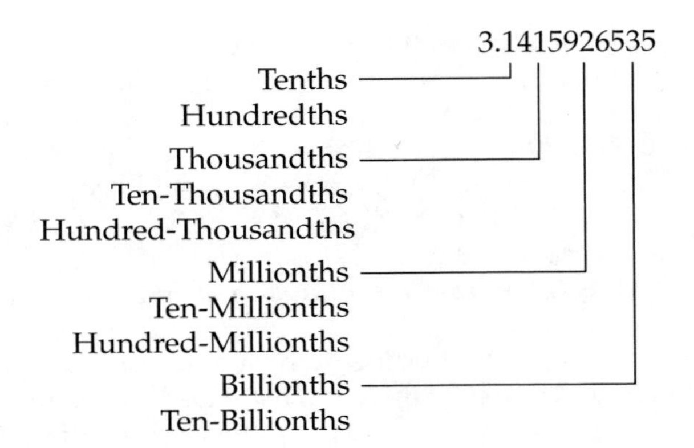

You should also recognize the pattern of place values after the decimal point. The word *ten* shows up in every third place again, just as the word *hundred* does. But the places are not exactly the same as those to the left of the decimal point, they have the suffix *-th* instead. So in the above number, the 9 is in the hundred thousandths place, so it has the value 0.00009, or $\frac{9}{100,000}$, or 9 hundred thousandths.

EXAMPLE 2

In the number 1,325,561.0458537, find the place values of the digits 2, 4, and 7.

SOLUTION

The digit 2 is in the ten thousands place, so its value is 20,000, or 20 thousand. The digit 4 is in the hundredths place, so its value is 0.04, or 4 hundredths, or $\frac{4}{100}$. (This fraction would reduce, but when the question is to determine a digit's place value, we normally do not reduce the fraction.) The digit 7 is in the ten-millionths place, so its value is 0.0000007, or 7 ten-millionths, or $\frac{7}{10,000,000}$.

Once we understand place values, we can read decimals easily. For instance, 0.7 is 7 tenths, 0.358 is 358 thousandths, and 2.68 is 2 and 68 hundredths.

Calculators can frequently supply decimal answers with 6 or 8 digits after the decimal point, or more. Sometimes, we need the accuracy given by those digits, especially if we are in the middle of a problem involving millions of dollars. On the other hand, we sometimes need to round those values, especially if we need a dollars and cents answer in order to make a payment.

Rounding decimals to a particular place is an easy process. Drop all of the digits after the place to be rounded. If the first digit dropped was a 5 or larger, add 1 to the last digit kept. Carry if necessary.

EXAMPLE 3

Round the number 3.74825 to the nearest hundredth.

SOLUTION

The hundredths place is occupied by the digit 4. Drop the digits after the 4. Since the first digit dropped was an 8, add 1 to the 4, it will become a 5. The result is 3.75.

Decimals, fractions, and mixed numbers are three ways of writing numbers. Often, any of the three of them can be used to write the same number. You should be able to change between the different forms of the same number.

Changing a decimal to a fraction is very easy. The denominator of the fraction will be given by the name of the place for the last digit. The number itself, stripped of all commas and decimal points, becomes the numerator.

Changing a decimal to a mixed number is also easy. Only the portion of the number to the right of the decimal point is turned into a fraction. The portion to the left of the decimal point remains unchanged.

EXAMPLE 4

Convert 2.68 to a fraction, and to a mixed number.

SOLUTION

The last digit 8 is in the hundredths place, so the denominator will be 100. Therefore, 2.68 in fraction form is $\frac{268}{100}$. In mixed number form, it is $2\frac{68}{100}$. These are answers, but not in simplest form. If simplest form is required, then we note that 268, 68, and 100 all have a (greatest) common factor of 4. After simplifying, our answers are $\frac{67}{25}$ and $2\frac{17}{25}$.

With a calculator, changing fractions to decimals is very easy. Simply divide the numerator by the denominator, using your calculator. A decimal will result.

To change a fraction to a mixed number, we recommend using the calculator to obtain a decimal first. Keep the whole number part of the decimal. Multiply the portion to the right of the decimal point by the original denominator. The result will be the remainder after dividing, and it is the numerator of the fraction we want.

EXAMPLE 5

Convert $\frac{131}{8}$ to a decimal, and to a mixed number.

SOLUTION

Using the calculator to divide, we can get the answer in decimal form.

$$\frac{131}{8} = 16.375$$

Since the original fraction was in eighths, we can find the numerator by multiplying.

$$8 \times 0.375 = 3$$

In mixed number form, our answer is $16\frac{3}{8}$.

Sometimes, when converting a fraction to a decimal, the calculator will fill its display with digits after the decimal point. Usually, some sort of rounding is in order, but extreme care must be taken to avoid rounding too much. Generally, try to keep as many decimal places as the dollars and cents expression of your problem or your answer would have, until you are done with the problem. If you are expecting dollar values on the order of $300.00, keep five decimal places. If you are pricing a new car at $30,000.00, keep seven places. In particular, avoid the mistake of saying that the decimal value $\frac{1}{3}$ is 0.33, since this will be sufficient only if you are working with amounts less than one dollar!

It is fairly easy to convert mixed numbers to fractions. Simply multiply the whole number by the denominator, then add the numerator. The result is the numerator of the new fraction. The denominator does not change.

To change a mixed number into a decimal, simply turn the fraction into a decimal, by dividing as we showed above.

EXAMPLE 6

Convert $5\frac{3}{4}$ to a fraction, and to a decimal.

SOLUTION

To find the numerator of a fraction, we compute:

$$4 \times 5 + 3 = 23$$

Therefore the fraction form of $5\frac{3}{4}$ is $\frac{23}{4}$.

To obtain a decimal, we divide 3 by 4 on the calculator, and obtain 0.75. The decimal form of $5\frac{3}{4}$ is 5.75.

1.2 Operations

In business situations, one cannot avoid working with fractions, decimals, and mixed numbers. In the last section, we reviewed how to convert between those types of numbers. In this section, we shall review some basic operations of fractions, decimals and mixed numbers, keeping in mind that calculators are available.

When working with fractions, the easiest operation to perform is multiplication. To multiply fractions, simply multiply the numerators to obtain a numerator, and multiply the denominators to obtain a denominator. Reduce to simplest form if necessary.

EXAMPLE 1

Evaluate $\frac{3}{5} \times \frac{4}{7}$.

SOLUTION

Multiplying the numerators, we have:

$$3 \times 4 = 12$$

Multiplying the denominators, we obtain:

$$5 \times 7 = 35$$

Putting these together, we have:

$$\frac{3}{5} \times \frac{4}{7} = \frac{12}{35}$$

The answer is $\frac{12}{35}$.

A **reciprocal** of a number is a second number which, when multiplied by the first number, produces a result of 1. The reciprocal of a fraction is easily found by swapping the numerator and the denominator. For example, the reciprocal of $\frac{3}{5}$ is $\frac{5}{3}$. To find reciprocals of mixed numbers, change them into fractions first.

Reciprocals make it easy to divide fractions. To divide one fraction by a second fraction, simply multiply the first fraction by the reciprocal of the second fraction.

EXAMPLE 2

Evaluate $\frac{3}{8} \div \frac{2}{3}$

SOLUTION

Dividing by a fraction is equivalent to multiplying by a reciprocal. Therefore, we have:

$$\frac{3}{8} \div \frac{2}{3} = \frac{3}{8} \times \frac{3}{2} = \frac{9}{16}$$

The answer is $\frac{9}{16}$.

The next example is a combination of both multiplication and division. Problems of this type will occur frequently in applications involving simple interest.

EXAMPLE 3

Evaluate $\dfrac{13}{17 \times \frac{7}{12}}$.

SOLUTION

We could begin by evaluating the denominator separately, then performing the division indicated by the fraction. With a calculator available, the intermediate step is not necessary. Remembering that dividing by a fraction is the same as multiplying by the reciprocal, we can rewrite the problem. Then we have:

$$\frac{13}{17 \times \frac{7}{12}} = \frac{13}{17} \times \frac{12}{7} = \frac{156}{119}$$

The result is $\frac{156}{119}$. Since the numerator is larger than the denominator, it can be turned into the mixed number $1\frac{37}{119}$.

If a whole number is being multiplied or divided with a fraction, the whole number can be converted into a fraction by placing it over 1. For example, 4 as a fraction is $\frac{4}{1}$.

If a mixed number and a fraction are being multiplied or divided, the mixed number should be converted into a fraction first. Then the rules for fraction operations may be used.

In general, the addition and subtraction of fractions is more difficult. In business math, there are only a few occasions when we need to add or subtract fractions. Most of these times, the fractions will have identical denominators (usually called a common denominator). In this special case, the fractions are added or subtracted by simply adding or subtracting the numerators, and leaving the denominator unchanged.

EXAMPLE 4

Evaluate $\frac{6}{21}+\frac{5}{21}$.

SOLUTION

The two fractions have a common denominator of 21. Therefore, we simply add the numerators.

$$\frac{6}{21}+\frac{5}{21}=\frac{11}{21}$$

The result is $\frac{11}{21}$.

When two fractions are to be added or subtracted, but they do not have a common denominator, then we must first find a common denominator. The common denominator will always be a multiple of each denominator, and multiplying the two denominators together will always produce a common denominator. However, multiplication may not produce the least common denominator, sometimes there are smaller common denominators. When the common denominator is known, we divide it by each of the denominators in turn, in order to determine the multiple needed to convert both the numerator and denominator of the original fraction. Once converted, the fractions can be added.

EXAMPLE 5

Evaluate $\frac{4}{9}+\frac{1}{6}$.

SOLUTION

These two fractions do not have a common denominator. Multiplying the denominators gives 54, which would work as a common denominator, but we notice that 18 is a multiple of both 9 and 6, and it is smaller, so it will be easier to work with. Dividing 18 by 9, we find a multiple of 2 is needed to convert the values in the first fraction. Similarly, dividing 18 by 6 produces a multiple of 3. So we have:

$$\frac{4}{9}+\frac{1}{6}=\frac{4\times 2}{9\times 2}+\frac{1\times 3}{6\times 3}=\frac{8}{18}+\frac{3}{18}=\frac{11}{18}$$

The answer is $\frac{11}{18}$.

Operations with decimals are easily handled by today's calculators. Generally, it is not necessary to handle any decimal operation by hand.

On the other hand, there are some issues which arise when working with decimals. Calculators can provide answers with many digits following the decimal point. Frequently, those answers provide a false sense of accuracy. Decimal answers frequently require rounding, and knowing how many decimal places to keep is not always an easy decision to make.

When adding or subtracting decimals without a calculator, the decimal points are lined up, and zeros can be added after a decimal point. In many practical situations, however, the answer should *not* contain more decimal places than any of the numbers in the original problem.

EXAMPLE 6

Evaluate 147.28 – 35.6.

SOLUTION

Computing, we obtain:

$$147.28 - 35.60 = 111.68$$

In most practical situations, this problem's answer should have only one decimal place. Therefore, we round 111.68 to 111.7.

When multiplying by decimals, you may remember that the number of decimal places in the answer is the sum of the number of decimal places in each factor. In practical situations, however, we should also consider the number of **significant digits** each decimal contains. The significant digits of a number are those digits which are known to carry a high degree of precision in their representation of the number. The answer to a multiplication (or division) problem should *not* contain more significant digits than any of the numbers in the original problem.

Identifying which digits in a number are significant is not always easy. All non-zero digits (i.e. 1 through 9) are significant. Zeros are significant when they fall somewhere between two non-zero digits. For example, 3700 has two significant digits, 0.0185 has three significant digits, and 13.0054 has six significant digits. These rules should be used for all problems whose context or application is not known, when the worst is assumed about the precision of the numbers given.

EXAMPLE 7

Evaluate 3.7×0.0154.

SOLUTION

Computing this product, we obtain:

$$3.7 \times 0.0154 = 0.05698$$

In most practical situations, however, our result would provide a false sense of precision. The two numbers being multiplied have two and three significant digits. Therefore, the answer should not have more than two significant digits. Thus, we round 0.05698 to two significant digits, and obtain 0.057.

Sometimes, trailing zeros are also considered significant, even though there is no non-zero digit following, because the trailing zero is meant to indicate a higher degree of precision. For example, $37.40 would most likely have four significant digits, since monetary values are much more frequently rounded to the nearest penny rather than the nearest dime.

Some numbers are meant to have exact precision, or an infinite number of significant digits. Pure mathematical problems are usually assumed to have exact precision. Numbers in some applied problems will also have exact precision. Suppose, for example, that you borrow a sum of money for the very short term of 6 days. The number 6 by itself would seem to have only one significant digit. In context, a banker will charge for exactly 6 days of interest (even though you may have repaid in 5.9 days). In the interest computation, the number 6 would be handled as if it were 6.000000000 . . . , having an exact precision with an infinite number of significant digits.

Estimation is the process by which approximately correct answers are quickly obtained for math problems. Perfect accuracy is sacrificed for speed of computation. Typically, the estimates are obtained by rounding numbers in the original problem. We shall discuss how problems involving whole numbers or decimals can be estimated.

When multiplying numbers, one common approach to estimating the answer is to round all numbers to one significant digit. The significant digits can be multiplied mentally, and the decimal point can be located by counting decimal places and/or zeros.

EXAMPLE 8

Obtain estimates for the following problems.

a. 482×6231
b. 0.0357×0.4514
c. 32.66×0.0855

SOLUTION

We shall round each of the numbers to one significant digit, and then perform the computations.

In the first estimate, 482 rounds to 500, and 6231 rounds to 6000. Now 5 times 6 gives 30. There are two extra zeros in the first factor and three extra zeros in the second, giving a total of 5 extra zeros. Therefore, the result is 3,000,000.

$$482 \times 6231 \approx 500 \times 6000 = 3000000$$

In the second estimate, the values round to 0.04 and 0.5. Now 4 times 5 is 20. There are two decimal places in the first factor and one in the second, for a total of three decimal places. The result, 0.020, should also have three decimal places.

$$0.0357 \times 0.4514 \approx 0.04 \times 0.5 = 0.020$$

In the third estimate, the values round to 30 and to 0.09, and 3 times 9 is 27. The first factor has one extra zero, and the second factor has two decimal places. When extra zeros and decimal places are mixed together in a multiplication problem, they have a cancelling effect. The extra zero cancels out one of the two decimal places, so the result should have one decimal place, and we obtain 2.7.

$$32.66 \times 0.0855 \approx 30 \times 0.09 = 2.7$$

Division estimates can be handled similarly, but they are much more difficult. The quotient of two digits may not be a whole number. Furthermore, determining the location of the decimal point can be tricky. We shall limit our discussion of division estimates to whole number operations only, and suggest that the calculator be used when decimals are involved.

EXAMPLE 9

Obtain estimates for the following problems.

a. $482 \div 6231$
b. $5883 \div 278$

SOLUTION

As before, we shall round each of the numbers to one significant digit, and then perform the computations.

In the first estimate, 482 rounds to 500 and 6231rounds to 6000. Now 5 divided by 6 is approximately 0.8 (rounded to one significant digit). The two extra zeros in 500 cancel two of the three extra zeros in 6000, leaving one extra zero in the denominator, which provides an extra decimal place in the answer. Therefore, 0.08 is the final estimate.

$$482 \div 6231 \approx \frac{500}{6000} \approx 0.08$$

In the second estimate, 5883 becomes 6000 and 278 becomes 300. Now 6 divided by 3 is 2. Again, two zeros are cancelled in each number, leaving one extra zero, but this time in the numerator. This provides an extra zero in the final estimate, and we obtain 20.

$$5883 \div 278 \approx \frac{6000}{300} = 20$$

When making estimates in addition or subtraction problems, all numbers should be rounded to the same place value (even though this could cause some numbers to be rounded to zero). The place value used in rounding depends on the precision desired. Often, the place value selected is the second significant digit of the largest number, which would give the final answer two significant digits.

EXAMPLE 10

Obtain estimates for the following problems.

a. $482 + 6231$
b. $0.0357 + 0.4514$
c. $32.66 - 0.0855$

SOLUTION

In each problem, we shall round so that the largest number retains two significant digits. In the first estimate, we round each number to the nearest hundred. Our final estimate is 6,700.

$$482 + 6231 \approx 500 + 6200 = 6700$$

In the second estimate, we round to the hundredths place, and after adding, obtain 0.49.

$$0.0357 + 0.4514 \approx 0.04 + 0.45 = 0.49$$

In the third estimate, we round to the ones place. This causes the second value, 0.0855, to be rounded to zero. Therefore, the final estimate is the same as the rounded value of the first number, namely 33.

$$32.66 - 0.0855 \approx 33 - 0 = 33$$

1.3 Graphs

According to ancient wisdom, "A picture is worth a thousand words", and it certainly holds true when trying to describe numbers. Information, or **data,** is frequently displayed in pictorial form. Already, we have seen the number line, a one-dimensional graph. In this section, we shall consider three basic types of two-dimensional graphs: bar graphs, line graphs, and circle graphs. These types of graphs are used whenever items can be grouped into classes, and each class has a numerical value.

A **bar graph** is a two-dimensional graph in which the lengths of bars are used to picture the numerical value assigned to each class. The bars may be aligned horizontally or vertically.

Figure 1.1 is an example of a bar graph, where the average housing price is displayed for five different cities. The length of the bar represents the average housing price for that city and can be estimated by the scale given parallel to that bar.

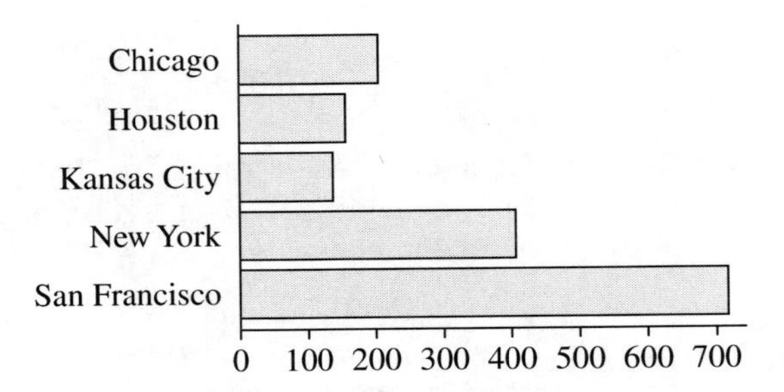

Figure 1.1 Median Housing Prices, 2011, in thousands of dollars

EXAMPLE 1

Estimate the average housing price in each of the cities represented in Figure 1.1.

SOLUTION

Examining the scale on the horizontal axis, we see that the tick marks occur every $100,000. When the right end of the bars is between a pair of tick marks, we estimate the value based on its position. Therefore, we conclude that the average housing price is about $210,000 in Chicago, about $160,000 in Houston, about $150,000 in Kansas City, about $410,000 in New York, and about $720,000 in San Francisco.

None of our estimates in the previous example used more than two significant digits, since the scale only provided one significant digit. Sometimes one significant digit beyond that provided in the scale can be estimated.

Many variations of the bar graph are used. A **histogram** is a bar graph in which the classes are themselves numerical (as in age groups or years), and the bars will usually be placed adjacent to each other, without spaces between, to emphasize the continuing nature of the classes combined. A **pictograph** is a bar graph, where the bars have been replaced by one or more pictures of some object representing the quantity being measured. In Figure 1.1, if we replaced the bars by rows of dollar signs, we would have a pictograph.

A **line graph** is a two-dimensional graph where the distance of a point from the axis is used to picture the numerical value assigned to each class. The points are connected by line segments. A line graph may also be called a **frequency polygon.**

Figure 1.2 is an example of a line graph, where the number of legal immigrants to the United States is given. Each year's number of immigrants was plotted as a point and the points were joined.

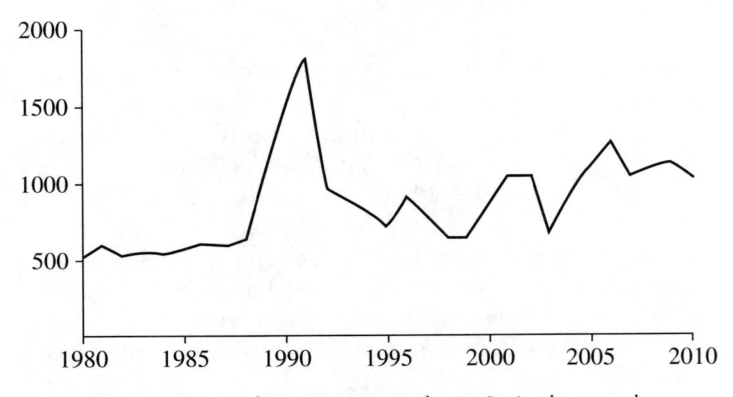

Figure 1.2 Legal Immigrants to the U.S., in thousands

EXAMPLE 2

Using Figure 1.2, in which years did the number of immigrants exceed one million?

SOLUTION

Imagine a horizontal line drawn through the value of one million (1000 thousands) that appears on the vertical axis. We look for those years in which the graph is above that horizontal line. Therefore, we estimate that the number of immigrants exceeded one million in each year from 1989 to 1991, and again in 2001 and 2002, and also in 2005 and in each year since.

Both the bar graph and the line graph use horizontal and vertical axes. In both cases, one of the two axes (the vertical axis in Figure 1.1 and the horizontal axis in Figure 1.2) was used to display the information describing the classes themselves. The other axis (the horizontal axis in Figure 1.1 and the vertical axis in Figure 1.2) was used to show the numerical information related to that class. It is very important that the scale on the numerical information axis be uniform. That is, the scale should start at zero and increase in equal sized increments. If this is not done, then the lengths of the bars (or the distances of the line from the axis) will not be proportional to the numerical information being shown, and the graph could be very misleading. At times, however, the author of the graph wishes to emphasize the differences rather than their values, and may truncate the graphs (start the scale at a number other than zero) for that reason. When this occurs, care must be taken to accurately interpret the information on the graph.

Figure 1.3 gives an example (slightly modified, to protect the guilty) of a misleading graph. As it originally appeared in a magazine advertisement, four brands of trucks were compared and the percentage of those remaining on the road after 10 years was graphed. From the appearance of the graph, one would conclude that Brand 1 trucks are much more reliable. However, the vertical numerical scale is not shown in Figure 1.3, and it was provided only in the original advertisement in very small print. The vertical scale in Figure 1.3 actually begins at 92% (not zero), and increases by 2% per tick mark. In other words, 98% of all Brand 1 trucks were still on the road after 10 years, as were 95% of all Brand 4 trucks. Not a whole lot of difference!

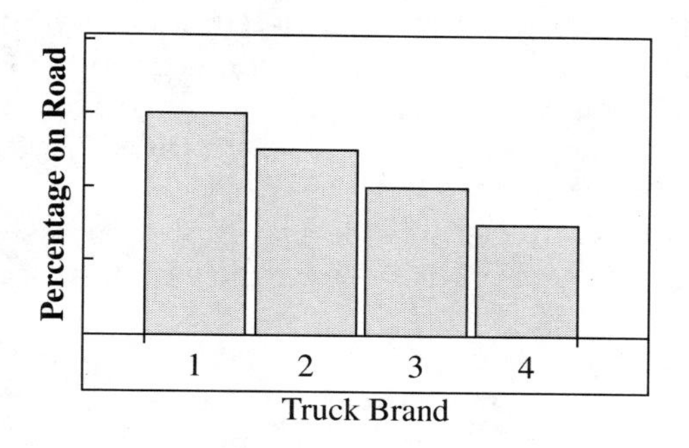

Figure 1.3 Trucks Still on the Road after 10 years

Unfortunately, misleading graphs are all too common in newspapers and magazines. As a consumer of graphical information, you must beware of such presentations. In this class, you will be asked to create graphs which accurately portray the numerical information. Figure 1.3 was provided as an example of what *not* to do and what to look for from unscrupulous purveyors of statistics. Don't take their lead.

Line graphs are also useful in displaying trends over time. Figure 1.4 shows wheat production in the United States. Numerical growth was the fastest during those times where the line on the graph is the steepest. (Percentage growth is not easy to determine from a line graph.)

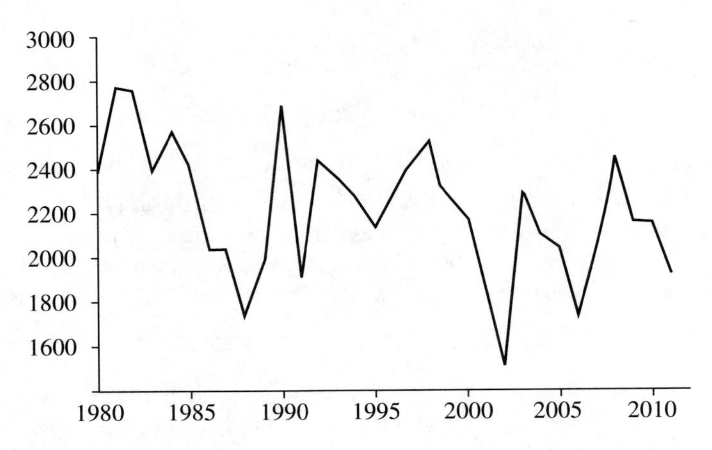

Figure 1.4 U.S. Wheat Production, in millions of bushels

EXAMPLE 3

During which time period (or periods) did the U.S. experience the greatest increase in wheat production?

SOLUTION

The steepest increasing part of the graph appears to occur between 1989 and 1990. The increases between 1980 and 1981, between 1991 and 1992, between 2002 and 2003, and between 2007 and 2008 also appear fairly steep. Therefore, these times were the times of the fastest numerical growth.

You should notice that the vertical scale on Figure 1.4 also does not start at zero. Many graphs are drawn in this fashion, not with the intent to mislead, but to show more clearly the variations between one year and the next. Even though the intention is good, you must still be careful when interpreting such a graph. For instance, the wheat production in 1990 was *not* three times the wheat production in 1988, even though the point on the graph for 1990 appears three times farther from the horizontal axis than for 1988.

A **circle graph,** or **pie chart,** is a two-dimensional graph which shows how various classes form a larger group. This is done by dividing a circle into sectors (similar to dividing a pie into slices).

Figure 1.5 is an example of a circle graph. It shows the distribution of active duty military personnel in the different branches of the armed forces of the USA. The army and navy together account for a majority (probably about 60%) of military personnel. The air force is also a significant segment of the armed forces, with about 25% of the graph.

If you have to prepare a graph from numerical information, you might wonder which type of graph will display your information best. Circle graphs are used when we want to show how the individual classes are related to the larger group. Bar graphs work best when we want to show differences between different classes. Line graphs are useful for showing trends when moving from one class to another. In fact, a line graph should not be drawn unless the classes themselves form a natural progression. Of the five figures provided, only Figures 1.2 and 1.4 displayed classes having a natural progression. Both of these cases displayed data by year, which is a numerically defined quantity.

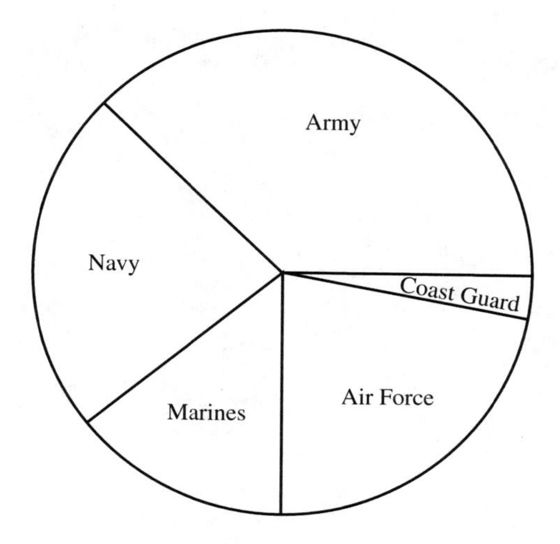

Figure 1.5 Relative Sizes of the U.S. Armed Forces, 2009

1.4 Averages

Our world is awash in data. Businesses need to continually digest the current economic trends in order to remain profitable. But with so many numbers to interpret, how does one keep from being overwhelmed by it all?

Averages can help. An **average** is a number deemed to be representative of the collection of data it is describing. An average may actually be one of the data values, or it may not. In fact, there are many different kinds of averages.

The most familiar average is officially called the **mean.** It is the value you obtain when you add up all of your data, and divide by the number of values you added. If someone refers to an average without specifying which kind they have in mind, the mean is probably being used.

EXAMPLE 1

To determine the gas mileage of a particular automobile model, the manufacturer tested 10 cars of that model and obtained the following data, in miles per gallon.

27, 25, 28, 29, 28, 27, 28, 25, 24, 28

Find the mean.

Solution

We add the values and divide by 10, since there were 10 data values. We obtain:

$$\frac{27+25+28+29+28+27+28+25+24+28}{10}=\frac{269}{10}=26.9$$

The manufacturer will advertise that this particular car model gets 26.9 miles per gallon.

Another commonly used type of average is the **median.** It is found by arranging all of the data in numerical order, then locating the value(s) in the middle of the list. If there are an odd number of values in the list, there will be a single value exactly in the middle of that list. If, however, there are an even number of values in the list, two values will be located in the middle. In this case, we add the two values together and divide by 2.

EXAMPLE 2

Using the gas mileage data from example 1, find the median.

SOLUTION

First, we arrange the data into numerical order. This gives:

24, 25, 25, 27, 27, 28, 28, 28, 28, 29

Since the list has ten numbers, there would be five values in each half. The middle of the list falls between the fifth and sixth values, which we have underlined below.

24, 25, 25, 27, <u>27, 28,</u> 28, 28, 28, 29

Therefore the median is:

$$\frac{27+28}{2}=27.5$$

The median fuel consumption of this car model is 27.5 miles per gallon.

You should notice that the answers from example 1 and 2 were not identical, even though the same data was used. Medians simply find the middle of the list, and the size of the numbers on the ends is irrelevant. The mean, however, takes every value into account and can be influenced by unusually large or small values. In these examples, the mean may have been less than the median simply because a few of the vehicles tested had extra equipment, or simply needed a tune-up.

A third type of average is the **mode,** or most common data value. It is possible for data to have two modes, if a tie occurs when finding the most common. It is also possible for data to have no mode if all data values occur with the same frequency. Despite these disadvantages, modes do have an advantage, in that numbers are not required. You can find an average favorite color, by collecting information on people's favorite colors and using the most common response.

EXAMPLE 3

Using the gas mileage data from example 1, find the mode.

SOLUTION

We shall use the already ordered list of data from example 2, since it will be easier to find the most common response. Here is that list once again.

24, 25, 25, 27, 27, 28, 28, 28, 28, 29

The value 28 is the most common, since it occurred four times, and all other values occurred fewer than four times. Therefore, the mode is 28 miles per gallon.

Averages can be estimated from graphs without estimating all of the data values used to construct the graph. We shall use Figure 1.6 to demonstrate.

The **modal class** is the class with the largest value, and in Figure 1.6 the modal class is a test score of 90. That is, more students earned a score of 90 on the test than any other score. Notice that based on an observation of the graph, it appears that these values were rounded to the nearest ten. Therefore, we don't actually find the mode, since the actual data values were lost when they were grouped into classes.

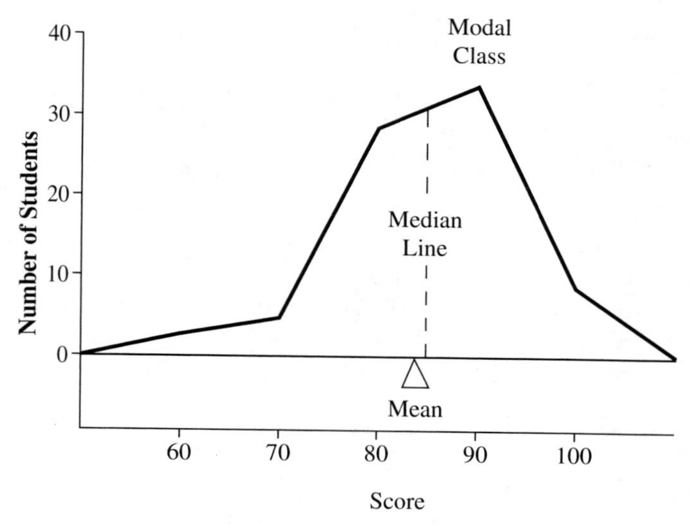

Figure 1.6 Student Test Scores

The median of the student test score data occurs at the point where half of the area falls on one side of a vertical line, and half of the area falls on the other side of that line. The vertical line in the graph above is the median line of the figure, and we estimate that the median score on the test was about 86.

The mean of the data in a graph is the point at which the graph would balance on a fulcrum (like weights on a child's see-saw). In Figure 1.6, we have indicated that balance point, or fulcrum, by the small triangle. The balance point appears to occur at about 84, so our estimate of the mean of the test scores is about 84.

Medians and modes are both conceptually and computationally easier than means, just as they were easier to find on graphs. However, means are still used most often, since they do take into account every value of data. When data is grouped into classes, we must be careful to take into account each value, not just each class. To do so, we can use a **weighted mean,** which averages the data values by recognizing how frequently each value occurs. This is done by first multiplying each score by how frequently it occurs, then proceeding with the mean computation and remembering to divide by the number of scores, not the number of classes.

EXAMPLE 4

Using Figure 1.6, estimate the number of students earning each test score. Then use these estimates to compute the mean test score.

Solution

From the graph above, we estimate that there are 3 students who earned scores of 60, 5 with scores of 70, 29 with scores of 80, 34 with scores of 90, and 9 with scores of 100. To find the mean, we do *not* want to average just the scores, but to recognize that some scores occurred more often than others. Therefore, our weighted mean computation is:

$$\frac{3\times60+5\times70+29\times80+34\times90+9\times100}{3+5+29+34+9}=\frac{6810}{80}\approx85.1$$

We estimate that the mean test score was approximately 85.1.

The use of averages is fraught with difficulties, even when one knows exactly how to do the computations. Consider the following example.

EXAMPLE 5

A company employs 28 individuals. Fifteen of them earn \$8.50 per hour, eight earn \$8.75 per hour, three earn \$9.00 per hour, one earns \$9.50 per hour, and one (the foreman) earns \$25.00 per hour. Find the average wage paid to these individuals.

SOLUTION

The problem does not specify which type of average to use, so we will have to use our best judgment. Let's try them all and see how each fares.

The mode is easy, more employees earn \$8.50 per hour than any other amount.

With 28 individuals, the median would be located between the 14th and 15th values. Since the first fifteen employees all earn \$8.50 per hour, both the 14th and 15th values are \$8.50, and the median is also \$8.50 per hour.

To find the mean, we use a weighted mean computation.

$$\frac{15\times 8.50+8\times 8.75+3\times 9.00+1\times 9.50+1\times 25.00}{15+8+3+1+1}=\frac{259}{28}=9.25$$

The mean wage is \$9.25 per hour.

So which is the most representative? Two of the averages were \$8.50, but \$8.50 is the lowest wage this company pays. Is it possible that the average can be so low that no one is earning less than average? (Yes.) The other average was \$9.25. This also seems pretty unrealistic, since almost every employee would be below average.

It seems unlikely that labor and management could even agree on which of these averages is the most appropriate, if that was the starting place for their negotiations.

Of course, the reason for the large discrepancies in the previous example between the different types of averages is the mean's inclusion of all values (including the \$25.00 per hour wage of the foreman) into its computation. We could decide that this extreme value, or **outlier,** should be removed from the discussion and recompute the averages. In this particular example, the median and mode would not change (they are not generally affected by extreme values), but the mean will be a much more reasonable \$8.67 per hour.

When numerical data is presented in a table, a weighted mean can be used, as it will take into account the frequency of each class. For classes which span a number of values, the midpoint of the class can be used in the weighted mean computation.

EXAMPLE 6

In a sample of 49 houses, the following distribution of floor areas (measured in square feet) was found.

Floor area	Number
800–1200	10
1200–1600	15
1600–2000	12
2000–2400	7
2400–2800	5

Find the mean, median, and modal class of the floor areas of a house in the sample.

SOLUTION

The modal class is the class with the largest frequency. The 1200–1600 class had the largest number of homes in the sample, so it is the modal class.

The median occurs in the middle of the list. With 49 homes, the 25th home is exactly in the middle (24 homes have less area, and 24 homes have more area). The first two classes account for 25 homes, so the 25th home falls at the upper end of the 1200–1600 class. The median floor area is about 1600 square feet (and possibly a bit less).

To compute the mean, we first assume that each house in every class has the size of the midpoint of the class. We compute the midpoints and put them in the table.

Floor area	Number	Midpoints
800–1200	10	1000
1200–1600	15	1400
1600–2000	12	1800
2000–2400	7	2200
2400–2800	5	2600

Now we can compute the weighted mean.

$$\frac{10\times1000+15\times1400+12\times1800+7\times2200+5\times2600}{49}=\frac{81000}{49}=1653.06$$

The mean floor area of a house in the sample is about 1,653 square feet.

1.5 Proportions

Virtually every business math problem can be solved in a non-algebraic fashion. In many cases, the problems can be solved by solving a simple proportion.

A **proportion** is a true equation where each side consists of exactly one fraction. For example $\frac{3}{6}=\frac{4}{8}$ is a proportion, since the two fractions are equal. When reduced, they are both equal to $\frac{1}{2}$.

The **cross products** of a proportion are the results obtained when the numbers in opposite corners of the proportion are multiplied. In the example above, the cross products are $4\times6=24$ and $3\times8=24$. The cross products of a proportion are *always* equal. This fact about proportions gives us the ability to solve (or find the missing value in) a proportion.

Before a math problem is solved, the answer is unknown. Often, a **variable** is used to represent this unknown quantity, and its presence is indicated by giving the variable a name, typically a letter. Common variable names include x, y, P, and r. Sometimes more than one letter may be used for a variable name, as in PV. The name which we give the variable may be an indication of the purpose of the variable. For example, r may stand for rate, and PV may stand for present value. The goal in most math problems is to find the value of the unknown quantity, or variable.

EXAMPLE 1

Solve the proportion $\frac{3}{10}=\frac{5}{k}$ for the variable k.

SOLUTION

Since one pair of opposite corners has only numbers, we can find the cross product of that pair, and it is $5\times10=50$. The other cross product must also be 50, so we must find the number which will allow $3 \times k = 50$. To find that missing number, we can use the operation that undoes multiplication, namely division. The computation is:

$$50 \div 3 = \frac{50}{3} = 16\frac{2}{3}$$

We find the value of k is $16\frac{2}{3}$.

This plan for solving proportions having one variable will always work. In summary:

> To solve a proportion:
> 1. Find the cross product using the corners having numbers.
> 2. Divide by the third number.

In fact, the steps to solve a proportion need not be done separately, they can be combined, as in the next example. Nor does the variable always have to appear in the same place, it may occur in any one of the four corners.

EXAMPLE 2

Solve the proportion $\frac{5.2}{8.9} = \frac{x}{7.4}$ for the variable x.

SOLUTION

We find the cross product, and divide by the third number. Our computation is:

$$5.2 \times 7.4 \div 8.9 = 4.3236\ldots \approx 4.3$$

Since each of the original quantities had just two significant digits, the answer should (unless the context would suggest otherwise) have two significant digits. Therefore, the variable x has the approximate value 4.3.

In the previous example, the quantities in both the numerator and denominator of the first fraction were decimals, but we did *not* simplify that fraction. When solving a proportion, there is no need to simplify fractions before the final answer. Usually, any complications will clean themselves up.

A great many situations involving pairs of quantities lend themselves to proportional analysis. When setting up a proportion, two related quantities must either appear in the same row or the same column of the proportion, but *not* in opposite corners. Then the proportion can be solved for the missing information. The remaining examples in this section will illustrate some of these situations.

EXAMPLE 3

Since 1 inch is equal to 2.54 centimeters, how many inches is 19 centimeters?

SOLUTION

There are three known quantities, and one unknown quantity. The two inch quantities must be in the same row or column, and the two centimeter quantities must be in the same row or column. Since the quantities 1 inch and 2.54 centimeters are related, they must also be in the same row or column. Also, the unknown inches and 19 centimeters must be in the same row or column. These are the requirements in setting up the proportion, and there are many different ways in which the proportion can be written. You should obtain *one* of the following eight proportions.

$$\frac{1\ in.}{2.54\ cm}=\frac{x\ in.}{19\ cm},\quad \frac{x\ in.}{19\ cm}=\frac{1\ in.}{2.54\ cm},\quad \frac{1\ in.}{x\ in.}=\frac{2.54\ cm}{19\ cm},\quad \frac{2.54\ cm}{19\ cm}=\frac{1\ in.}{x\ in.},$$

$$\frac{2.54\ cm}{1\ in.}=\frac{19\ cm}{x\ in.},\quad \frac{19\ cm}{x\ in.}=\frac{2.54\ cm}{1\ in.},\quad \frac{x\ in.}{1\ in.}=\frac{19\ cm}{2.54\ cm},\quad \frac{19\ cm}{2.54\ cm}=\frac{x\ in.}{1\ in.}$$

Next, we solve the proportion by finding the cross-product and dividing by the third number. No matter which of the eight proportions you have written, the computation is:

$$1\times 19\div 2.54\approx 7.48$$

Therefore, 19 centimeters is equal to approximately 7.48 inches.

In the previous example, we went to great lengths to show every possible proportion that could be used to solve the problem. You will notice in any one proportion, the inches always occur in the same row or the same column, as do the centimeters. Similarly, the relationship 1 inch equals 2.54 centimeters always occurs in the same row or column. Unfortunately, there are twice as many ways to set up the proportion incorrectly. (Based on our comments, it shouldn't be hard to find one.) Always be sure that you put related quantities in the same row or column.

EXAMPLE 4

The scale on a set of house plans indicates $\frac{1}{4}$ *in.* = 2 *ft.* Find the length of a room which measures $2\frac{3}{8}$ *in.* on the plans.

SOLUTION

One possible proportion is:

$$\frac{\frac{1}{4}\ in.}{2\ ft.}=\frac{2\frac{3}{8}\ in.}{L\ ft.}$$

To solve this proportion, our computation is:

$$2\times 2\frac{3}{8}\div\frac{1}{4}=2\times\frac{19}{8}\times\frac{4}{1}=\frac{152}{8}=19$$

The length of the room is 19 feet.

Exchange rates are used to convert from one nation's currency into another. Proportions can easily solve these currency exchanges.

EXAMPLE 5

Stephanie changed \$500 into British pounds. If one British pound was worth \$1.5668 at the time of Stephanie's exchange, how many pounds did she receive?

SOLUTION

We can use the proportion:

$$\frac{\$500}{£x} = \frac{\$1.5668}{£1}$$

Note that £ is the symbol for British pounds. To solve, our computation is:

$$500 \times 1 \div 1.5668 \approx 319.12$$

Stephanie will receive 319 pounds and 12 pence, or £319.12.

Name: ______________________________ Date: __________

Exercises 1.1

* In the number 26,750.3894, find the digit in the:

1. tens place

2. tenths place

3. thousands place

4. thousandths place

In the number 739,462.5108, find the place values of the digits.

5. 5

6. 6

7. 7

8. 8

Simplify the following fractions.

9. $\frac{16}{22}$

10. $\frac{20}{48}$

11. $\frac{18}{39}$

12. $\frac{75}{135}$

Round the number 275,384.646752 to the nearest

13. hundredth

14. hundred

15. tenth

16. ten thousand

Complete the table.

	Decimal	Fraction	Mixed Number
17.	2.94	________	________
18.	13.071	________	________
19.	________	$\frac{17}{8}$	________
20.	________	$\frac{47}{3}$	________

21. __________ __________ $7\frac{4}{5}$

22. __________ __________ $14\frac{2}{7}$

Name: ______________________________ Date: __________

Exercises 1.2

* Find the reciprocal of each number.

1. $\frac{2}{5}$

2. $\frac{17}{9}$

3. 4

4. $\frac{1}{8}$

5. 2.92

6. $6\frac{3}{11}$

Evaluate.

7. $\frac{4}{5} \times \frac{1}{2}$

8. $\frac{7}{3} \times \frac{5}{8}$

9. $\frac{2}{3} \div \frac{7}{4}$

10. $\frac{5}{8} \div \frac{1}{7}$

11. $4\frac{2}{5} \times 3\frac{1}{4}$

12. $7 \times 2\frac{1}{2}$

13. $5\frac{1}{3} \div 8\frac{3}{4}$

14. $12 \div 2\frac{2}{3}$

15. $\frac{4}{21} + \frac{10}{21}$

16. $\frac{31}{5} - \frac{16}{5}$

17. $\frac{2}{5} + \frac{4}{7}$

18. $\frac{7}{8} - \frac{2}{3}$

19. $\dfrac{12}{14 \times \frac{3}{4}}$

20. $\dfrac{27}{6 \times \frac{5}{8}}$

21. $6.25 + 13.473$

22. $39.81 - 7.416$

23. 9.85×0.4722

24. $24.33 \div 5.1$

How many significant digits does each number contain?

25. 57.4682

26. 108.509

27. 0.3758

28. 0.00841

29. 2.870

30. 0.10506

Estimate the values of the following.

31. 313×477

32. 612×966

33. 0.5725×0.0481

34. 62.357×0.0911

35. $6923 \div 420$

36. $285 \div 39447$

37. $2890 + 7855$

38. $0.0752 + 4.3375$

39. $16.5225 - 4.8811$

40. $9.25 - 0.8872$

Name: ______________________________ Date: __________

Exercises 1.3

**Use Figure 1.7 to answer each question.

1. Estimate the per capita income of California and of Kansas.

2. How much higher was the per capita income in Hawaii than in New Mexico?

3. Which state had the highest per capita income? How much was it?

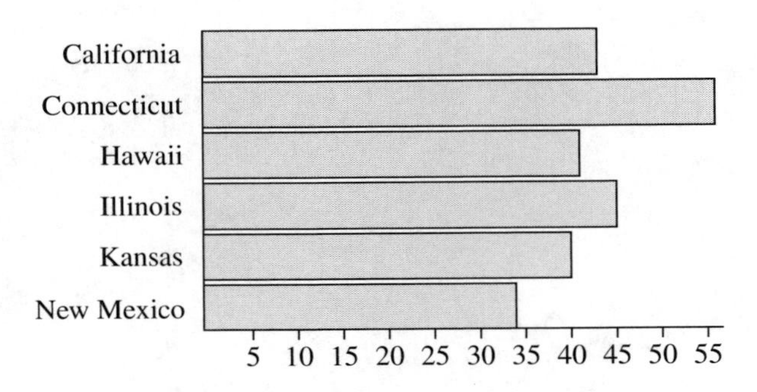

Figure 1.7 Per Capita Personal Income, 2010, in thousands of dollars

Use Figure 1.8 to answer each question.

4. Estimate the number of cases in 1990.

5. How many more cases were heard in 1994 than in 1987?

6. In which year shown did the court hear the fewest cases?

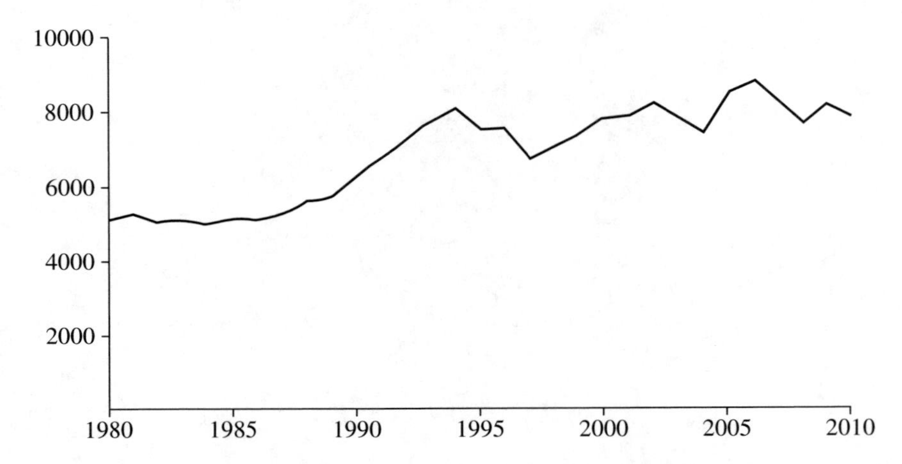

Figure 1.8 U.S. Supreme Court Caseload, in number of cases

Use Figure 1.9 to answer each question.

7. Estimate the number of participants in 1992.

8. How many more people received food stamps in 1995 than in 1990?

9. Explain how this graph can be misleading.

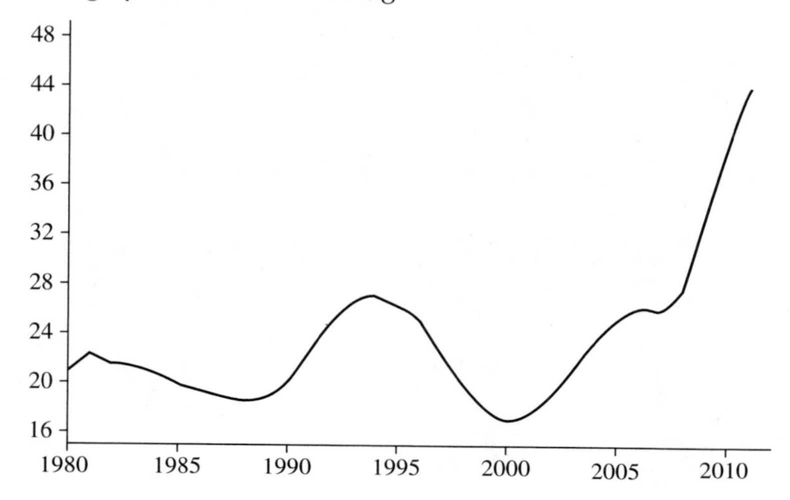

Figure 1.9 Food Stamp Participants, in millions

Use Figure 1.10 to answer each question.

10. Approximately what percent of energy is produced through petroleum products?

11. Approximately what percent of energy is not nuclear power?

12. Approximately how much more energy is produced through natural gas than through hydroelectric power?

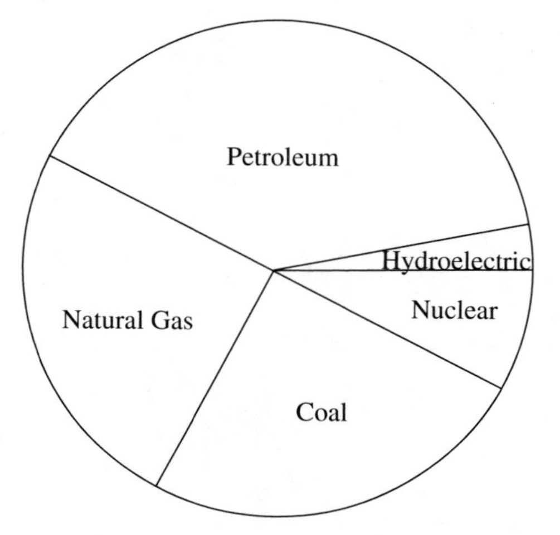

Figure 1.10 Relative Amounts of U.S. Energy Consumption, 2009

Name: ____________________ Date: __________

Exercises 1.4

✳Find the mean, median, and mode of the following sets of numbers.

1. 15, 22, 28, 28, 47

2. 16, 16, 21, 22, 24, 31

3. 71, 83, 44, 57, 45, 69, 57, 83

4. 45, 69, 27, 84, 18, 44, 88, 81, 49

**Use Figure 1.11 to answer each question.

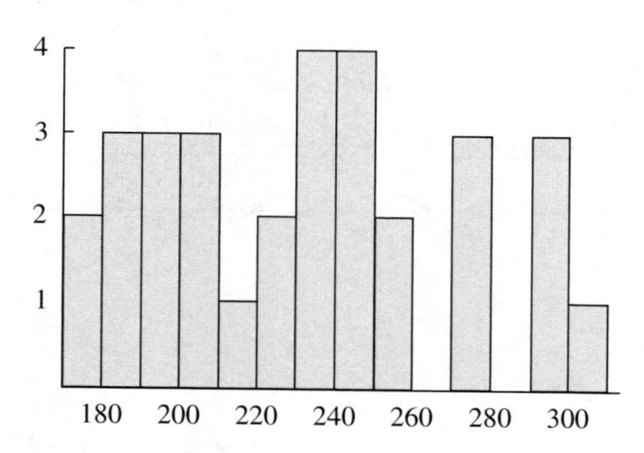

Figure 1.11 Worldwide Tin Annual Production Frequency, in thousands of metric tons per year

5. Estimate the mean annual worldwide production of tin.
6. Estimate the median annual worldwide production of tin.
7. Find the modal class for the annual worldwide production of tin.

Use Table 1.1 to answer each question.

Table 1.1
Highest grade completed by a sample of adults

Grade	Number
8	3
9	1
10	2
11	5
12	21
13	3
14	4
15	1
16	9
17	2

8. Compute the mean educational level of the 51 adults in the sample.

9. Compute the median educational level of the 51 adults in the sample.

10. Find the mode of the educational levels in the sample.

Use Table 1.2 to answer each question.

Table 1.2
Household size, 2010, in millions

Size	Number
1	31.4
2	39.5
3	18.6
4	16.1
5	7.4
6	2.8
7	1.7

11. Compute the mean U.S. household size.

12. Compute the median U.S. household size.

13. Find the mode of the U.S. household sizes.

Name: ______________________________ Date: __________

Exercises 1.5

✱ Solve each proportion.

1. $\frac{2}{5} = \frac{8}{x}$

2. $\frac{4}{7} = \frac{12}{x}$

3. $\frac{x}{5} = \frac{20}{45}$

4. $\frac{x}{8} = \frac{21}{56}$

5. $\frac{4}{x} = \frac{36}{11}$

6. $\frac{5}{x} = \frac{27}{4}$

7. $\frac{2.38}{1.12} = \frac{x}{19.4}$

8. $\frac{5.11}{4.1} = \frac{x}{31.66}$

✱✱ 9. Find the number of quarts in 27 gallons, given that 1 gallon has 4 quarts.

10. Find the number of inches in 22 feet, given that 1 foot has 12 inches.

11. How many pounds are in 375 ounces, if 1 pound has 16 ounces?

12. How many meters in 2,857 centimeters, if 1 meter has 100 centimeters?

13. Since 1 square yard is 9 square feet, how many square feet are in 17 square yards?

14. Since 1 cubic foot has 1,728 cubic inches, how many cubic inches are in 2.6 cubic feet?

15. If 1 pound is 453.6 grams, find the number of pounds in 6,733 grams.

16. If 1 square kilometer is 247.1 acres, find the number of acres in 3.72 square kilometers.

17. Convert $860 to British pounds, given the exchange rate is $1.5668 per pound.

18. Convert 450 British pounds to U.S. dollars, given the exchange rate is $1.5668 per pound.

19. How many Indian rupees are equal to $525, if the exchange rate is 50.28 rupees per dollar?

20. How many U.S. dollars are equal to 6,350 Indian rupees, if the exchange rate is 50.28 rupees per dollar?

21. Find the number of U.S. dollars in 22,400 Japanese yen, when the exchange rate is 83.29 yen per dollar.

22. Find the number of Japanese yen in $900, when the exchange rate is 83.29 yen per dollar.

23. If the exchange rate is $0.1314 per rand, how many U.S. dollars is 1,800 South African rand?

24. If the exchange rate is $0.1314 per rand, how many South African rand is $2,400?

Name: ______________________________ Date: __________

Chapter 1 Review

Summary of Important Concepts

- ▲ Place value, significant digits
- ▲ Fractions, mixed numbers, simplest form
- ▲ Converting fractions, mixed numbers, and decimals
- ▲ Adding, subtracting, multiplying, dividing
- ▲ Rounding, estimating
- ▲ Graphs: bar, line, circle
- ▲ Averages: mean, median, mode, weighted mean
- ▲ Proportions

Exercises

1. In the number 205,367.4819, what is the place value of the digits 2, 4, and 9?

2. How many significant digits does the number 0.0308640 have? Explain.

3. Simplify the fraction $\frac{6}{21}$.

4. Convert 2.04 to a fraction and a mixed number.

5. Convert $\frac{3}{8}$ to a decimal.

6. Convert $3\frac{7}{16}$ to a fraction and a decimal.

Evaluate.

7. $\frac{4}{5} \times \frac{3}{8}$

8. $\frac{3}{7} \div \frac{4}{9}$

9. $2\frac{3}{4} \times 5\frac{2}{3}$

10. $\frac{5}{12} + \frac{13}{12}$

11. $\frac{5}{6} + \frac{3}{8}$

12. $3.16 + 12.0543$

13. 2.701×0.0834

14. Round 344.7725 to the nearest ten, and to the nearest tenth.

15. Find an estimate of 577×391.

16. Find an estimate of 23.474 + 15.482.

17. Estimate the difference in inflation rates between the U.S. and Venezuela using Figure 1.12.

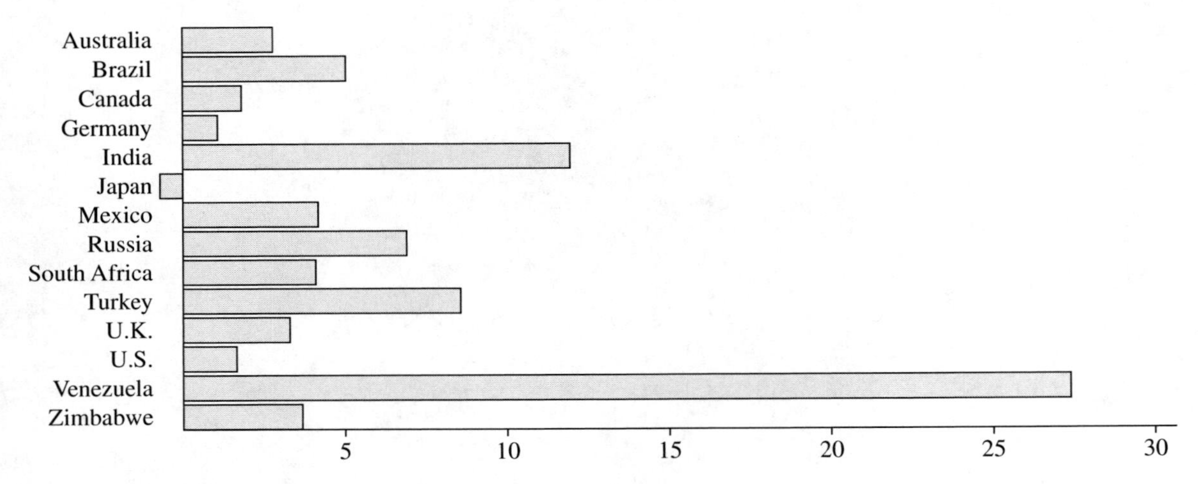

Figure 1.12 Annual Inflation Rates, 2010, as a percent

18. For the numbers 17, 22, 25, 27, 27, 38, 41, 46, and 49, find the mean, median, and mode.

19. Solve $\frac{5}{7} = \frac{12}{x}$.

2 Percents

2.1 Interpretation of Percents

Problems involving business math very frequently require an understanding of percents. We use percents in everyday situations both in our personal lives and in our business lives. Without an understanding of percent, you will never be able to truly grasp many common situations.

Consider the following three statements:

- ▲ During the 2008 election, Barack Obama received 53% of the vote.
- ▲ Tom's earnings place him in the 28% federal income tax bracket.
- ▲ In January, 2012, the average unemployment rate in Louisiana was 6.9%.

How do we interpret each of these statements? We shall take them one at a time.

EXAMPLE 1

Interpret the following statement: "During the 2008 election, Barack Obama received 53% of the vote."

SOLUTION

To say that Obama received 53% of the vote means that 53 out of every 100 voters, or 53 hundredths of the voters, cast their ballots for Obama. The other 47% voted for someone else.

The meaning of percent is incorporated in the above description. A **percent** is a hundredth, or the number of parts out of 100. The word *percent* contains the root *cent,* which is related to the 100 cents that make up a dollar. This idea is the foundation upon which all percent problems stand.

EXAMPLE 2

Interpret the following statement: "Tom's earnings place him in the 28% federal income tax bracket."

SOLUTION

We know that 28% means 28 out of every hundred. But what is the context? Income taxes are paid on income, so we might conclude that out of every $100 of income, the federal government will get $28 tax.

So far, we have incorporated the idea of percent as a hundredth, but taxes are slightly more complicated. The federal tax code allows exemptions to income to go untaxed, and some income may be taxed at a lower rate than other income. So Tom, in the 28% tax bracket, will pay $28 tax on every $100 of a certain part of his income, a lesser rate on another part of his income, and no tax on yet another part of his income.

Although this example did not change how we interpret the number 28 in the quantity 28%, it does bring forth the idea that the percent is based on another quantity. That is, of what were we taking 28%? The quantity to which the percent refers is called the **base.** For a correct understanding of this problem, we needed to recognize that only some of Tom's income is taxed at 28%, not all of it. That is, the base of the 28% is a certain portion of Tom's income. (We will specify exactly what portion in a later section.) For a correct understanding of percent problems in general, we always need to identify the base of any statement incorporating a percent. The base is usually the object following the words "percent of".

EXAMPLE 3

Interpret the following statement: "In January, 2012, the average unemployment rate in Louisiana was 6.9%."

SOLUTION

The unemployment rate describes that portion of the people in the labor pool (all those who are willing to work) who do not have a job. So the base is the number of people in the labor pool. This example says 6.9 out of every 100 people in the labor pool are unemployed. But how can we have 6.9 people? We might want to round and say that about 7 people out of every 100 are unemployed, but the unemployment rate was not given as 7%. So 7 would be wrong. To visualize 6.9 people out of every 100, we need to think of a labor pool ten times as large. In a group of 1000 people from the labor pool, 69 would be unemployed.

By now, you might realize that even though all percents are interpreted in much the same way, the context of each problem will often require you to think a little farther in order to express the meaning of the percent in a suitable fashion. Here are a few more such situations.

EXAMPLE 4

Interpret the following statement: "Tomorrow there is a 30% chance of rain."

SOLUTION

The number 30% means 30 out of 100, but what is the base? Is it 30 chances out of 100? That would be a rather vague answer. The weather prediction is about rain tomorrow, and tomorrow is a day. So a 30% chance of rain means that on 100 days having similar weather conditions to this day's conditions, the weather records indicate that it rained on the day following 30 times. That is, 30 days out of 100 days experienced rain. The base was the number of days with similar weather conditions.

Problems which deal with the likelihood, chance, or probability of a certain event occurring, are best described by assuming the event does occur with that percentage frequency.

EXAMPLE 5

Interpret the following statement: "The credit card offered by BigBank has a 12.9% interest rate."

SOLUTION

Since interest is based on principal (amount borrowed), we would guess that the interest is 12.9 dollars for every 100 dollars of balance. Since dollars are involved, this is more correctly written as $12.90 interest out of every $100 balance. But there is a flaw in this answer. Credit card issuers usually require monthly payments, but interest rates are stated annually. So the interest charged on your monthly statement for every $100 balance would be one-twelfth of $12.90, or $1.08 (rounded to the nearest penny). For every $100 balance, $12.90 interest *per year* will be charged.

This is an example of a rate per unit of time. Interest is often stated with the assumption that the unit of time is a year. Therefore, when other time periods are involved, we either have to adjust the answer, or state specifically what time period we are describing. In other words, for some problems we not only need to know the rate and base, but also the time. We will investigate this situation in later chapters.

EXAMPLE 6

Interpret the following statement: "The inflation rate in Zimbabwe in 2007 was 976%."

SOLUTION

Inflation rates are a measure of the change in prices. Zimbabwe's rate, 976%, means 976 out of every 100. So if a loaf of bread cost 100 Zimbabwean dollars at the beginning of 2007, then the price would change by 976 Zimbabwean dollars during the year. Therefore, the price at the beginning of 2008 would be 1,076 Zimbabwean dollars (the original 100 plus the 976 increase in price).

This example illustrates that percents can be very large, and even larger than 100%. The situation in which the percent occurs determines whether a percent larger than 100% is possible. Obama could not have had more than 100% of the vote (see example 1), the unemployment rate could not be more than 100% (example 3), and the chance of rain could not be more than 100% (example 4). These examples each used the percent to describe a part of the whole. But the other three examples used the percent to describe some aspect of a change, and each of them can have rates over 100%.

Percents form a convenient way of expressing relationships between quantities. When we interpret them, we need to know not only the rate, but also the base to which the rate refers. In some problems, we also need to know the time period used. If we have a good understanding of these aspects of percents, then we can interpret percentages in any context, assuming we are familiar with the context.

2.2 Percent Conversions

In this section, we shall describe the relationship between percents and other forms of numbers, namely decimals and fractions. This is a necessary part of being able to work with percents in problems. We shall build upon the ideas we introduced in the last section when we discussed the interpretation of percents.

Let us begin by converting percents to decimals. Recall that percents describe the number of parts out of 100, or hundredths. Therefore, when we change percents to decimals or fractions, we simply need to change the "percent" to "hundredths".

EXAMPLE 1

Change each of the following percents to a decimal.

a. 35%
b. 128%
c. 3.57%

SOLUTION

Since percent means hundredths, 1% is the same as 0.01, or one-hundredth. Each solution will involve multiplying by 0.01. We have:

$$35\% = 35 \times 0.01 = 0.35$$

$$128\% = 128 \times 0.01 = 1.28$$

$$3.57\% = 3.57 \times 0.01 = 0.0357$$

Therefore, 35% is the same as 35 hundredths, 128% is written as 1.28 in decimal form, and 3.57% is the same as 3 and 57 hundredths.

You may remember from your previous studies that you can change a percent into a decimal by moving the decimal point two places to the left. That still works, of course, but your understanding will increase if you concentrate on the connection between percent and hundredth, which contains the reason why the decimal point can be moved two places to the left.

EXAMPLE 2

Change $36\frac{2}{7}\%$ to a decimal.

SOLUTION

Although you may be tempted to simply put a decimal point in front of the 36, that would not be enough. To change this problem to a decimal, we cannot let the fraction remain. First, use your calculator to change the fraction to a decimal. Then finish the problem.

$$36\frac{2}{7}\% \approx 36.286\% = 36.286 \times 0.01 = 0.36286$$

Therefore, $36\frac{2}{7}\%$ is written as approximately 0.36286 in decimal form.

The appropriate rounding position in a problem like the previous example frequently depends on the context of the problem. Since the example did not have a context (it did not come from a word problem), the proper number of decimal places to keep will depend on one's personal preference. However, if this result was obtained in the middle of some other problem, you may need to keep all of the decimal places your calculator provided, in order to avoid losing accuracy in your final answer. In other words, beware of rounding in the middle of a problem.

Now we will change some percents to fractions. Once again, we simply need to change percents to hundredths, or parts out of 100, but this time written as a fraction.

EXAMPLE 3

Change each of the following percents to a fraction.
a. 12%
b. 300%
c. 7.3%

SOLUTION

Since percent means hundredths, 1% is the same as $\frac{1}{100}$, or one-hundredth. Each solution will involve multiplying by the fraction $\frac{1}{100}$. We have:

$$12\% = 12 \times \frac{1}{100} = \frac{12}{100} = \frac{3}{25}$$

$$300\% = 300 \times \frac{1}{100} = \frac{300}{100} = 3$$

$$7.3\% = 7.3 \times \frac{1}{100} = \frac{7.3}{100} = \frac{7.3 \times 10}{100 \times 10} = \frac{73}{1000}$$

Therefore, 12% is written as $\frac{3}{25}$ in fraction form, 300% becomes the number 3, and 7.3% becomes $\frac{73}{1000}$. Notice that when a fraction was requested, a whole number answer might be provided. When a fraction reduces to a whole number, the whole number is considered to be the correct answer. Also, in part c, we did not leave decimals in our fractions.

EXAMPLE 4

Change $16\frac{2}{3}\%$ to a fraction.

SOLUTION

We will first turn the mixed number into an improper fraction, then proceed as before.

$$16\frac{2}{3}\% = \frac{50}{3}\% = \frac{50}{3} \times \frac{1}{100} = \frac{50}{300} = \frac{1}{6}$$

In fraction form, $16\frac{2}{3}\%$ becomes $\frac{1}{6}$.

On occasion, we shall also need to convert numbers into percents. Essentially, this is the inverse operation of converting percents into numbers, so we use an inverse operation. Instead of multiplying by one-hundredth, we need to divide by one-hundredth. But since one-hundredth can be written as a fraction, and dividing by a fraction is the same as multiplying by its reciprocal, we can multiply by 100 to turn numbers into percents. In fact, since 100% = 1, multiplying by 100% is the same as multiplying by 1, and allows us to put the % sign into the answer. This method is valid whether you begin with a decimal or a fraction.

EXAMPLE 5

Change the following decimals into percents.
a. 0.85
b. 0.006
c. 5

SOLUTION

Since 100% is equal to one, we will multiply each quantity by 100%.

$$0.85 = 0.85 \times 100\% = 85\%$$

$$0.006 = 0.006 \times 100\% = 0.6\%$$

$$5 = 5 \times 100\% = 500\%$$

In percent form, 0.85 becomes 85%, 0.006 is 0.6%, and the whole number 5 becomes 500%.

EXAMPLE 6

Change each of the following fractions into percents.

a. $\frac{4}{5}$

b. $2\frac{3}{4}$

c. $\frac{3}{7}$

SOLUTION

Once again, we multiply each fraction by 100%.

$$\frac{4}{5} = \frac{4}{5} \times 100\% = \frac{400}{5}\% = 80\%$$

$$2\frac{3}{4} = 2\frac{3}{4} \times 100\% = \frac{11}{4} \times 100\% = \frac{1100}{4}\% = 275\%$$

$$\frac{3}{7} = \frac{3}{7} \times 100\% = \frac{300}{7}\% \approx 42.86\%$$

Therefore, the fraction $\frac{4}{5}$ is equal to 80%, the mixed number $2\frac{3}{4}$ is equivalent to 275%, and $\frac{3}{7}$ is approximately equal to 42.86%.

In this last example, we see that some numbers will not change into percents neatly, and may require rounding. As we mentioned before, since this problem does not have a context, (it did not come from a word problem), the proper number of decimal places to keep will depend on personal preferences. But if this result was obtained in the middle of some other problem, you may need to keep all of the decimal places your calculator provided, in order to avoid losing accuracy in later computations.

2.3 Basic Percent Problems

When percents appear in the context of an application or word problem, some quantity related to the percent, or even the percent itself, is to be found. Before we work with applied problems involving percents, we will first study some generic percent problems. There are many valid approaches to solving percent problems. In this book, we will concentrate on the use of proportions, and occasionally introduce simple formulas.

Consider the following three generic percent problems.

- ▲ 40% of 108 is what number?
- ▲ 40% of what number is 108?
- ▲ What percent of 108 is 40?

Each of these problems is different, and each has a different answer. We might notice a superficial similarity, since each problem uses 40 and 108. But there is a more general similarity that we need to notice. Each problem has the form:

Some percent of some number is some other number.

In this form, we recognize that there are three quantities in each problem, described as "some percent", "some number", and "some other number". They also have official names, specifically rate, base, and part, and we will generally use the letters R, B, and P as abbreviations (or variables) for these quantities. So we have:

Some percent of	some number	is	some other number.
R% of	B	is	P
rate	**base**		**part**

The rate is always the quantity which has the percent sign. The base is the total, or whole, to which the percent refers. It typically follows the phrase "percent of". (Sometimes the word "of" will be by itself, and it may or may not be an indication that the base follows. In such cases, you must consider the context.) The part is the portion of the base which the rate is describing. If you have identified the rate and base, then the part is often the leftover quantity, but you must be sure that the number for part is describing the same quantity to which the rate refers.

Percent problems can be solved by use of the following proportion.

$$\frac{R}{100} = \frac{P}{B}$$

We learned how to solve proportions in an earlier section, and this proportion is no different. The presence of the 100 in the proportion is an indication that the rate has already been turned into a fraction. Do not attempt to change the percent into a fraction or decimal when using this proportion, since the proportion automatically takes care of this conversion.

Now we shall consider the three generic examples which we introduced at the beginning of this section.

EXAMPLE 1

40% of 108 is what number?

SOLUTION

The rate is 40, since 40 has the percent sign. The number following the phrase "% of" is 108, so it is the base. The missing value is the part. This gives us the proportion:

$$\frac{40}{100} = \frac{P}{108}$$

We solve this by cross-multiplying, and dividing by the third quantity.

$$P = 40 \times 108 \div 100 = 43.2$$

So 40% of 108 is the number 43.2.

EXAMPLE 2

40% of what number is 108?

SOLUTION

The rate is 40, and the part is 108. We are looking for the base. The proportion is:

$$\frac{40}{100} = \frac{108}{B}$$

Solving the proportion, we obtain:

$$B = 100 \times 108 \div 40 = 270$$

Therefore 40% of 270 is 108.

EXAMPLE 3

What percent of 108 is 40?

SOLUTION

The rate is the missing number, the base is 108, and the part is 40. The proportion is:

$$\frac{R}{100} = \frac{40}{108}$$

Therefore, our computation is:

$$R = 100 \times 40 \div 108 \approx 37.037\%$$

We have found that 40 is approximately 37.037% of 108. We did have to round the answer, and the matter of how many decimal places to keep was one of personal preference.

In the three examples above, we covered each type of percent problem. We found the part in example 1, the base in example 2, and the rate in example 3. But we solved each of the three problems in essentially the same way. For each problem, we identified the quantities, wrote a proportion, and solved that proportion by cross-multiplying and dividing by the third quantity.

Now we shall turn to some applied examples. The process involved is the same as we used in the three generic examples.

EXAMPLE 4

A newspaper reports "Yesterday the new unemployment figures were released, showing a countywide unemployment rate of 7.5%, which is equivalent to 14,350 unemployed persons." What is the size of the labor force in that county?

Solution

Rewriting, we have 7.5% of the labor force is 14,350. Therefore, 7.5 is the rate, 14,350 is the part, and we are looking for the base. We obtain:

$$\frac{7.5}{100} = \frac{14350}{B}$$

This proportion leads to the following computation.

$$B = 100 \times 14350 \div 7.5 \approx 191333$$

So approximately 190,000 people are part of the labor force in that county.

Notice that we rounded the final answer in the previous example to 190,000, rather than keeping the result of 191,333. The accuracy which 191,333 appears to have is misleading, since the rate with which we began, 7.5%, only had two significant digits. So we kept just two significant digits in the result, and rounded to the nearest ten thousand.

You should also notice that we put the original decimal numbers directly into the proportion, and did not convert the resulting fraction. Our goal was not to write the percent as a fraction, but to find the base. So there was no need to remove the decimals from the fractions, as this was only a middle step in our problem. If it was the last step, we would need to be concerned about those fractions.

EXAMPLE 5

Tom is one of several partners in a business. His share of the income (based on his share of the investment) is $37\frac{1}{3}$%. If the income of the business this year is 6 million dollars, what portion is Tom's share?

Solution

Rewriting, we have $37\frac{1}{3}$% of 6 million is Tom's share. The rate is $37\frac{1}{3}$, the base is 6 million, and we need to find the part. The word *million* may be considered as part of the units, rather than a part of the number, in which case the base becomes 6. We obtain:

$$\frac{37\frac{1}{3}}{100} = \frac{P}{6}$$

Solving, we find:

$$P = 37\frac{1}{3} \times 6 \div 100 = \frac{112}{3} \times 6 \div 100 = 2.24$$

So Tom's share of the income is 2.24 million dollars.

In the previous example, the mixed number needed to be changed. Normally, it does not matter whether you convert a mixed number into a decimal or a fraction. But if you opt for a decimal, beware of rounding too much. In fact, unless you use your calculator carefully, you may have trouble obtaining the correct answer with a decimal approach. Use the calculator's memory, and don't reenter decimals, because reentering them often means rounding them, which may produce incorrect results.

EXAMPLE 6

At one company, 34% of its employees are women, and 165 employees are men. How many employees does the company have?

SOLUTION

At first glance, you may be tempted to write "34% of the employees is 165". But this is not correct. In a percent problem, the rate and the part must describe the same quantity. In this problem, 34% describes the women, and 165 describes the men, and these are different quantities.

First, we shall find the rate of employees who are men. The employees are either men or women, and they must total 100%. So if 34% are women, then the number of men is:

$$100\% - 34\% = 66\%$$

That is, 66% of the employees is 165. The rate is 66 and the part is 165 (and both these numbers describe men). Now we obtain:

$$\frac{66}{100} = \frac{165}{B}$$

Solving, we find:

$$B = 100 \times 165 \div 66 = 250$$

Therefore, the company has 250 employees.

The method we have chosen to solve percent problems, namely proportions, has several advantages. Every problem can be solved with this method, every problem is done in exactly the same way, and no algebraic manipulations are necessary. If you have studied algebra, you can also use it to solve every percent problem. There is another useful non-algebraic approach, which generates formulas for each of the quantities you might want to find. This approach is based on the following **PBR diagram.**

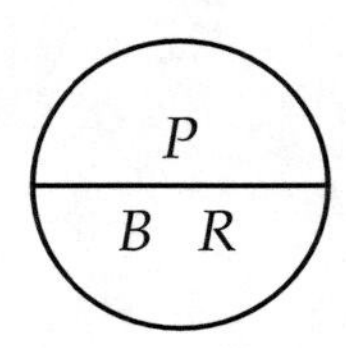

This diagram contains the formulas for each of the quantities in the percent problem. To find them, cover up the quantity you want to find, and what is left is the formula. The **PBR formulas** are:

$$P = B \times R,\ B = \frac{P}{R},\ R = \frac{P}{B}$$

It is much easier to remember the PBR diagram than to remember the three separate PBR formulas. When you use these formulas, remember that percents must be changed into fractions or decimals, and vice versa.

EXAMPLE 7

In one year's time, a $250 deposit earned $8 interest. What was the interest rate?

SOLUTION

Rewriting, we have "Some percent of $250 is $8". The base is 250 and the part is 8. We are looking for the rate.

$$R = \frac{P}{B} = \frac{8}{250} = 0.032 = 3.2\%$$

Therefore, the interest rate was 3.2%.

EXAMPLE 8

Find the sales tax on a $300 chair, if the tax rate is 6.9%.

SOLUTION

Rewriting, 6.9% of $300 is the tax. The rate is 6.9% and the base is 300. The part is missing.

$$P = B \times R = 300 \times 6.9\% = 300 \times 0.069 = 20.70$$

The sales tax is $20.70.

We have now introduced two methods for solving percent problems, proportions and the PBR diagram. The PBR diagram often involves less work, but produces different formulas for different situations. The proportion method solves all problems in exactly the same fashion. Either method can solve any percent problem.

2.4 Percent Change

Percents are not only used to measure parts of some whole quantity, but also as comparisons, or changes, between two amounts. In business, the comparison is often between old and new prices. Percent change problems still have the basic features of base, rate, and part. However, they are different than basic percent problems in that the part is either added to or subtracted from the base to produce a new total.

EXAMPLE 1

The average price of a house in Kansas City in 2011 was $137,000. If housing prices increased 4.7% over the next year, what was the average price in 2012?

SOLUTION

One approach is to find the size of the increase, and add it to the original price. The number 137000 is the base, and the rate is 4.7%. Either proportions or a PBR formula would work. But rather than immediately proceeding to the answer in this fashion, we would like to organize this information in a different way, so that we can apply a new method to any percent change problem.

There are actually three rates and three dollar amounts in this problem (some of which are not yet known), and we shall organize them in a **percent change diagram,** shown below.

100.0%	*Old*	137000
4.7%	*+ Change*	____
____%	*New*	____

Now any two rows of this percent change diagram form a proportion, which can be solved by cross-multiplying two quantities, and dividing by the third. Let's take the first two rows (which happen to contain the rate and base we identified earlier).

100.0%	*Old*	137000
4.7%	*+ Change*	____

Then we solve the proportion.

$$137000 \times 4.7 \div 100 = 6439$$

The increase in the housing prices from 2011 to 2012 is $6439. Putting that information into our diagram, we have:

100.0%	*Old*	137000
4.7%	*+ Change*	6439
____%	*New*	____

The central column of the percent change diagram describes the relationship between the three quantities. That is, the old and change quantities add to the new quantity. To obtain the new dollar amount, we add the old and change dollar amounts. (We shall add the old and change percents also.) This gives:

100.0%	*Old*	137000
4.7%	*+ Change*	6439
104.7%	*New*	143439

So the average housing price in Kansas City in 2012 is the new price, $143,439.

The basic process by which any percent change diagram is solved is summarized by the following steps.

> To solve a percent change diagram:
> 1. The old percent is always 100%.
> 2. If two quantities appear on the same side, add or subtract to find the third quantity.
> 3. Use two rows (having three entries total) and solve the proportion.
> 4. Add or subtract to find any remaining quantities.

EXAMPLE 2

Complete the following percent change diagram.

____%	*Old*	____
9%	+ *Change*	____
____%	*New*	455.62

Solution

First, we know that the old percent must be 100%. That puts two entries in the left column, so we can add them to obtain the new percent, 109%. Now we have:

100%	*Old*	____
9%	+ *Change*	____
109%	*New*	455.62

Now we use two rows of the diagram and solve the proportion. The first two rows won't work, since they only have two known entries among them. We can use the first and third rows.

100%	*Old*	____
109%	*New*	455.62

Alternatively, we can use the second and third rows.

9%	+ *Change*	____
109%	*New*	455.62

Either of those choices has three known entries among the two rows. To continue, we shall choose to use the second and third rows. Solving the proportion, we get:

$$9 \times 455.62 \div 109 = 37.62$$

Now our percent change diagram reads:

100%	*Old*	____
9%	+ *Change*	37.62
109%	*New*	455.62

Since the old and the change add to the new, we can find the old by subtracting the change from the new. Then the completed diagram is:

100%	*Old*	418.00
9%	+ *Change*	37.62
109%	*New*	455.62

There are several advantages to using percent change diagrams. First, as we mentioned before, the diagram is an organizational tool. That is, it will help you sort out and identify the various information provided in a word problem involving a percent change. Fewer errors in identification will occur when you realize that there are actually six quantities involved in a percent change problem. Second, any missing quantity in a percent change diagram can be found, as long as there are two known quantities (in addition to the 100%), and at least one of them is in the dollar column. Third, the diagram works for both percent increase and percent decrease problems. (Simply change the sign from + to – on the change line.) Fourth, the process by which percent change diagrams are solved, which we described above, is essentially the same in every problem. The only real disadvantage is that the process may be slower than other methods.

EXAMPLE 3

A 7″ television originally sells for $299, but the dealer marks the price down 20% for a sale. What is the sale price?

SOLUTION

The percent change diagram in this situation would be:

____%	*Old*	299.00
20%	– *Change*	____
____%	*New*	____

Notice that the change is subtracted, since the price is being marked down. The old percent is always 100%, so that makes the new percent 80%. We want to find the new (sale) price, so we shall use the first and third rows of the following percent change diagram.

100%	*Old*	299.00
20%	– *Change*	____
80%	*New*	____

Then we solve the proportion.

$$80 \times 299 \div 100 = 239.20$$

Therefore, the sale price is $239.20.

You might notice that we did not complete the percent change diagram above. Since the question asked only for a specific component of that diagram, we solved the problem only as far as we needed.

EXAMPLE 4

After a 22% increase, a lawn tractor sells for $1,785. What was the original price?

SOLUTION

After including the 100% base and completing the percent column, the percent change diagram is:

100%	*Old*	______
22%	*+ Change*	______
122%	*New*	1785.00

Since we want to find the original, or old, price, we will solve the proportion using the first and third rows. This gives:

$$1785 \times 100 \div 122 \approx 1463.11$$

The original price of the lawn tractor was $1,463.11, before the 22% increase.

Although it might seem very tempting, the above example can not be done by subtracting 22% from the new price. Every rate has a base, and in a percent change problem the base is always the old price, and never the new price. So we can't take 22% of the new price and subtract; it simply won't work.

EXAMPLE 5

Sales at Marla's Music were $292,000 last month, and $328,000 this month. What was the percent increase in sales?

SOLUTION

The percent change diagram is:

100%	*Old*	292000
_____%	*+ Change*	______
_____%	*New*	328000

Using the first and third rows and solving the proportion, we get:

$$100 \times 328000 \div 292000 \approx 112.33$$

This result is the new percent, but our question is asking for the percent change. So we subtract the old percent from the new.

$$112.33 - 100 = 12.33$$

Therefore, there was a 12.33% increase in sales.

As we previously mentioned, the percent change diagram method is not necessarily fast, but it does always work. Since many percent change problems involve finding the new dollar amount from the old, given a percent change, we should consider a more efficient way of handling this type of problem. A PBR formula will work, and will be very fast if we choose the new percent as the rate.

In a percent decrease problem, the new percent is always obtained by subtracting the change percent from 100%, and is referred to as the **complement** of the change percent. For example, 80% is the complement of 20%.

EXAMPLE 6

Tina earns $833 per week, but 29% of it is withheld for taxes. What is her pay after taxes?

SOLUTION

Since 29% is withheld, Tina retains the complement of 29%, or 71%, of her income. So we use 71% as the rate, and 833 as the base. We get:

$$P = B \times R = 833 \times 0.71 = 591.43$$

Tina's net pay is $591.43 per week.

In a percent increase problem, the new percent is obtained by adding the change percent to 100%. We shall refer to this new percent as an **augmented percent.** For example, 120% is the augmented percent of 20%.

EXAMPLE 7

Carol's purchases at the grocery store subtotal $135.42, before the 5.5% sales tax is added. What is the total after sales tax is added?

SOLUTION

Carol must pay the subtotal plus tax. So the rate is 5.5% augmented, or 105.5%, of the $135.42 subtotal. Using a PBR formula, we get:

$$P = B \times R = 135.42 \times 1.055 \approx 142.87$$

The total, including tax, is $142.87.

2.5 Compounding of Percents

Many situations exist where two or more percent changes must be performed on the same quantity. When percents are **compounded,** or several percent changes occur in succession, they must be handled carefully to avoid incorrect results. Intuitive reasoning misleads many people, because wrong answers are easy to obtain. But when you have understood the basic concepts behind rate and base, the reason that compounding produces nonintuitive results will become clear.

Tom received a 10% raise last year, and another 10% raise this year. What was the percent increase in his salary for the two-year period?

SOLUTION

We do not know Tom's original salary. Actually, it doesn't matter what his original salary was, so we can pick an arbitrary number. Let's suppose he earned $24,000 last year. We can find his new salary by using augmented percents. For two years, we need to do this multiplication twice. So we obtain:

$$24000 \times 1.10 \times 1.10 = 29040$$

Tom's salary in two years will be $29,040, if it was $24,000 last year. We can determine the percent increase by using the following percent change diagram.

100%	*Old*	24000
_____%	*+ Change*	_____
_____%	*New*	29040

Using the first and third rows, and solving the proportion, we get:

$$29040 \times 100 \div 24000 = 121$$

Therefore, the new percent is 121%, and Tom received a 21% increase.

When the two 10% raises were combined, the answer was *not* 20%. Surprised? There are several ways by which we can recognize why the percent increases did not add. Tom's first 10% raise was 10% of last year's salary, but his second 10% raise was 10% of this year's salary. The bases were different. In other words, the two percents were not equal, even though they were both 10%.

There is a faster way in which percent changes can be combined. Toward the beginning of the process of solving the problem, we had written the following computation.

$$24000 \times 1.10 \times 1.10 = 29040$$

That computation was straightforward, but if we had stopped and thought a minute, we might have realized that we were very close to having the final answer. Instead of multiplying from left to right, if we had chosen to multiply the augmented percents first, we would have obtained:

$$24000 \times 1.21 = 29040$$

In percent form, 1.21 is 121%, which is the augmented percent of 21%. The percent increase over the two-year period was 21%. In fact, using this analysis, we see that the $24,000 salary really does not matter.

Whenever percents are to be compounded, (that is, two or more percent changes are to be combined consecutively), a simple computation can be done. Percent increases are turned into augmented percents, and percent decreases are turned into complements. Augmented percents and complements can be multiplied. The result of this multiplication is either the augmented percent or the complement of the final answer.

EXAMPLE 2

When Bob purchased pencil sharpeners to place in his store's inventory, his supplier gave him a 15% discount, followed by a 5% discount. What was the total discount?

SOLUTION

The 15% discount means Bob paid the complement, or 85%, of the quoted price, and the 5% discount means Bob paid 95% of the discounted price. We don't know the quoted price, nor do we need to know it. The complements can be multiplied.

$$0.85 \times 0.95 = 0.8075$$

In percent form, 0.8075 is 80.75%, which is the complement of 19.25%. So Bob received a total discount of 19.25%.

Many people are at first deceived by the next example, which combines a percent increase and percent decrease.

EXAMPLE 3

A bookcase originally costs a dealer $50. The dealer marks it up 20% above his cost, and later reduces it 20% for a sale. What is the sale price?

SOLUTION

If you are tempted to say $50, think again. The rates do *not* cancel each other out. The markup of 20% produces an augmented percent of 120%. That makes the new (before the sale) price:

$$P = B \times R = 50 \times 1.20 = 60$$

The reduction by 20% gives a complement of 80% for the customer to pay. Then we have:

$$P = B \times R = 60 \times 0.80 = 48$$

So the sale price is $48, not $50.

Why didn't the 20% decrease cancel out the 20% increase? Because the base had changed. The 20% increase was based on a different price than the 20% decrease. In fact, we can approach this problem using augmented percents and complements as we did the previous two examples. The computation is:

$$1.20 \times 0.80 = 0.96$$

Now 0.96 is 96%, which is the complement of 4%. Therefore, a 20% increase followed by a 20% decrease (or vice versa) always produces a 4% decrease. The implication of this result is important.

> Percent decreases will *NOT* cancel out percent increases, and vice versa.

EXAMPLE 4

A dealer normally marks up his merchandise 30% above his cost. What percent markdown from regular price can he advertise, if he wants to place merchandise on sale at his cost?

Solution

No dollar amounts are given for this problem. The original cost, before the 30% markup, would be represented by 100%, and the cost after the markup would then be the augmented percent, 130%. (If you wish, you can imagine some item whose original cost was $100, and was marked up to $130.) For the markdown, we want to change the 130% into 100%. We shall use these figures in place of the dollar amounts in a percent decrease problem. The diagram is now:

100%	*Old*	130
______%	*– Change*	30
______%	*New*	100

Using the first two rows as a proportion, we get:

$$30 \times 100 \div 130 \approx 23.08$$

Therefore, a 30% increase is cancelled out by a 23.08% decrease. The dealer can advertise a 23.08% markdown. (Maybe "prices marked down over 20%" would look better in the dealer's advertisement.)

The basic idea behind using the percent change diagram to cancel a percent change is to recognize that the roles of part and base have changed. Therefore, we need to reverse those numbers in the percent change diagram. The 100 that used to be an old percent is now a new dollar amount, and what used to be a new percent is now an old dollar amount.

If we examine the final computation from example 4, we can obtain faster methods for reversing percent changes. The goal of example 4 was to reverse a 30% increase, and the final computation was:

$$30 \times 100 \div 130 \approx 23.08$$

The 100 is present in the computation because percents were *not* expressed in decimal form. If they were expressed in decimal form, the 100 would be unnecessary, and we would have:

$$0.30 \div 1.30 \approx 0.2308$$

In other words, a 30% increase is reversed by dividing by its augmented percent, and using the result as a decrease. Analogously, a percent decrease is reversed by dividing by its complement, and using the result as an increase. The operation which undoes the percent change is called the **inverse** of that percent change.

EXAMPLE 5

Find the inverse of a 40% decrease.

SOLUTION

The inverse can be found by dividing by the complement of 40%. Therefore, the computation is:

$$0.40 \div 0.60 \approx 0.6667$$

A 66.67% increase is the inverse of a 40% decrease.

Sometimes we want to find the additional percent change needed to change one percent change into another. Complements and augmented percents can be used for this situation also. Consider the following example.

EXAMPLE 6

What additional percent change is needed to change a 25% decrease into a 30% decrease?

SOLUTION

It is tempting to claim an additional 5% decrease is needed. An additional 5 percentage point decrease is needed, but that is not the same as an additional 5% change. Changing the rates into complements, we get 75% and 70%. Therefore, we need to change a 75% complement into a 70% complement. The percent change diagram is:

100%	*Old*	75
____%	*– Change*	____
____%	*New*	70

Using the first and third rows, we solve the proportion and obtain:

$$100 \times 70 \div 75 \approx 93.33$$

Subtracting this new percent from 100%, we get the change percent, 6.67%. Therefore, a 6.67% additional decrease is needed to change a 25% decrease into a 30% decrease.

Name: ______________________________ Date: __________

Exercises 2.1

✳ Identify the base.

1. "In a survey, 23.3% of adults said they formerly smoked."

2. "With 98% of the precincts reporting, Treen had 25% of the vote."

3. "Save up to 60% off factory retail."

4. "Health care premiums will rise 40% for next year."

✳✳ Interpret the following statements.

5. "About 20% of the bank robbers convicted nationwide last year were repeat offenders."

6. "Nearly 75% of the hospital's patients have criminal backgrounds."

7. "Automakers will cut tailpipe emissions by an average of 80%."

8. "Automobiles are 97% cleaner than they were 30 years ago."

9. "Automobiles account for about 22% of nitrogen oxide pollution nationwide."

10. "Lease payment based on average capitalized cost of 91.47% of manufacturer's suggested retail price."

11. "Small and mid-sized businesses account for 90% of all businesses and 50% of the GNP."

12. "Get 8.25% interest on a home equity loan of 80% of home value or less."

13. "The overall increase in salary and benefits is nearly 6%."

14. "The city experienced a –16.8% population change over the last ten years."

15. "The corporation reports a 55.4% increase in profits."

Name: ______________________________ Date: __________

Exercises 2.2

✳ Change to a decimal.

1. 46%

2. 59%

3. 172%

4. 400%

5. 7.29%

6. 0.18%

7. $2\frac{3}{4}\%$

8. $7\frac{5}{9}\%$

Change to a fraction.

9. 37%

10. 72%

11. 700%

12. 852%

13. 24.9%

14. 7.25%

15. $7\frac{3}{5}\%$

16. $8\frac{1}{3}\%$

Change into a percent.

17. 0.68

18. 0.9

19. 0.0034

20. 3.16

21. 12.6

22. 18

23. $\frac{2}{5}$

24. $\frac{3}{8}$

25. $\frac{7}{12}$

26. $\frac{1}{78}$

27. $3\frac{11}{20}$

28. $8\frac{5}{6}$

Name: ____ Date: __________

Exercises 2.3

∗ Solve each problem.

1. 15% of 138 is what number?

2. 22% of what number is 275?

3. What percent of 350 is 84?

4. 34,794 is 18% of what number?

5. What number is 73% of 169?

6. 16.38 is what percent of 24?

∗∗ 7. Stone Age Keepsakes had $174,500 in sales last year, and spent $7,350 on advertising. What percent was spent on advertising?

8. Tom buys a sofa sleeper for $754, plus 6% sales tax. What is the amount of the sales tax?

9. Eudora Industries announces a layoff of 465 employees, or 3% of its workforce. What was the size of its total workforce?

10. RadioLand is having a storewide 15% off sale. What will the markdown be on a radio normally selling for $39?

11. On his tax return this year, Steve reports $575 income from interest. Assuming an interest rate of about 4.6%, about how much does Steve have invested?

12. There are 40.5 million immigrants among the 312 million people living in the United States. What percent of the U.S. population is foreign-born?

13. Carole's new job will pay $3,525 per month, but about 30% will be withheld for taxes. Estimate her pay after taxes.

14. The price of a laser printer is reduced from $379 to $299. What percent markdown can be advertised?

15. Susan has $35,000 invested in bonds, and the other 45% in stocks. What is the total amount invested?

Name: ______________________________ Date: __________

Exercises 2.4

∗ Complete the following percent change diagrams.

No.	Percent		Amount
1.	_____%	Old	5400
	14%	+ Change	_____
	_____%	New	_____
2.	_____%	Old	_____
	29%	+ Change	186.34
	_____%	New	_____
3.	_____%	Old	_____
	31%	+ Change	_____
	_____%	New	278.13
4.	_____%	Old	169
	11%	– Change	_____
	_____%	New	_____
5.	_____%	Old	_____
	57%	– Change	84.10
	_____%	New	_____
6.	_____%	Old	_____
	3.6%	– Change	_____
	_____%	New	125
7.	_____%	Old	69.50
	_____%	Change	_____
	125%	New	_____
8.	_____%	Old	_____
	_____%	Change	33.22
	104.5%	New	_____

9.	_____%	Old	_____
	_____%	Change	_____
	251%	New	168.33
10.	_____%	Old	923
	_____%	Change	_____
	92%	New	_____
11.	_____%	Old	_____
	_____%	Change	775
	46%	New	_____
12.	_____%	Old	_____
	_____%	Change	_____
	83.5%	New	12.50
13.	_____%	Old	36
	_____%	+ Change	10
	_____%	New	_____
14.	_____%	Old	_____
	_____%	+ Change	49
	_____%	New	215
15.	_____%	Old	78
	_____%	– Change	13
	_____%	New	_____
16.	_____%	Old	_____
	_____%	– Change	3.85
	_____%	New	9.14
17.	_____%	Old	58
	_____%	Change	_____
	_____%	New	42

18. | | | |
|---|---|---|
| _____% | Old | 129 |
| _____% | Change | _____ |
| _____% | New | 365 |

** 19. Last year, Tom earned $35,700. What will be his earnings this year, after a scheduled 3.2% raise?

20. Greg invested $300 in the stock market last year. Today, its value is $365. What was the percent increase in his investment?

21. A bookstore offers 20% off on all books. If a book normally sells for $29.95, what will the sale price be?

22. Shannon earned $746.52 last week, but only received $532.59 after taxes. What percent was withheld for taxes?

23. A sofa is discounted 30% resulting in a sale price of $199. What was the price before the discount?

24. Total sales (including 5.9% sales tax) at Terry's Music Salon today was $685.52. What were Terry's net receipts?

25. A restaurant had sales of $395,000 last year, and $572,600 this year. What was the percent increase in their sales?

26. Ann has $18,900, which she would like to use as a 15% down payment on a house. What is the maximum price of a house which she can afford?

*** 27. Interest rates dropped a half percentage point, to 7.25%. What was the percent decrease?

28. Is there a largest possible percent decrease? Explain.

29. Is there a largest possible percent increase? Explain.

Name: ____________________ Date: __________

Exercises 2.5

✳ Find each percent change.

1. a 12% increase followed by a 16% increase

2. a 29% decrease followed by a 17% decrease

3. a 17% increase followed by a 12% decrease

4. a 20% decrease followed by a 20% increase

5. a 60% decrease followed by a 70% decrease

6. increases of 8%, 12%, and 5%, in succession

7. decreases of 14%, 22%, and 16%, in succession

8. the inverse of a 22% increase

9. the inverse of a 147% increase

10. the inverse of a 16% decrease

11. the additional percent increase needed to change a 7% increase into a 14% increase

12. the additional percent decrease needed to change a 9% decrease into a 15% decrease

13. the additional percent change needed to change a 4% increase into a 6% decrease

** 14. Carolyn will receive a 5% increase in pay this year, and a 6% increase next year. What is the percent increase for the two years combined?

15. A kitchenware company receives a 30% discount, followed by a 20% discount, from its supplier. What is the total percent discount?

16. Congress plans 4% funding increases for a popular program for each of the next 4 years. What total percent increase will they announce?

17. A state legislature plans 10% motor vehicle tax cuts for each of the next 3 years. What will the total percent reduction be?

18. A supplier provides a merchant a 40% discount from list price. If the merchant sells the goods at list price, what percent markup over his cost will he get?

19. A supplier normally offers a 30% discount. Due to competition, he wants to increase the discount to 40%. What additional discount is needed?

20. A store is advertising a 30% off sale. From the customer's point of view, should the discount be computed before or after the 7% sales tax? Explain.

Name: ______________________________ Date: __________

Chapter 2 Review

Summary of Important Concepts

- ▲ Percent as hundredths
- ▲ Conversions to and from fractions and decimals
- ▲ Rate, base, and part
- ▲ Percent change
- ▲ Compounding percents
- ▲ Inverses of percents

Exercises

1. Interpret "Poorly adjusted brakes can be found in 46% of the trucks on the road, and will be a leading cause of accidents involving trucks."

2. Convert 23.07% to a decimal and a fraction.

3. Convert 0.086 to a percent.

4. Convert $\frac{5}{8}$ to a percent.

5. 16% of what number is 350?

6. What percent of 55 is 420?

7. What number is 72% of 688?

8. Complete

____%	Old	____
4.8%	– Change	____
____%	New	147.30

9. The unemployment rate is 8.3%, which means 12.8 million workers are out of a job. What is the size of the total workforce?

10. Sales are up 8% over last year and now total $49,000. What were the sales last year?

11. After a 10% down payment, Tim's mortgage was for $155,700. What was the price of the house?

12. Tim received raises of 4.2%, 6.3%, and 5.1% in three consecutive years. What is the total percent increase?

13. Due to the poor economy, the budget was cut 15% last year. What percent increase will restore the budget to its previous size?

3 Payroll

3.1 Salaries and Wages

Employees earn income from their labor, and are paid by their employers. **Gross earnings** are the total earnings made, before taxes and other deductions are subtracted. There are four common methods by which the amount of the gross earnings is computed. Salary and hourly wages are discussed in this section, and commission and piecework will be discussed in the next section.

An employee who receives a **salary** receives a fixed income at regular intervals for his or her labor. The time interval for a salary quote may not be the same as the frequency that the paycheck is issued. Many administrative and professional workers are paid a salary.

EXAMPLE 1

Maryanne, a teacher, receives a salary of $30,000 per year. Find her gross pay for one paycheck, assuming she is paid a) monthly, b) semimonthly, c) weekly, d) biweekly.

SOLUTIONS

If paid **monthly,** she would receive 12 paychecks per year. Dividing her annual salary by 12, we obtain:

$$30000 \div 12 = 2500$$

If paid **semimonthly,** she would receive paychecks twice each month, or 24 times per year. This would be the case if she received a check on the 13th and 28th of every month. Dividing her annual salary by 24, we obtain:

$$30000 \div 24 = 1250$$

If paid **weekly,** she would be paid 52 times per year. We obtain:

$$30000 \div 52 \approx 576.92$$

If paid **biweekly,** she would be paid every other week, or 26 times per year. We obtain:

$$30000 \div 26 \approx 1153.85$$

You should notice that when we computed the earnings in each case, we always used the original annual salary. If we had found her biweekly pay from her weekly pay, a small rounding error may have occurred.

Some people will argue that since a year really has 52 weeks plus one day, that we should use $52\frac{1}{7}$ weeks in a year. This is true, but the loss of accuracy by using 52 weeks per year is much smaller than the gain in ease of computation. However, there may be some situations in which the accuracy is necessary. In those cases, we might use $52\frac{1}{7}$ weeks in a year (or $52\frac{2}{7}$ weeks in a leap year), and $26\frac{1}{14}$ biweekly pay periods in a year (or $26\frac{1}{7}$ biweekly pay periods in a leap year). Or we might use 53 weeks (or 27 biweekly pay periods) in a year for those years having an "extra" payday. In this book, we will always use 52 and 26.

Converting salaries always involves multiplying and/or dividing by the appropriate number of pay periods per year. When changing a salary into a shorter pay period, we divide, as in the previous example. When changing the salary into a longer pay period, we multiply.

EXAMPLE 2

Susan earns $527 per week. What is the equivalent monthly salary?

SOLUTION

Most months contain more than four weeks, so we cannot multiply by 4. We shall change Susan's weekly salary into an annual salary, then back into a monthly salary. This is accomplished by multiplying by 52 and dividing by 12.

$$527 \times 52 \div 12 \approx 2283.67$$

Therefore Susan's pay is equivalent to $2,283.67 per month.

If you are looking for a more efficient method to change weekly pay into monthly pay, you may want to know how many weeks there are in an average month. The previous example provides a hint to this answer. Since we multiply by 52 and divide by 12 to change weekly pay into monthly pay, then dividing 52 by 12 will give the number of weeks in an average month. Doing this, we find there are $4\frac{1}{3}$ weeks per month. In the previous example, we could have multiplied Susan's weekly pay by $4\frac{1}{3}$ to obtain her monthly pay.

A person who receives an **hourly wage** will receive a certain fixed rate of pay for each hour worked. In order to find gross earnings for a paycheck, we only need to know the number of hours worked. Many companies will also pay higher **overtime** wages, when employees work beyond a certain minimum number of hours in some period of time. A common overtime method is to pay **time-and-a-half,** or 1.5 times the regular wage, for overtime hours.

EXAMPLE 3

Rita earns $7.55 per hour, and worked 35 hours and 45 minutes last week. What were her gross earnings for last week?

SOLUTION

To find gross earnings, we will need to multiply the number of hours worked by the rate of pay. But first, 45 minutes must be changed into parts of an hour. Since there are 60 minutes in one hour, 45 minutes is equal to $\frac{45}{60}$ of an hour, or, in decimal form, 0.75 hour. So Rita worked 35.75 hours last week. Therefore, we get:

$$35.75 \times 7.55 \approx 269.91$$

Rita had gross earnings of $269.91 last week.

EXAMPLE 4

Jana worked 47 hours last week. She earns $8.25 per hour, with time-and-a-half paid for all hours over 40 per week. Find her gross earnings.

Solution

This computation can be handled efficiently by considering regular and overtime hours separately.

$$\begin{aligned} \text{Regular:} \quad & 40 \times 8.25 = 330.00 \\ \text{Overtime:} \quad & 7 \times 1.5 \times 8.25 = \underline{86.625} \\ & 416.625 \end{aligned}$$

Rounding to the nearest penny, Jana's gross earnings totaled $416.63 last week.

If you should choose to obtain Jana's overtime rate of pay in the previous problem, do not round the result. When working overtime, Jana earned $12.375 per hour, not $12.37 or $12.38 per hour. Although a half-cent per hour seems like a trivial amount, if the 1,000 employees of a large company all worked the same hours and earned the same wage as Jana, the company would be overpaying (or underpaying, depending on the direction of rounding) over $1,500 per year in gross earnings. Therefore, rounding in the middle of a gross pay computation is to be avoided. The final answer for gross earnings, however, is always rounded.

EXAMPLE 5

Pete earns $9.38 per hour, with time-and-a-half paid for all hours over 8 per day. Find his gross earnings for this week, if he worked the schedule given below.

Mon.	Tues.	Wed.	Thurs.	Fri.	Sat.
5	5	9	10	10	4

Solution

Pete worked a total of 43 hours. Of these, five hours were overtime (one on Wednesday, and two each on Thursday and Friday). Therefore, he had 38 regular hours.

$$\begin{aligned} \text{Regular:} \quad & 38 \times 9.38 = 356.44 \\ \text{Overtime:} \quad & 5 \times 1.5 \times 9.38 = \underline{70.35} \\ & 426.79 \end{aligned}$$

Pete earned $426.79 last week.

We have looked at two overtime policies so far, one in which overtime is paid for over 40 hours per week, and the other in which overtime is over 8 hours per day. Many people assume that one of these policies is always better for the worker, but it is not so. Each policy favors different work schedules. Consider the following example.

EXAMPLE 6

Ben and Cathy are two employees at the same company. Each earns $8.40 per hour, with time-and-a-half for overtime. Their work schedules are:

	Mon.	Tues.	Wed.	Thurs.	Fri.	Sat.
Ben	8	8	8	8	8	8
Cathy	10	10	10	10		

Find their gross earnings, if overtime is paid for working:
a) over 40 hours per week
b) over 8 hours per day

SOLUTIONS

If overtime is paid for over 40 hours per week, then Ben receives overtime (he worked 48 hours last week) but Cathy does not. Their gross earnings would be:

	Ben		Cathy
$40 \times 8.40 =$	336.00	$40 \times 8.40 =$	336.00
$8 \times 1.5 \times 8.40 =$	100.80		
	436.80		

If overtime is paid for over 8 hours per day, then Cathy receives overtime (she worked 8 overtime hours last week) but Ben does not. Their gross earnings would be:

	Ben		Cathy
$48 \times 8.40 =$	403.20	$32 \times 8.40 =$	268.80
		$8 \times 1.5 \times 8.40 =$	100.80
			369.60

So an 8-hour-per-day rule for overtime favors Cathy's work schedule, but the 40-hour-per-week rule favors Ben's schedule.

The **Fair Labor Standards Act,** passed by the U.S. Congress in 1938, stipulates that employees who are covered by the act must be paid at least time-and-a-half for all hours worked over 40 per week. Some employees, due to their occupation or the size of their employer, may not be covered by this law, and may not be entitled to any overtime. Companies who wish to exceed this minimum overtime policy are permitted to pay wages beyond what the law provides.

Companies whose employees are covered by the Fair Labor Standards Act and who adopt an overtime policy different than time-and-a-half for over 40 hours per week may be violating the law (or may not, depending on the work schedules involved). In Example 6b above, if Ben is an employee covered by the Fair Labor Standards Act, then the company would be illegally underpaying him. His pay must be at least $436.80, as computed in Example 6a. (The law has no objection to Cathy receiving or not receiving overtime in this situation).

3.2 Commission and Piecework

In the last section, we considered how gross pay is computed for employees who are paid on the basis of their time. In this section, we consider those employees whose earnings are based on their output.

Salespeople may receive a commission for the net sales they generate for their employer. Employees who receive a **commission** earn a certain percent of the net sales they generate.

EXAMPLE 1

Ken receives an 8% commission on his net sales. If he sold $28,000 in merchandise during the last month, what were his gross earnings?

SOLUTION

We need to find 8% of $28,000.

$$8\% \times 28000 = 0.08 \times 28000 = 2240$$

Ken received $2,240.00 in gross earnings last month.

In the previous example, Ken received a **fixed commission,** where all of his net sales earn the same percent commission. Some salespeople earn a **variable commission,** where the rate of commission can vary according to the level of net sales, as in the next example.

EXAMPLE 2

Lola is paid commission according to the following scale:

4% on the first $5,000 in net sales each month

6% on the next $7,000 in net sales each month

9% on net sales exceeding $12,000 each month

If she sold $25,537 in merchandise last month, what was her commission?

SOLUTION

Lola does not earn 9% on all of her net sales, but only on that portion of her net sales beyond her first $12,000 for that month. Computing that portion, we get:

$$25537 - 12000 = 13537$$

The first $12,000 in net sales are paid at the lower rates. Her commission can be found by the following computation.

$$\begin{aligned} 0.04 \times 5000 &= 200.00 \\ 0.06 \times 7000 &= 420.00 \\ 0.09 \times 13537 &= \underline{1218.33} \\ & 1838.33 \end{aligned}$$

Lola's commission was $1,838.33 last month.

When commissions are paid, provisions are often included for **sales returns,** or items brought back by dissatisfied customers for refunds. A salesperson's commission is usually based on **net sales,** which are found by subtracting the returns from the **gross sales,** or total sales. Examples 1 and 2 assumed that the difference was already found. Example 3 will require us to find it.

EXAMPLE 3

Terry earns 8% commission on the first $7,000 of his monthly net sales, and 12% commission on his net sales over the first $7,000 per month. Find his commission for last month, when he sold $12,255 of merchandise, and had $472 in returns.

SOLUTION

First, returns are subtracted from gross sales to get net sales.

$$12255 - 472 = 11783$$

The first $7,000 of sales receives the lower rate, and the balance earns the higher rate. We get:

$$\begin{aligned} 7000 \times 0.08 &= 560.00 \\ 4783 \times 0.12 &= \underline{573.96} \\ & 1133.96 \end{aligned}$$

Terry earned $1133.96 commission last month.

Another common situation involving commission involves an employee who earns a **salary plus commission**. This scenario helps the salesperson through the slow economic times, while still providing an incentive for boosting the sales of their employer. The quantities involved will be computed separately, then added.

EXAMPLE 4

Linda earns a salary of $300 per week, plus a 3% commission on her net sales. Last week she sold $15,866 in goods, and had $924 in returns. Find her earnings.

SOLUTION

We deduct the returns from her gross sales, and then compute 3% of that amount for her commission. Then her weekly salary is added.

$$\begin{aligned} 15866 - 924 &= 14942 \\ 14942 \times 0.03 &= 448.26 \\ 448.26 + 300 &= 748.26 \end{aligned}$$

Linda earnings for the week were $748.26.

The jobs of some people involve **piecework,** where their work is paid according to the quantity of their output, not the dollar value of the output (as with commission). Piecework jobs are more common in manufacturing situations, where items are produced for resale. Piecework computations are very similar to commission computations, except that no percent is involved. The rate of pay is a dollar amount per item, rather than a percentage of the dollar value.

EXAMPLE 5

Susan works in the shipping department filling orders. She earns $0.70 for each box packed. If she packed 375 boxes this week, what were her earnings?

SOLUTION

Multiplying the quantity by the rate, we find:

$$375 \times 0.70 = 262.50$$

Susan earned $262.50 last week.

Some companies use a **differential piecework** plan, where piecework rates vary according to the output of the worker. Just as piecework is similar to commission, the computation of differential piecework earnings is similar to the computation of variable commission.

EXAMPLE 6

John sews shirts at a garment factory. His weekly piecework rate is $0.19 per shirt for the first 1,500 shirts, and $0.21 for each additional shirt. Last week he sewed 1,825 shirts. What were his earnings?

SOLUTION

The first 1,500 shirts receive the lesser piecework rate; only the last 325 shirts receive the higher rate. We get:

$$\begin{aligned} 1500 \times 0.19 &= 285.00 \\ 325 \times 0.21 &= \underline{68.25} \\ &\ 353.25 \end{aligned}$$

John earned $353.25 for the week.

The evidence of poor output by piecework employees are the defective items they produce. However, not all defective items are necessarily due to the employee's negligence, so defective output may yet earn some income, but not as much as good output. A **chargeback,** or **docking,** is a deduction for the defective items produced.

EXAMPLE 7

Cathy assembles electrical switches at $1.35 per switch, and is charged back $0.95 for each defective switch. Last week she produced 358 switches, of which 11 were defective. Find her gross earnings.

SOLUTION

We compute both the total earned if all switches were good, and the chargeback for the defective switches. We get:

$$\begin{aligned} 358 \times 1.35 &= 483.30 \\ 11 \times 0.95 &= \underline{-10.45} \\ &\ 472.85 \end{aligned}$$

Cathy earned $472.85 last week.

3.3 FICA and FUTA

The previous two sections of this chapter discussed the computation of gross earnings. Typically, employees do not receive the amount of their gross earnings in their paycheck, because various employment taxes, and possibly other benefits, are deducted. In addition, there are employment taxes which are paid directly by the employer, and not deducted from an employee's paycheck. Self-employed persons are also subject to employment taxes.

Employment taxes are basically computed as a percentage of wages or income. However, taxable income is not always the same as gross income, since some wages are often excluded from tax. Tax rates and wage bases change annually, to reflect cost of living adjustments or the desires of Congress. Each year, the Internal Revenue Service releases the Employer's Tax Guide (Publication 15, Circular E), which will contain employment tax information for the current year. The information in this book is current for the year 2012.

Some taxes assess the same rate on every taxpayer, and some taxes use a scale of rates. In this section, we shall discuss **flat taxes,** where (almost) every taxpayer pays the same rate. Flat employment taxes include the FICA (Social Security and Medicare) taxes, the Self-Employment Tax, and the Federal Unemployment Tax.

Although flat taxes always use the same computational rate, definitions of the base on which the rate is assessed can alter the effect a tax has on different taxpayers. A flat tax may have an income **floor,** below which no income is taxed (alternatively, income below the floor is taxed at a 0% rate). Flat taxes may also have an income **ceiling,** above which no income is taxed (alternatively, income above the ceiling is taxed at a 0% rate.) The **wage base** of a flat employment tax is the income earned between the floor and the ceiling.

In 1935, the U.S. Congress passed the Social Security Act, which provided basic retirement benefits to old age survivors. The portion of the act which mandates tax withholding is sometimes referred to as the **Federal Insurance Contributions Act,** or **FICA.** Since 1935, because of changes to the system, disability and medical benefits are also provided. Due to the increasing availability of benefits, the proportion of eligible recipients in the population, and the increasing cost of living, the revenue required from the FICA tax has also increased. Figure 3.1 shows the increase in FICA rates. From an original rate of 1% on each employee's first $3,000 of gross earnings in 1937, the tax reached 7.65% on the first $51,300 of each employee's gross earnings in 1990.

In the following year, the portion of the tax which provided for medical benefits was separated from the rest of the tax, so two separate computations became necessary. These are the **Social Security** tax (or **Old Age Survivors and Disability Insurance,** abbreviated **OASDI**) and the **Medicare** tax (or **Hospital Insurance,** sometimes abbreviated **HI**). **Supplemental Medical**

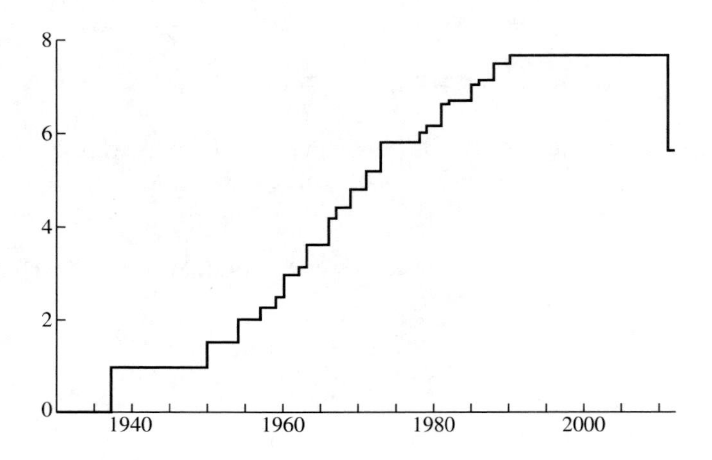

Figure 3.1 FICA Rates, as a percent

Insurance, or **SMI,** is also part of the Medicare program, and is partially funded by the tax, and partially paid for by recipients of that program. Unfortunately, the combined FICA tax is sometimes called the Social Security tax, even in some official descriptions. This leads to confusion between the whole FICA tax and the part designated for OASDI. In this text, we shall use the term Social Security only for the OASDI portion of FICA.

In 2011, due to the languishing economy, Congress legislated a reduction in the tax rate for the employee deduction for Social Security. Therefore, the 2012 rates for these taxes are:

- Social Security, employee: 4.2% of the first $110,100 of gross wages
- Social Security, employer: 6.2% of the first $110,100 of gross wages
- Medicare: 1.45% of all gross wages

Employers will deduct the tax amounts, using these rates, from the gross earnings of their employees. Furthermore, employers are also obligated to pay these taxes themselves, but at a higher rate than the employee. Both the employee deductions and the employer's shares will be forwarded to a financial institution authorized to collect these taxes. Although they are submitted together, Social Security and Medicare taxes are generally reported separately, since the tax returns for businesses require separate accounting for these two taxes.

The Medicare tax is truly a flat tax, in which every taxpayer pays exactly the same rate of their gross income. The Social Security tax, however, has a wage ceiling, beyond which no tax is assessed. Neither tax has a floor. This creates three cases into which a taxpayer's paycheck may fall:

- cumulative wage will remain under the ceiling
- cumulative wage will change from under to over the ceiling
- cumulative wage is already beyond the ceiling

The following trilogy of examples illustrates these three different cases.

EXAMPLE 1

Brenda had $1,186 in gross earnings for her current pay period, and her prior cumulative earnings were $104,582. How much will be deducted from her current paycheck for FICA taxes?

Solution

The sum of her current and her prior cumulative earnings,

$$104582 + 1186 = 105768$$

does *not* exceed the $110,100 ceiling (as it won't for most employees). Therefore, we tax all of her current earnings at the rates given above. The Social Security computation is:

$$1186 \times 0.042 \approx 49.81$$

and the Medicare computation is:

$$1186 \times 0.0145 \approx 17.20$$

Brenda's Social Security and Medicare tax deductions are $49.81 and $17.20, respectively.

EXAMPLE 2

Chesley had gross earnings of $1,352 for her current pay period, and her prior cumulative earnings were $109,338. How much will be deducted for FICA taxes for this pay period?

SOLUTION

The sum of Chesley's current and prior cumulative earnings,

$$109338 + 1352 = 110690$$

does exceed the $110,100 earnings ceiling for Social Security tax. Only that portion of the current $1,352 earnings *below* the $110,100 ceiling can be taxed for Social Security. The Social Security computation is:

$$110100 - 109338 = 762$$

$$762 \times 0.042 \approx 32.00$$

All of her current earnings are taxed for Medicare.

$$1352 \times 0.0145 \approx 19.60$$

Chesley's Social Security and Medicare tax deductions for this pay period are $32.00 and $19.60, respectively.

EXAMPLE 3

Danielle had gross earnings of $1,251 for the current pay period, and had prior cumulative earnings of $112,655. How much will be deducted from her check for FICA taxes?

SOLUTION

Her prior cumulative earnings exceed the Social Security wage ceiling of $110,100, so her current earnings are not subject to Social Security tax. But all of her current earnings are taxed for Medicare.

$$1251 \times 0.0145 \approx 18.14$$

Therefore, Danielle's Medicare deduction is $18.14, and she has $0 deducted for Social Security tax.

The most difficult case of the three examples is the middle case, when a taxpayer's cumulative income increases from below the Social Security ceiling to above the ceiling. When you do this computation, take caution that you are taxing the taxable amount below the ceiling, not the non-taxable portion above the ceiling.

Self-employed persons were first included in the Social Security program in 1951. The **Self-Employment Tax** is the method by which self-employed people make contributions for Social Security and Medicare. In 2012, the self-employed tax rates are:

13.3% of the first $110,100 of net earnings
2.9% of net earnings above $110,100

The 13.3% and 2.9% rates are the sum of the rates for employee deductions and employer shares. Essentially, self-employed people are required to pay both the employee's share and the employer's share, since they effectively employ themselves. Notice also that the tax is assessed on net earnings, not on gross earnings. The reason is that self-employed people are taxed in the same manner as businesses, on their net profit. Generally, self-employed people pay quarterly estimated taxes, as opposed to a more frequent withholding from an employee paycheck.

Since the employer half of the Self-Employment Tax represents a business expense, current law provides a reduction in a self-employed person's earnings before the tax is applied. The sum of the tax rates for the employer shares of Social Security and Medicare is 7.65%, and the Self-Employment Tax includes this reduction for all earnings levels, not just earnings below the Social Security ceiling. After the 7.65% reduction, a self-employed person will be taxed on the remaining 92.35% of his earnings.

EXAMPLE 4

Mike is self-employed, and had $34,533 in earnings for the first quarter of the year. How much will he owe in Self-Employment Tax?

SOLUTION

First, we reduce the earnings by 7.65% (which means 92.35% of the earnings will be taxed).

$$34533 \times 0.9235 \approx 31891.23$$

Since this is the first quarter, there are no prior cumulative earnings, and Mike's net earnings of $31,891.23 do not exceeded the $110,100 level. Therefore, we tax the net earnings at 13.3%.

$$31891.23 \times 0.133 \approx 4241.53$$

Mike will owe $4,241.53 for Self-Employment Tax for the first quarter, which represents his share of the Social Security and Medicare taxes.

The Social Security Act of 1935 also made provision for federal unemployment taxes and benefits, in a section often called the **Federal Unemployment Tax Act,** or **FUTA.** Employers, not employees, are required to pay the unemployment tax. Every state has also enacted a **state unemployment tax,** frequently referred to as **SUTA.** The federal government encouraged states to maintain their own unemployment programs by making the federal unemployment tax rate that a company pays depend on their state unemployment tax obligation. For this reason, we shall begin with a discussion of state unemployment taxes.

Many states use an **experience rating** system to determine state unemployment tax rates. That is, companies whose ex-employees receive more unemployment benefits pay a higher rate than companies whose ex-employees receive fewer benefits. For example, the 2012 state unemployment tax rate in Kansas varies from 0.11% to 9.4%. This rate is paid by the employer (not deducted from the employee's earnings) on the first $8,000 of each employee's gross earnings in each year.

Employers are required to pay both federal and state unemployment taxes. The official 2012 FUTA rate is 6.0% of the first $7,000 of each employee's gross earnings in each year. However, employers in states where the highest state unemployment rate is at least 5.4% are entitled to a 5.4% credit toward their FUTA taxes, unless the state has had outstanding loans from the federal government for their unemployment compensation programs, in which case the credit is smaller. Since the highest state rate in Kansas is greater than 5.4%, a credit is available to every Kansas employer, though certain conditions apply (e.g. timely payment of SUTA taxes). This provision effectively produces a net FUTA rate in Kansas of 0.6% of the first $7,000 of each employee's gross earnings in each year. In this book, we shall use the net FUTA rate in Kansas, rather than the official FUTA rate, in each example and exercise.

EXAMPLE 5

Joe Murphy's last biweekly gross earnings were $1,895. His previous cumulative income was $5,750. His employer has a state unemployment tax rate of 4.80% on the first $8,000. Find his employer's federal and state unemployment tax liability.

SOLUTION

The computations for unemployment taxes proceed in a manner very similar to the computations for the FICA taxes. The sum of Joe's current and prior cumulative gross earnings,

$$5750 + 1895 = 7645$$

exceeds the $7,000 earnings ceiling for the Federal Unemployment Tax, but not the $8,000 earnings ceiling for the state unemployment tax. Only those amounts below the ceilings are taxed. The FUTA computation is:

$$7000 - 5750 = 1250$$

$$1250 \times 0.006 = 7.50$$

The state unemployment tax computation is:

$$1895 \times 0.0480 = 90.96$$

Joe's employer will be paying $7.50 in federal unemployment tax, and $90.96 in state unemployment tax, as a result of Joe's earnings during the last two weeks.

Notice that the FUTA ceiling of $7,000 was passed in the previous example. This means that Joe's employer will not owe any more FUTA tax as a result of Joe's employment in future weeks this year, though some state unemployment tax may be owed.

Most employers have more than a single employee. Unemployment taxes are paid on all employees, and computation methods can combine their taxable earnings.

EXAMPLE 6

Sunflower Doodads has three employees. The earnings of each of their employees is given below. Sunflower's state unemployment tax rate is 2.57% on the first $8,000. Find the federal and state unemployment taxes Sunflower owes on its employees' current gross earnings.

Employee	Current Gross Earnings	Prior Cumulative Gross Earnings
Earl	$3,522	$4,132
Janet	$6,944	$7,133
Samuel	$8,442	$9,113

SOLUTION

For the FUTA tax, only the first $7,000 of each employee's gross earnings can be taxed. Janet and Samuel both made their first $7,000 before the current earnings, and none of their current earnings are taxable. Earl did not have $7,000 in previous earnings, but the sum of his prior and current earnings,

$$3522 + 4132 = 7654$$

does exceed $7,000. Earl's current taxable earnings can be computed by subtracting the prior cumulative earnings from the wage ceiling. That is,

$$7000 - 4132 = 2868$$

Therefore, the taxable earnings (for FUTA) for all employees were:

Employee	Taxable Earnings
Earl	2868
Janet	0
Samuel	0
Total	2868

Sunflower's FUTA liability for its three employees is:

$$2868 \times 0.006 \approx 17.21$$

For the state unemployment tax, the first $8,000 of each employee's gross earnings is taxed. Samuel made his first $8,000 previously, so none of his earnings are taxable. The sum of Janet's current and previous earnings,

$$6944 + 7133 = 14077$$

will put her earnings over the $8,000 ceiling, and only that portion under the ceiling,

$$8000 - 7133 = 867$$

is taxable. The sum of Earl's current and previous earnings, $7654 (computed above), does not put him over the $8,000 ceiling, so all of his earnings are taxable.

Therefore, the taxable earnings (for the state unemployment tax) were:

Employee	Taxable Earnings
Earl	3522
Janet	867
Samuel	0
Total	4389

Based on the total, we can compute the state unemployment tax (rounding to the nearest cent).

$$4389 \times 0.0257 \approx 112.80$$

These tax amounts, $17.21 for federal and $112.80 for state unemployment tax, are paid by Sunflower Doodads, and are *not* deducted from the earnings of their employees.

3.4 Withholding for Income Tax

Since 1913, the federal government has collected a **Federal Income Tax,** based on the incomes of individual citizens. Today it is the largest single source of revenue for the federal government. Since its inception, the federal income tax has assigned higher tax rates (not simply higher amounts of tax) to taxpayers with larger incomes, and lower rates to taxpayers with lower incomes. That is, the federal income tax is a multi-rate tax, and uses **tax brackets.**

In order to facilitate collection of the federal income tax, employers are required by law to deduct amounts from the gross earnings of each of their employees. The required deduction for the payment of federal income taxes is called the **Federal Withholding Tax,** or **FWT.** The withholding tax computation is designed to predict each employee's income tax obligation. After an employer deducts the withholding tax, it is sent to a financial institution authorized to collect taxes for the U.S. Treasury. When individual taxpayers file their returns after the end of the year, the accumulated Federal Withholding Taxes are applied to their Federal Income Tax bill.

Most states also tax the income of individuals. **State withholding taxes** are usually collected from employees through payroll deductions, in the same fashion that federal withholding taxes are collected. Sometimes the state withholding tax is abbreviated as **SWT.**

The amount of the withholding tax (for federal and state taxes) depends on five factors. These factors are:

- ▲ Gross earnings for the payroll period
- ▲ Marital status
- ▲ Number of allowances claimed
- ▲ Length of the payroll period
- ▲ Method used for the computation

The first four factors are used to attempt to reach some sort of fairness in our tax system. Income taxes are based on the principle that those individuals who earn larger incomes ought to be subject to larger taxes. Therefore, gross earnings must be a part of the withholding computation. However, the tax code also recognizes that some incomes are used to support only a single individual, and some incomes support large families. In an effort to recognize the greater needs of a family, the income tax code includes different tax tables for married individuals, as well as exemptions for each family member. Exemptions on the income tax correspond to allowances on the withholding tax. Each employee provides this information to their employers at the time they are hired when they fill out a W-4 form. Lastly, employees who are paid less frequently will need to have larger tax deductions from each paycheck in order to meet their income tax obligation.

There are two basic methods by which withholding taxes may be computed. These methods provide approximately, but not exactly, the same withholding tax amounts. The method we shall use is the **Percentage Method of Withholding.** This method requires fewer tables, and the computations are based on the conceptual framework of the tax system. The main advantage of the other method (the **Wage-Bracket** or **Table Method of Withholding**) is that the percentages are built into the tables and do not need to be computed.

TABLE 2 — BIWEEKLY Payroll Period

(b) MARRIED person—

If the amount of wages (after subtracting withholding allowances) is:		The amount of income tax to withhold is:	
Not over $312		$0	
Over—	**But not over—**		**of excess over—**
$312	—$981	10%	—$312
$981	—$3,031	$66.90 plus 15%	—$981
$3,031	—$5,800	$374.40 plus 25%	—$3,031
$5,800	—$8,675	$1,066.65 plus 28%	—$5,800
$8,675	—$15,248	$1,871.65 plus 33%	—$8,675
$15,248		$4,040.74 plus 35%	—$15,248

Figure 3.2 A portion of the Percentage Method of Withholding Tables for 2012

Due to the many factors involved in computing withholding for federal income tax, as well as the presence of tax brackets, the Percentage Method of Withholding uses several tables. The combination of a taxpayer's marital status (single or married) and payroll period (weekly, biweekly, semimonthly, monthly, quarterly, semiannually, annually, or daily/miscellaneous) determine the table to be used. (There are 16 possible combinations, but the tables are numbered 1a, 1b, 2a, 2b, etc., up to 8b.) In Figure 3.2, you will find the 2012 biweekly-married table for the Percentage Method of Withholding. The most commonly used Percentage Method of Withholding Tables for the 2012 Federal Income Tax can be found in the appendix.

Each table, as can be seen in the excerpt from Figure 3.2, contains a set of rules for computing the withholding tax, depending on the wage and withholding allowances. The range of wages for each separate rule is usually referred to as a **tax bracket,** and identified by the tax rate. For example, the Federal Withholding Tax for a married person receiving biweekly checks of $3,555 (after subtracting withholding allowances) would be found in Table 2b (shown in Figure 3.2), in the range of wages from $3,031 to $5,800. This range of wages is the 25% tax bracket for a married person paid biweekly.

Before using any of the Percentage Method tables, a taxpayer's withholding allowances must be subtracted from their gross income. The 2012 federal withholding allowance values are given in Figure 3.3. The value of each withholding allowance depends on the payroll period. For example, the weekly allowance value is simply the annual allowance value divided by 52. The amounts are subject to change annually.

Payroll Period	Allowance
Weekly	$ 73.08
Biweekly	$ 146.15
Semimonthly	$ 158.33
Monthly	$ 316.67
Annually	$3,800.00

Figure 3.3 Federal Withholding Allowance Values, 2012

When using these tax tables to compute the withholding tax, you will generally do the following steps:

1. Find the value of the employee's withholding allowances.
2. Find the taxable earnings by subtracting the allowances from the gross earnings.
3. Find the correct tax bracket in the correct table.
4. Use the rule provided to compute the tax. Information in the rule is always used from right to left.

EXAMPLE 1

During 2012, Albert, a married employee, was paid $890 biweekly. On his W-4 form, he claimed two allowances. Compute the Federal Withholding Tax.

SOLUTION

Each 2012 biweekly allowance was worth $146.15. So two allowances were worth:

$$2 \times 146.15 = 292.30$$

The allowances estimate the portion of the gross income which is not subject to federal income tax. This amount is subtracted from the gross income to find the taxable income, as follows:

$$890.00 - 292.30 = 597.70$$

For Albert's tax, we need to find the table for a married person paid biweekly. This is found in table 2b (Figure 3.2). His taxable income (after subtracting withholding allowances), puts him in the 10% tax bracket. This row reads:

Over $312 But not over $981 10% of excess over $312

According to this tax rule, we compute the "excess over \$312" by subtracting it from the taxable income, as follows:

$$597.70 - 312.00 = 285.70$$

and then compute 10% of that amount, rounding to the nearest cent:

$$285.70 \times 0.10 = 28.57$$

We have found that Albert's federal withholding tax deduction was \$28.57.

EXAMPLE 2

Barry, a single employee, was paid \$3,746.65 semimonthly during 2012. On his W-4 form, he claimed 3 allowances. Compute his Federal Withholding Tax.

Solution

The procedure is almost identical, except that Barry is in a higher tax bracket than Albert was. Three federal withholding allowances are worth:

$$3 \times 158.33 = 474.99$$

This leaves a taxable income of:

$$3746.65 - 474.99 = 3271.66$$

On Table 3a (in the appendix), this income puts Barry in the 25% tax bracket. This row reads:

Over \$1,563 But not over \$3,658 \$202.85 plus 25% of excess over \$1,563

The tax is then computed as follows:

$$3271.66 - 1563.00 = 1708.66$$

$$1708.66 \times 0.25 \approx 427.17$$

$$427.17 + 202.85 = 630.02$$

Therefore, Barry's federal income tax withholding was \$630.02. Notice that in this example, one additional step was necessary. The reason is that Barry was not in the lowest non-zero tax bracket, and therefore the \$202.85 amount was the tax on the first \$1,563 of his taxable income.

When you work problems involving withholding taxes, remember that the order of operations is critical. Using the steps in the wrong order, or omitting steps, will produce incorrect answers.

These examples illustrate the standard approach to computing withholding taxes. However, if an employee receives supplemental pay (usually resulting in a separate paycheck), the rules for withholding are often different.

In addition to withholding for the Federal Income Tax, 41 states (as of 2009) assess a state income tax on the earnings of employees. In all of these states, withholding from an employee's paycheck is required. In general, the **state withholding tax** computation proceeds in a fashion similar to the Federal Withholding Tax, but variations are common. State withholding tax is often abbreviated as **SWT.** Excerpts from the Kansas SWT tables can be found in the appendix.

EXAMPLE 3

Kara earned $2,235 for the last two weeks. She is single and claims 2 allowances. Find her state withholding tax.

Solution

Each state biweekly allowance is worth $86.54. So two allowances are worth:

$$2 \times 86.54 = 173.08$$

We then subtract to obtain the taxable income.

$$2235.00 - 173.08 = 2061.92$$

From Table 2a of the SWT table (in the appendix), we find that Kara's taxable earnings are in the 6.45% tax bracket. So the computation proceeds as follows:

$$2061.92 - 1269.00 = 792.92$$

$$792.92 \times 0.0645 \approx 51.14$$

$$51.14 + 56.25 = 107.39$$

Therefore, $107.39 will be withheld from Kara's paycheck for state withholding tax on Kara's paycheck.

3.5 After Taxes

In the previous two sections we discussed six specific taxes, namely federal and state withholding tax, Social Security and Medicare, and federal and state unemployment tax. (In this discussion, we are considering the Self-Employment Tax as Social Security and Medicare for the self-employed person, rather than as a separate tax.) These six payroll taxes are those which are incurred by either the employee or the employer as a result of the employee-employer relationship. Both employees and employers pay many other taxes, but most others are not as a result of employment. (For example, employees pay sales tax on purchases, and employers pay income taxes on profits.)

Some payroll taxes are deducted from the gross earnings of employees, and some are paid by the employer from his revenues. It is very important to remember which taxes are paid by which party. We can summarize the situation regarding required payroll taxes as follows:

Employee Deductions	Employer Expenses
Federal Withholding Tax (FWT)	Social Security (OASDI)
State Withholding Tax (SWT)	Medicare (HI, SMI)
Social Security (OASDI)	Federal Unemployment Tax (FUTA)
Medicare (HI, SMI)	State Unemployment Tax (SUTA)

The FICA taxes (Social Security and Medicare) show up in each list, since they are both an employee deduction and an employer expense. That is, the employer must also set aside a certain amount in addition to that deducted from an employee's check, and submit both portions to the federal government.

Both employer and employee shares of the two FICA taxes, and the employee deductions for the federal withholding tax, are sent to a financial institution authorized by the U.S. Treasury to collect these taxes. Businesses with large tax liabilities may be required to make these payments almost daily, whereas very small businesses may only need to make annual payments. In any case, businesses must submit a quarterly federal tax return (Form 941) reporting the details. Federal unemployment taxes are paid separately from FICA and FWT, and are reported annually (on Form 940). State withholding and unemployment taxes are, of course, paid and reported to the state, not the federal, government.

In addition to these required payroll taxes, employees often choose to have the costs of other benefits deducted from their earnings (e.g. union dues, medical benefits, retirement annuities, and savings bonds), while employers may often provide other benefits for their employees (e.g. medical benefits, pension plans, and vacation time). All of the tax deductions, and any other deductions, are subtracted from an employee's gross earnings to obtain his **net earnings.** Also, additional taxes and other costs to the employer will increase the employer's cost of doing business beyond the gross earnings of his employees.

EXAMPLE 1

Gina is married, claims 5 withholding allowances, and earned $2,533 on her last weekly check. Her prior cumulative earnings were $4,987.33. Gina's employer, Nelson Automotive, has a state unemployment tax rate of 3.88% on the first $8,000. Find Gina's net pay for the week.

Solution

There are four required deductions, federal and state withholding taxes, and Social Security and Medicare. We first compute the Federal Withholding Tax.

$$5 \times 73.08 = 365.40$$

$$2533.00 - 365.40 = 2167.60$$

$$\text{Table 1b: } \$187.15 \text{ plus } 25\% \text{ of excess over } \$1515$$

$$2167.60 - 1515.00 = 652.60$$

$$652.60 \times 0.25 = 163.15$$

$$163.15 + 187.15 = 350.30$$

A similar computation will produce the state withholding tax.

$$5 \times 43.27 = 216.35$$

$$2533.00 - 216.35 = 2316.65$$

$$\text{Table 1b: } \$56.25 \text{ plus } 6.45\% \text{ of excess over } \$1269$$

$$2316.65 - 1269.00 = 1047.65$$

$$1047.65 \times 0.0645 \approx 67.57$$

$$67.57 + 56.25 = 123.82$$

The total of Gina's $4,987.33 prior cumulative earnings and $2533 current earnings is only $7,520.33, and does not exceed the Social Security ceiling of $110,100. Therefore, Social Security tax is computed at the 4.2% rate.

$$2533 \times 0.042 \approx 106.39$$

Similarly, we compute the Medicare tax at a 1.45% rate.

$$2533 \times 0.0145 \approx 36.73$$

So Gina has deductions of $350.30 for Federal Withholding Tax, $123.82 for state withholding tax, $106.39 for Social Security, and $36.73 for Medicare. We can add these to obtain the total deductions, and subtract from gross pay to obtain Gina's net pay.

$$350.30 + 123.82 + 106.39 + 36.73 = 617.24$$

$$2533.00 - 617.24 = 1915.76$$

Gina's net pay was $1,915.76 for the week.

EXAMPLE 2

Using Example 1, find the cost to Nelson Automotive for employing Gina this week.

SOLUTION

Nelson Automotive incurred four payroll taxes, Social Security and Medicare, and federal and state unemployment taxes. The employer share of Social Security is taxed at a 6.2% rate.

$$2533 \times 0.062 \approx 157.05$$

The Medicare employer share will be exactly the same as for the employee, $36.73, as computed in Example 1.

To compute the Federal Unemployment Tax, we note that the sum of her prior cumulative earnings and her current earnings ($7,520.33, from adding the quantities in example 1) did exceed the $7,000 limit. Therefore, we must be careful to tax only that portion of her first $7,000 in earnings.

$$7000.00 - 4987.33 = 2012.67$$

$$2012.67 \times 0.006 \approx 12.08$$

Since Gina has not yet earned her first $8,000, all of her current earnings are subject to state unemployment tax. The SUTA rate was provided in example 1.

$$2533 \times 0.0388 \approx 98.28$$

Therefore, the taxes incurred by Nelson Automotive include $157.05 for Social Security, $36.73 for Medicare, $12.08 for federal unemployment tax, and $98.28 for state unemployment tax. To complete the computation, we add all of these taxes to Gina's gross pay for the week.

$$157.05 + 36.73 + 12.08 + 98.28 = 304.14$$

$$2533.00 + 304.14 = 2837.14$$

In addition to Gina's $2,533 gross pay, Nelson Automotive incurred $304.14 in payroll taxes, for a total cost of $2,837.14 for employing Gina this week.

Employment taxes are a large cost to employers, and a large deduction from an employee's gross pay. Economists measure this tax burden through the use of an **effective tax rate,** which computes the rate of tax paid based on the gross salary, as if all income were taxed at the same rate. Effective tax rates can be computed for single taxes, for all tax deductions, or for both tax deductions and hidden taxes (those paid by the employer are essentially hidden from the employee).

EXAMPLE 3

Using the details from example 1, find Gina's effective Federal Withholding Tax rate.

SOLUTION

From Gina's $2,533 gross salary, she paid $350.30 in withholding for the federal income tax. Using a PBR diagram, we find

$$R = \frac{P}{B} = \frac{350.30}{2533.00} \approx 0.1383 = 13.83\%$$

Gina paid an effective federal income tax rate of 13.83%.

Notice that Gina's effective tax rate, 13.83%, is not the same as the 25% rate of the tax bracket for her salary. The tax bracket rate is a **marginal tax rate,** or rate paid on the next dollar of earnings. Since much of Gina's income was taxed at a rate lower than her 25% marginal rate, her effective rate was also lower than 25%.

The use of multirate taxes, or the use of tax floors or ceilings, will generally cause the marginal tax rate to be different than the effective tax rate. When the tax rates increase for larger salaries, then the tax is called a **progressive tax,** and the effective tax rate will be lower than the marginal rate. The Federal Withholding Tax is an example of a progressive tax. On the other hand, when tax rates decrease for larger salaries, then the tax is called a **regressive tax,** and the effective tax rate will be larger than the marginal rate. The use of wage ceilings produces regressive taxes, since the tax bracket for the highest incomes is basically 0%. The Social Security tax and the unemployment taxes are examples of regressive taxes.

EXAMPLE 4

Using all of the tax deductions from example 1, find Gina's effective tax rate.

SOLUTION

This question differs from the first example in that a general tax rate is requested, and a specific tax is not named. The total of Gina's deductions, $617.24, was computed in Example 1. Using a PBR formula, we find:

$$R = \frac{P}{B} = \frac{617.24}{2533.00} \approx 0.2437 = 24.37\%$$

Gina's tax deductions produced an effective tax rate of 24.37%. In other words, Gina had 24.37% of her gross pay withheld for taxes.

For comparison, we might also consider Gina's marginal tax rate. Her wages put her in the 25% FWT bracket and the 6.45% Kansas SWT bracket. She also had 4.2% withheld for Social Security and 1.45% for Medicare. All of these rates would apply to her next dollar of earnings, so these rates will have the same base and can be added. The sum of those rates produces a 37.1% marginal tax rate. In other words, even though Gina had 24.37% of her current earnings withheld for taxes, any raise she would receive would be taxed at 37.1%. Effective tax rates of 15% to 30% are quite common, and marginal tax rates can reach 50%.

However, economists will (rightly) point out that the computations we have done so far ignore the taxes hidden from the employee, those that the employer is required to pay without deducting them from the employee's salary. Their argument is that the employer paid a certain amount in labor costs, and if the government had not taken some of that amount, it would all have gone to the employee as salary. This approach will have us compare the total taxes (whether deducted or hidden) to the employer's cost. For example 4, an economist would combine the $617.24 tax deductions (from example 1) with the $304.14 in employer taxes (from example 2), and compare that total with the employer's cost of $2,837.14 (from example 2), for an effective tax rate of 32.48%. That is, 32.48% of the costs paid for Gina's labor went for taxes. In this book, though, we will assume that the base is the employee's gross pay, unless a problem states otherwise.

Name: ______________________________ Date: __________

Exercises 3.1

* Convert each salary.

1. $39,000/year into a monthly salary

2. $45,000/year into a weekly salary

3. $27,550/year into a biweekly salary

4. $32,000/year into a semimonthly salary

5. $1,895/month into a biweekly salary

6. $1,580/month into a weekly salary

7. $2,350/month into a semimonthly salary

8. $2,480/month into an annual salary

9. $685/week into an annual salary

10. $925/week into a semimonthly salary

11. $725/week into a monthly salary

12. $550/week into a biweekly salary

13. $1,035 biweekly into a semimonthly salary

14. $1,400 biweekly into an annual salary

15. $1,754 biweekly into a weekly salary

16. $955 biweekly into a monthly salary

17. $1,855 semimonthly into a weekly salary

18. $1,137 semimonthly into a monthly salary

19. $1,533 semimonthly into an annual salary

20. $1,325 semimonthly into a biweekly salary

Find gross earnings. Overtime (OT) is paid at time-and-a-half.

21. 26 hours at $8.85 per hour

22. 33 hours at $8.17 per hour

23. 36.5 hours at $9.23 per hour

24. 38.25 hours at $11.55 per hour

25. 42 hours at $8.56 per hour, OT for over 40 hours/week

26. 48 hours at $9.53 per hour, OT for over 38 hours/week

27. 45.5 hours at $7.75 per hour, OT for over 40 hours/week

28. 53.25 hours at $8.63 per hour, OT for over 37.5 hours/week

Find gross earnings. Overtime is paid at time-and-a-half for over 8 hours per day.

	Rate	M	Tu	W	Th	F	Sat	Sun
29.	$8.50	8	8	10	8	5		
30.	$10.35		7	8	9	10.5	8	4
31.	$9.76	6	6	8		8	8	8
32.	$11.43	9.5	5.25	5.5	9.25	11.5	9.75	

** 33. Carol has two job offers. One pays $655 per week, and the other pays $2,800 per month. Which is the better offer?

34. Kristy has two job offers. One pays $32,000 per year, and the other pays $620 per week. Which is the better offer?

35. John worked 46 hours last week, with time-and-a-half for over 40 hours per week. Find his gross pay, if he earns $8.95 per hour.

36. Tammy worked 51 hours last week, with time-and-a-half for over 38 hours per week. Find her gross pay, if she earns $9.23 per hour.

37. Frank worked 49 hours and 15 minutes last week, with time-and-a-half for over 35 hours per week. Find his gross pay, if he earns $11.53 per hour.

38. Jean worked 47 hours and 45 minutes last week, with time-and-a-half for over 40 hours per week. Find her gross pay, if she earned $10.87 per hour.

***The following employees are covered by the Fair Labor Standards Act. Is the amount of gross wages they received legal? Explain.

39. $400 for the week, for 44 hours at $8.75 per hour

40. $855 for two weeks, for 86 hours at $9.20 per hour

41. $1,800 for four weeks, for 200 hours at $8.95 per hour

Name: ______________________________ Date: __________

Exercises 3.2

* Find each gross pay.

1. net sales $342,400, with a 7% commission

2. net sales $57,200, with an 11% commission

3. net sales $17,500, with a 5% commission on sales below $4,000, and 8% on sales in excess of $4,000

4. net sales $31,045, with a 6% commission on sales below $17,500, and 7.5% on sales in excess of $17,500

5. gross sales $23,402, sales returns $855, with a 9% commission

6. gross sales $16,580, sales returns $1,340, with a 5% commission

7. salary $250, gross sales $12,714, sales returns $922, with a 4% commission

8. salary $400, gross sales $9,384, sales returns $685, with a 3% commission

9. output 480 pieces, with a rate of $2.40 per piece

10. output 540 pieces, with a rate of $1.95 per piece

11. output 375 pieces, with a rate of $2.80 per piece on output below 300 pieces, and $3.50 per piece on output in excess of 300 pieces

12. output 622 pieces, with a rate of $1.95 per piece on output below 450 pieces, and $2.35 per piece on output in excess of 450 pieces

**13. Barb earns 7% commission on the sale price of each house she sells. Find her commissions for October, when her sales totalled $465,300 for 3 houses.

14. Ken earned 3.5% commission on sales of $197,500. What is his commission?

15. Drewry Furniture pays 6% commission on the first $4,000 of sales, and 9% on sales over $4,000. Find Dave's commission, if he made $7,500 in sales.

16. Lemaster's pays a 9% commission on the first $5,500, and 12% on sales in excess of $5,500. Find Ellen's commission, if she made $6,495 in sales.

Commissions at Computer Heaven are paid on the following scale:

8% on the first $7,000 in net sales
11% on the next $14,000 in net sales
16% on any additional net sales

Find each person's commission.

17. Frank made $16,385 in sales, with $210 in returns.

18. Brenda made $24,577 in sales, with $308 in returns.

19. Carl made $13,268 in sales, with $171 in returns.

20. Rob made $4,057 in sales, with $89 in returns.

21. Anne made $7,058 in sales, with $92 in returns.

Florence Farms pays its pickers 75 cents per pound for the first 40 pounds of blueberries, and pays $1.05 per pound for each additional pound.

22. Find Hank's gross earnings, if he picked 42.3 pounds of blueberries.

23. Find Steve's gross earnings, if he picked 47.6 pounds of blueberries.

The Pie Shop pays $1.75 for each pie baked, with a $0.95 chargeback for pies not meeting the standard.

24. Find Trella's gross earnings, if she baked 126 pies, all meeting the standard.

25. Find Rick's gross earnings, if he baked 117 pies, all meeting the standard.

26. Find Karen's gross earnings, if she baked 142 pies, with 3 chargebacks.

27. Find Tom's gross earnings, if he baked 98 pies, with 5 chargebacks.

Name: ______________________________ Date: __________

Exercises 3.3

∗ Find the amounts of each of the FICA deductions for the current pay period for each of the following employees. Use the 2012 rates of 4.2% on the first $110,100 of gross earnings, and 1.45% on all gross earnings.

	Employee	Current Gross Earnings	Prior Cumulative Earnings
1.	S. Turner	$358.41	$8,662.15
2.	M. Bell	$583.16	$30,411.18
3.	F. Whitecross	$1,225.22	$15,596.12
4.	T. Baker	$1,801.61	$63,017.41
5.	C. Gould	$2,533.61	$110,811.59
6.	M. Towne	$3,142.53	$115,972.44
7.	P. Baldwin	$1,184.21	$109,986.14
8.	G. Falk	$952.41	$109,504.33
9.	N. Schwarz	$1,538.44	$108,989.41
10.	T. Talley	$955.41	$109,321.33
11.	Z. McCombs	$1,246.33	$108,732.18
12.	O. Ledwith	$2,013.59	$107,992.44

Find the amounts of the FUTA and state unemployment taxes for the current pay period for each of the following employees. Assume that the state tax rate is based on the first $8,000.

	Employee	Current Gross Earnings	Prior Cumulative Gross Earnings	State Tax Rate
13.	F. Todd	$1,088.64	$6,959.28	3.15%
14.	T. Silverman	$827.44	$7,882.51	5.11%
15.	R. Manley	$1,528.99	$7,136.44	0.89%
16.	F. Chastain	$952.38	$6,485.47	0.65%

∗∗ Use the 2012 tax rates to find the taxes for the current pay period.

17. Philip earned $1,589 last week, and had previous earnings of $108,894 for the year. Calculate the amounts for the Social Security and Medicare deductions.

18. Bill earned $3,592 on his last biweekly check, and had previous cumulative earnings of $107,841. Calculate the deductions for Social Security and Medicare.

19. Linda earned $2,095 on her last check, and had previous earnings of $28,338. Find the deductions for each of the FICA taxes.

20. Laura earned $2,095 on her last check, and had previous earnings of $146,338. Find the deductions for each of the FICA taxes.

21. Grace had previous earnings of $109,866, and earned $1,335 on her last check. Find the deductions for each of her FICA taxes.

22. Tom had previous earnings of $111,866, and earned $1,335 on his last check. Find the deductions for each of his FICA taxes.

23. Kelly is self-employed, earned $795 last week, and had previous earnings of $19,443. Find the amount of his Self-Employment Tax.

24. Karen is self-employed, earned $3,522 last month, and had previous earnings of $32,495. Find the amount of her Self-Employment Tax.

25. Frederick is married, earned $655 last week, and had previous cumulative earnings of $109,559. Find the deductions for his FICA taxes.

26. Jessie is single, earned $1,335 for the last two weeks, and her previous cumulative earnings were $108,982. Find the deductions for her FICA taxes.

27. Zebulon earned $3,258 on his last check, which brings his current cumulative earnings up to $111,921. Find the deductions for his FICA taxes.

28. Althea earned $2,598 on her last check, which brings her current cumulative earnings up to $109,985. Find the deductions for her FICA taxes.

29. Quincy earned $816.51 on his last weekly check, and had prior cumulative earnings of $6,543.26. Find the unemployment taxes on those earnings, if his employer's state tax rate is 5.70% on the first $8,000.

30. Yuri earned $925.43 on his last weekly check, and had prior cumulative earnings of $6,827.55. Find the unemployment taxes on those earnings, if his employer's state tax rate is 6.20% on the first $8,000.

31. Linda earned $2,433.88 on her last semimonthly check, and had prior cumulative earnings of $5,931.47. Find the unemployment taxes on those earnings, if her employer's state tax rate is 2.77% on the first $8,000.

32. Terry earned $1,478.25 on her last biweekly check, and had prior cumulative earnings of $6,829.33. Find the unemployment taxes on those earnings, if her employer's state tax rate is 0.11% on the first $8,000.

Find the federal and state unemployment tax liability for the current pay period for the following employers. Assume that the state tax rate is based on the first $8,000.

	Employer	State Tax Rate	Employee	Current Gross Earnings	Prior Cumulative Gross Earnings
33.	Speedy Sneakers	5.28%	E. Bender	$864.22	$4,251.33
			T. DeLeon	$1,141.92	$7,851.33
			F. Raleigh	$952.33	$6,431.22
34.	Herb's Herbs	0.34%	J. Thompson	$966.44	$9,231.88
			P. Waters	$455.20	$5,842.33
			L. Wilson	$633.51	$6,588.39
			E. Wings	$826.87	$7,466.53
			S. Zoellner	$966.32	$8,668.80

Name: ______________________________ Date: __________

Exercises 3.4

✶ Find the federal and state withholding taxes for the current pay period for each of the following employees.

	Employee	Earnings	Pay period	Status	Allowances
1.	D. Carter	$1,800	monthly	M	3
2.	F. Ellis	$625	weekly	M	2
3.	H. Gardner	$958.25	semimonthly	S	1
4.	P. Tuttle	$1,014.18	biweekly	S	1
5.	V. Sanchez	$948.51	weekly	S	3
6.	K. Johnson	$2,958.41	biweekly	M	0
7.	L. Porter	$6,853.55	monthly	S	0
8.	T. Prichett	$7,341.88	semimonthly	M	6

✶✶ 9. Joe is married and claims three allowances. The gross earnings on his last biweekly check were $1,895. Find Joe's federal and state withholding taxes for this pay period.

10. Diana's gross earnings for last week were $589. She is single and claims two allowances. Find the deductions for her federal and state withholding taxes for this pay period.

11. Walter's gross earnings were $4,596 on his last monthly check. He is single and claims one allowance. Find his federal and state withholding taxes for this pay period.

12. Lorraine is married and claims 5 allowances. Her gross earnings on her last semimonthly check were $2,095. Find her federal and state withholding taxes for this pay period.

13. Carla is married and claims no allowances. On last week's semimonthly check, her gross earnings were $8,399.52. Find her federal and state withholding taxes for this pay period.

14. John is single and claims 3 allowances. His gross earnings were $2,533.41 for the last two weeks. Find his federal and state withholding taxes for this pay period.

15. Linda is married and claims 6 allowances. Her gross earnings last week were $952.44. Find her federal and state withholding taxes for this pay period.

16. Steve is married and claims 10 allowances. The gross earnings on his last monthly check were $3,152.44. Find his federal and state withholding taxes for this pay period.

17. Jeanne receives gross earnings of $2,554.33 every month. She is married and claims 4 allowances. Find her federal and state withholding taxes for this pay period.

18. Don receives gross earnings of $679.92 every week. He is single and claims one allowance. Find his federal and state withholding taxes for this pay period.

19. Lucille is single and claims two allowances. Her gross earnings for the last two weeks were $1,336.50. Find her federal and state withholding taxes for this pay period.

20. Larry is married and claims three allowances. His gross earnings for the last half-month were $1,446.25. Find his federal and state withholding taxes for this pay period.

Name: ______________________________ Date: __________

Exercises 3.5

** 1. Joan earns $1,700 biweekly. She is married and claims three allowances. Her employer has a state unemployment tax rate of 4.6%.

a. Find her net pay for the first pay period of the year.

b. Find Joan's effective tax rate.

c. How much does it cost to employ her for the first pay period of the year?

d. Express the net pay as a percent of the employer's cost.

2. Felix is paid $2,000 per month. He is single and claims two allowances. So far this year he has earned $6,000. His employer has a 2.9% state unemployment tax rate.

a. What is his net pay for this month?

b. Find the effective tax rate.

c. How much does it cost to employ him for this month?

d. Express the net pay as a percent of the employer's cost.

3. Karl has earned $12,000 so far this year. He is married, claims no allowances, and is paid $1,350 weekly. His employer has a state unemployment tax rate of 5.7%.

   a. What is his net pay for the next week?

   b. Find Karl's effective tax rate.

   c. How much does it cost to employ him during the next week?

   d. Express the net pay as a percent of the employer's cost.

*** 4. John McDonald is employed by Lee & Sterling. He is married, claims two withholding allowances, and earns $16.97 per hour. He has also chosen to have his union dues ($405 annually) and medical insurance ($5,500 per year, of which his employer pays 70%) deducted from his weekly paycheck. His cumulative gross earnings prior to this paycheck were $7,858.26. This week he worked 49 hours and 45 minutes. The union contract states that time-and-a-half is paid for all hours worked over 38 hours per week. Lee & Sterling's state unemployment tax rate is 3.25% on the first $8,000.

   a. Find John McDonald's net pay for this week.

   b. Find John's effective tax rate.

   c. Find Lee & Sterling's total cost for employing John McDonald this week.

   d. Express the net pay as a percent of the employer's cost.

Name: ______________________________ Date: __________

Chapter 3 Review

Summary of Important Concepts

- ▲ Pay periods: monthly, semimonthly, biweekly, weekly
- ▲ Salary
- ▲ Hourly wages and overtime
- ▲ Commission and returns
- ▲ Piecework and chargebacks
- ▲ FICA: Social Security and Medicare
- ▲ FUTA & SUTA (unemployment) taxes
- ▲ FWT & SWT (withholding) taxes
- ▲ Gross pay, net pay, and employer cost
- ▲ Effective tax rates

Exercises

1. Ron earns $2,584 monthly. How much is that each week?

2. Sheila earns $8.55 per hour, with time-and-a-half paid for working over 40 hours per week. How much is her gross pay, if she works 45 hours and 15 minutes this week?

3. Tom earns a 4% commission on the first $16,000 worth of sales each month, and 7% on all sales in excess of $16,000. How much is his commission if he sells $44,200 this month and has returns of $2,490?

4. Sally boxes peaches. She earns 35 cents per box for the first 200 boxes per week, and 40 cents per box for boxes beyond the first 200. If she packs 375 boxes, what are her gross earnings?

5. Lynn is married and claims four allowances. The gross wages on her biweekly paycheck are $2039.88. How much are Lynn's federal and state withholding taxes?

6. Mark had prior cumulative gross earnings of $110,025.41. The gross wages on this week's paycheck are $1,566.97. What are the amounts of this week's Social Security and Medicare deductions?

7. Nora is self-employed. If she earned $19,428.23 during the first quarter of this year, what will be the amounts of her first quarter Self-Employment Tax?

8. Brian earned $4,889.92 during the first quarter of the year. His employer, Stevens Industries, has a state unemployment tax rate of 2.66% on the first $8,000. For the first quarter of this year, how much does Stevens owe for federal and state unemployment taxes due to employing Brian?

9. Cathy is single and claims five allowances. She earned $1,925.57 for the last week. Her prior cumulative earnings were $34,562.71. What will be her net pay for the current paycheck? What is Cathy's effective tax rate?

10. Don is married and claims two allowances. He earned $2,688.42 during this month, and his prior cumulative earnings were $5,277.83. What is the cost to Don's employer for having Don on the payroll this month? Use a SUTA rate of 4.28% on the first $8,000.

4 Retailing

4.1 Profitability

Every successful business will generate a profit for its owner or owners. This is true whether the business is a **manufacturer** which produces goods, a **retailer** who offers goods for sale to the general public, a **wholesaler** who buys goods from manufacturers and sells them to retailers, or a company which provides a **service** but does not sell goods. If a business never produces a profit, it will not be able to stay in business. In this chapter, we shall usually describe concepts in terms of a retail business, though they are usually applicable to other types of businesses as well.

All businesses produce **revenue,** or **income,** which is money paid to that business for its goods or services. In a retail business, most income is due to **sales,** or cash received from customers in exchange for goods. All business also have **costs,** or **expenses,** which is money paid by businesses for goods or services performed by others. Costs in a retail business include the merchandise, salaries of employees, utilities, taxes, advertising, and so on. **Profit** is simply the amount by which income exceeds expenses. Written as a simple formula, we have:

$$\text{Profit} = \text{Income} - \text{Cost}$$

Profit should be a positive number. If not, because costs are larger than income, then the business has incurred a loss. We will discuss losses later in this section.

Retailers (and their accountants) separate costs into two types, cost of goods sold and operating expenses. **Cost of goods sold,** or **net cost,** refers to the cost of the merchandise which the retailer paid the supplier. Usually we use the term cost of goods sold when describing all of the goods sold by the retailer during the year, and we use the term net cost to describe the cost to the retailer for a single item. **Operating expenses,** or **overhead,** refers to most other expenses incurred when operating the business. Salaries, utilities, taxes, and advertising are some of the operating expenses businesses encounter.

In order to make a profit, a business must cover both of these types of costs. The **breakeven point** is the amount which a business must earn in income to cover their total costs. That is, the total cost in dollars equals the breakeven point.

There are also two types of profit. **Gross profit** refers to the profit when only the cost of the goods sold, or net cost, is used. In other words, gross profit is the profit before operating expenses are taken into account. **Net profit** refers to the profit when all costs, both cost of goods sold and operating expenses, are taken into consideration. When we say that businesses need to be profitable, we are referring to their net profit.

Profitable businesses will have more income than their total costs, since that is what the definition of net profit implies. So we can summarize this discussion of the income of profitable retail businesses by drawing the following **number line diagram.**

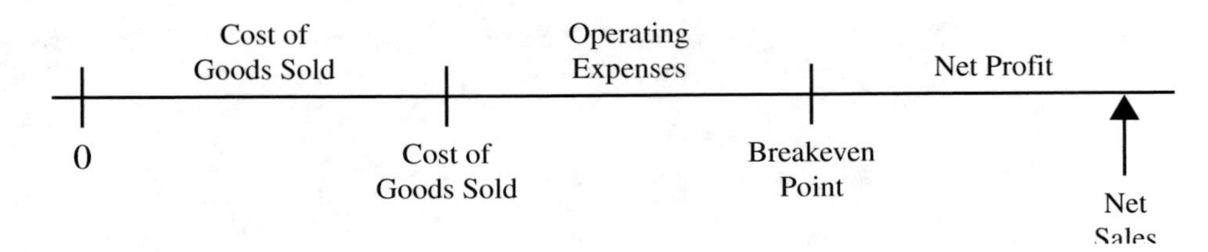

Notice that this number line begins at zero and ends at net sales. That is, the length of the number line is the amount of net sales. **Net sales** is the income for a retail business after any returns made by customers have been deducted. Therefore, the length of the number line represents income for the retailer. That income is divided into three sections. Two of the sections represent the two different types of costs a retailer incurs, and the third section is the net profit, or the amount by which the income exceeds the total expenses. Notice that the breakeven point occurs after the two cost sections on the number line.

A number line diagram can be very useful in organizing information regarding costs, and determining profit or loss. There are three basic rules regarding computations on a number line.

- A position and the following section can be added to produce the next position. (Add when moving to the right.)
- A position and the previous section can be subtracted to produce the previous position. (Subtract when moving to the left.)
- Two consecutive positions can be subtracted to produce the intervening section. (Subtract to find distance between two points.)

Furthermore, if you remember how numbers are added or subtracted on a number line, you can use the number line instead of formulas for profit computations.

EXAMPLE 1

Bob's Music Shack had net sales of $495,000 last year, with cost of goods sold of $255,000 and operating expenses of $223,000. Complete a number line diagram for Bob, and find his profit.

SOLUTION

We begin by placing the given information on the diagram.

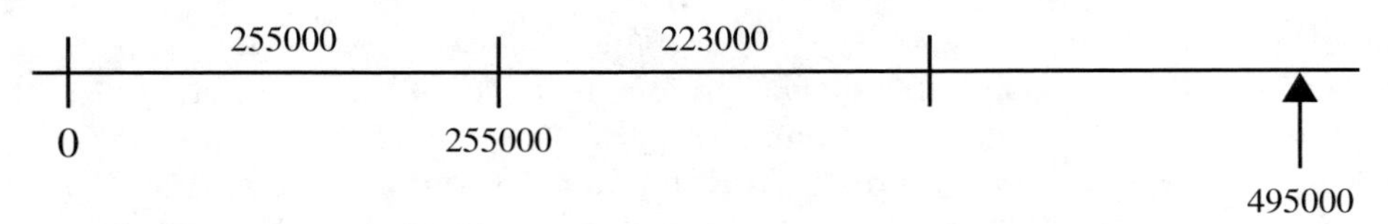

To produce the number at the breakeven point position, we add the cost of goods sold and operating expense sections. Then our number line diagram is:

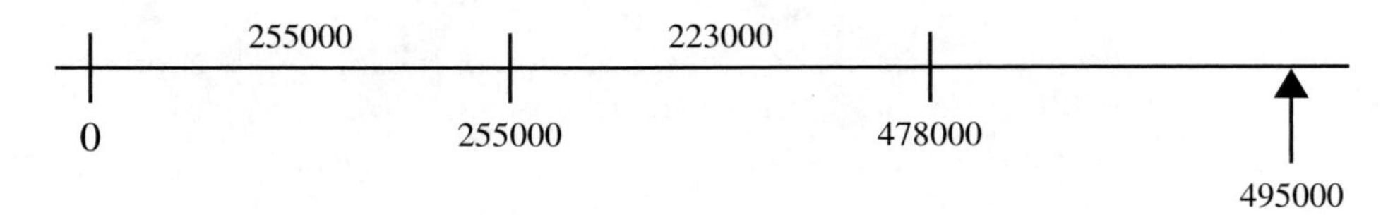

To find the length of the section for net profit, we subtract the breakeven point from the net sales.

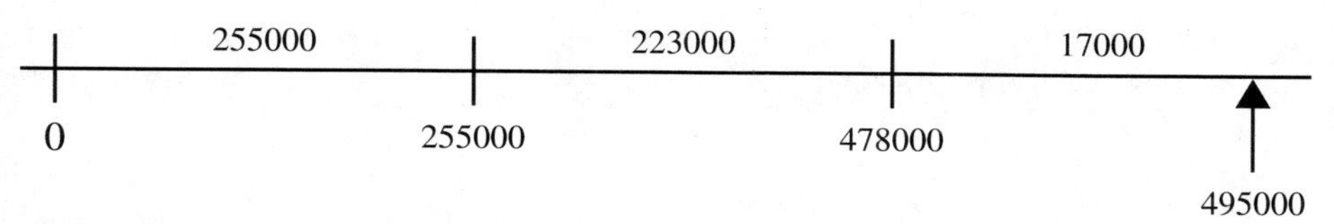

Therefore, Bob's profit was $17,000 last year.

The information provided on the number line diagram can also be displayed in an income statement. An **income statement** is a financial statement which gives a summary of income, expenses, and profit for some period of time. Displayed in Figure 4.1 is a very simplified income statement for Bob's Music Shack.

Bob's Music Shack Income Statement For the Year Ended December 31, 2012	
Net Sales:	$495,000
Cost of Goods Sold:	–$255,000
Gross Profit:	$240,000
Operating Expenses:	–$223,000
Net Profit	$ 17,000

Figure 4.1 A simplified income statement

An actual income statement would provide a lot more detail regarding expenses than this statement does, and we will study these financial statements in a later section. The five entries in this simplified income statement correspond to the five major sections of a more detailed income statement. In this example, we can still see the relationship between the parts of the number line diagram and the major components of the income statement.

We can also use the number line diagram when discussing profit from the sale of a single item of merchandise. To do this, we use net cost in place of cost of goods sold, and selling price in place of net sales. The revised number line would be

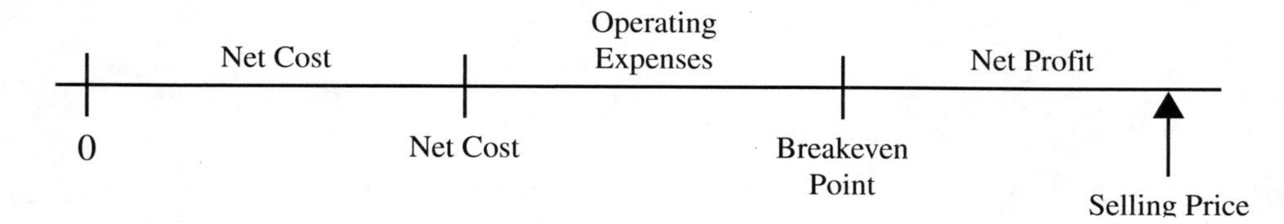

EXAMPLE 2

Valleyview Toys sells a particular model of bicycle for $125 each. It purchased these bicycles for $65 each from its supplier, and estimates that each bicycle ought to be responsible for $40 worth of overhead expenses. Complete the number line diagram.

SOLUTION

First, we place the given information on the number line.

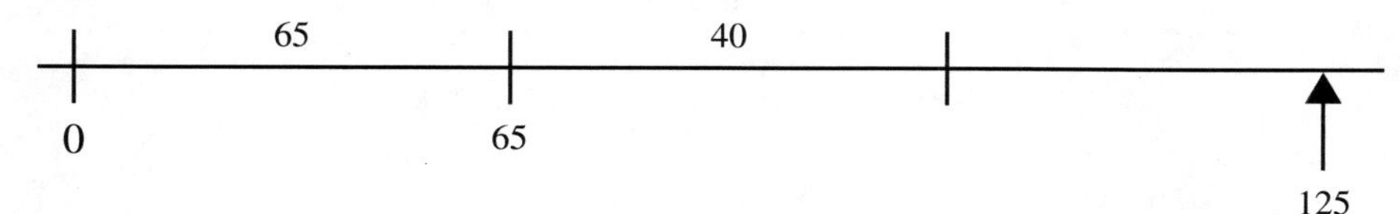

We can add to find the breakeven point, and subtract to find net profit. (In fact, you may have recognized that these were the necessary steps without the number line.) The completed number line diagram is:

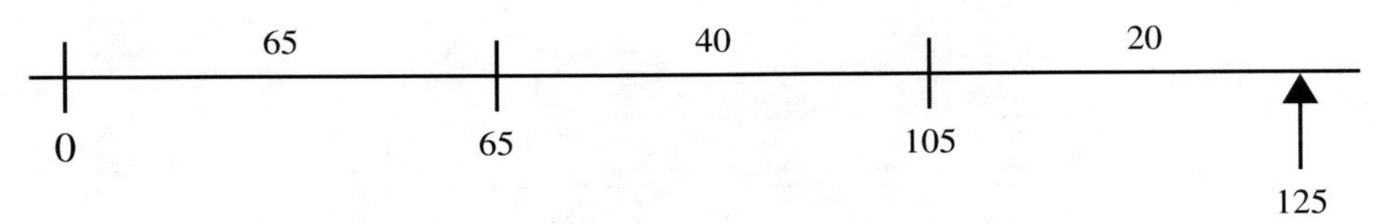

Therefore, Valleyview Toys has a breakeven point of $105 per bicycle, and hopes to earn $20 net profit per bicycle.

EXAMPLE 3

For the sale of a wrench, a store covers $6 in operating expenses, earns $2 net profit, and has a breakeven point of $14. Complete the number line diagram.

SOLUTION

First, we place the given information on the number line.

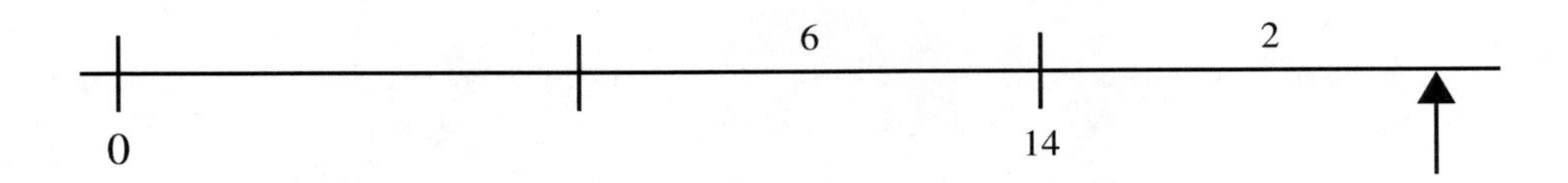

We see that we can add to obtain selling price, and subtract to get net cost.

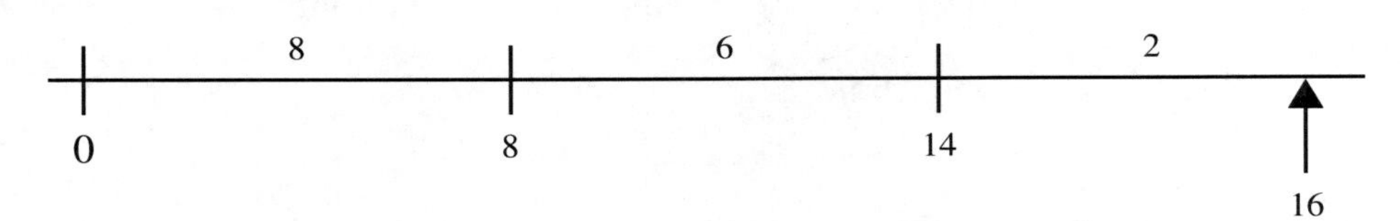

The store's cost for the wrench was $8, and their selling price is $16.

A **loss** occurs when the costs of doing business exceed the income. To use the number line diagram in this situation, we need to make some minor modifications.

The first type of loss we will consider is the **operating loss,** or **net loss.** This type of loss is the amount by which all of the costs, both cost of goods sold and operating expenses, exceed the income. Put another way, it is the amount by which the selling price falls below the breakeven point. The operating loss represents the total loss from the transaction or the year. Do not confuse the operating loss with the operating expenses. Here is the number line diagram for this situation.

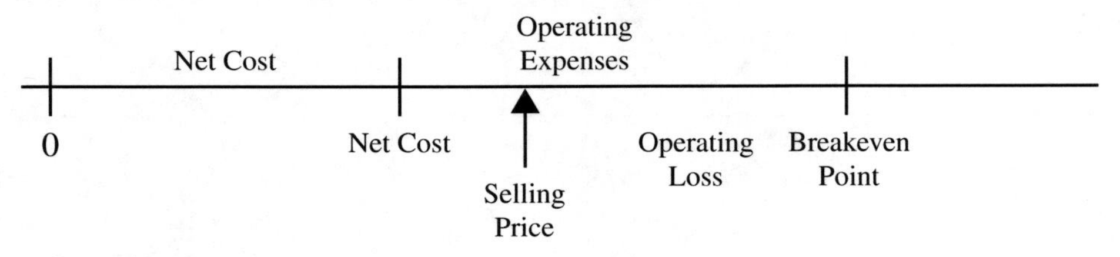

EXAMPLE 4

A kitchen store purchases a mixer for $45 and sells it for $55. Operating expenses are 30% of cost. Find the breakeven point and the operating loss.

SOLUTION

We first compute the operating expenses.

$$45 \times 0.30 = 13.50$$

Therefore, our number line diagram is:

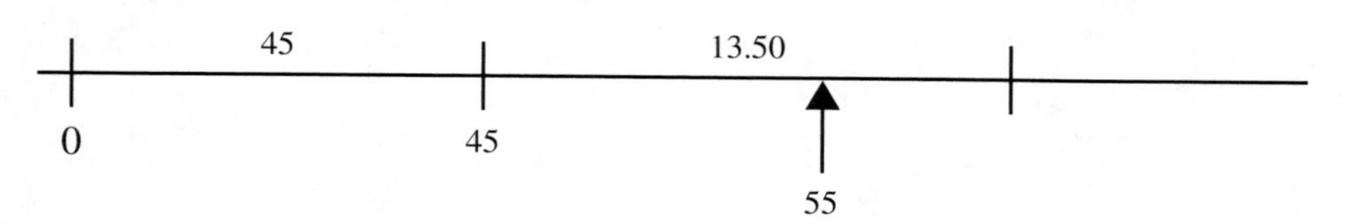

We can complete the number line by adding 45 and 13.50 to get the breakeven point, then subtracting 55 from the breakeven point to get the size of the operating loss.

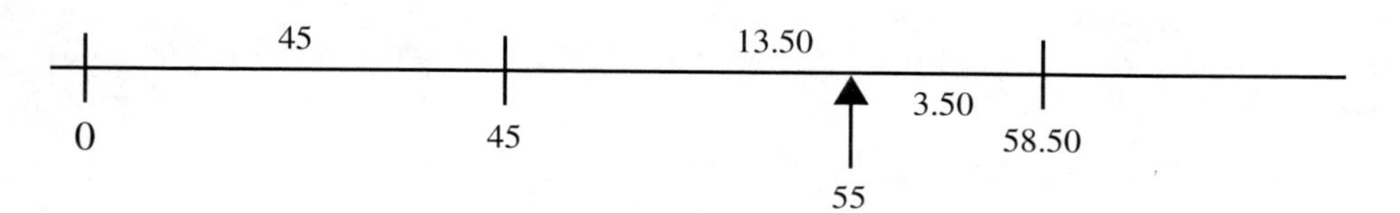

The breakeven point of the sale of the mixer is $58.50, and the operating loss is $3.50.

Losses are not generally described as negative number profits, since the negative sign is too easily overlooked. On financial statements, a loss is typically reported in parentheses, as ($3.50). In other contexts, the word loss should be clearly reported.

Occasionally, a retailer will sell an item below his cost. Here is the number line diagram for this situation.

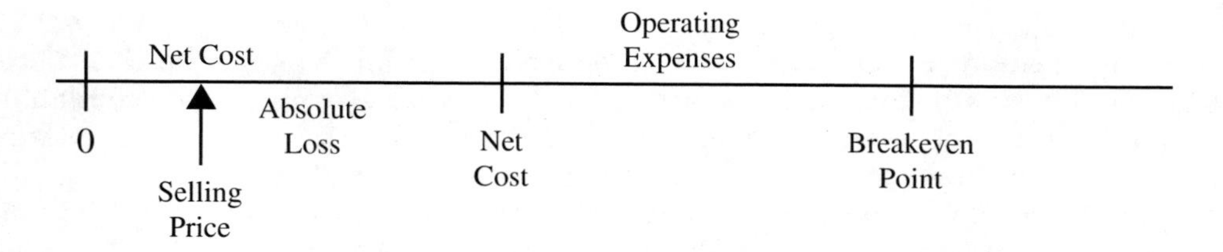

The **absolute loss** is the amount by which the selling price or net sales, falls below the net cost or cost of goods sold. In these situations, a retailer will incur both an absolute loss and an operating loss. The operating loss is still the amount by which the total costs exceed the selling price, or the amount by which the selling price falls below the breakeven point. The absolute loss is a portion of the operating loss, and is never added to it.

EXAMPLE 5

Radios 'n' Phones purchased a certain model of telephone for $35, and operating expenses are 23% of cost. Customers were not impressed with the phone, so the store has put it on sale for $25. What are the operating and absolute losses for the proposed sale?

SOLUTION

The operating expenses are found first.

$$35 \times 0.23 = 8.05$$

The completed number line diagram is:

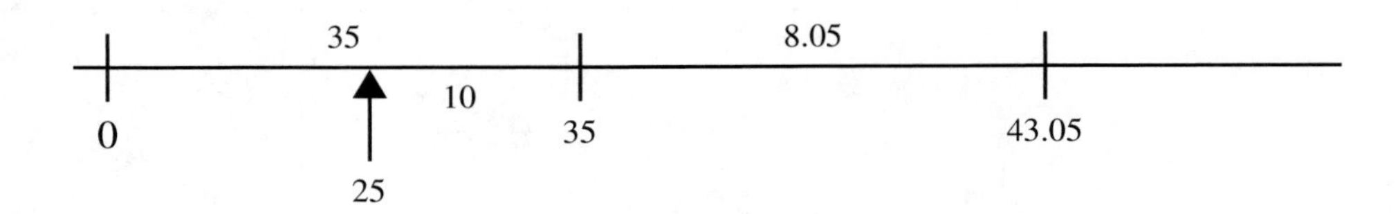

The absolute loss is the amount by which the sale price falls below the net cost. In this case, the absolute loss is $10. The operating loss is the amount by which the sale price falls below the breakeven point. By subtracting $25 from $43.05, (or by adding $10 and $8.05), we get an operating loss of $18.05.

4.2 Trade Discounts

In the remaining sections of this chapter, we will look at some of the details of how a retailing business operates. In the next three sections, we shall begin by looking at how the retailer obtains merchandise to place on the shelves of his store.

As we saw in the last section, retailers need to make a profit to remain in business. That is, they must be able to cover both the cost of the goods they plan to sell, and their overhead expenses. A manufacturer may suggest a **list price** for his merchandise, a price which the final consumer can expect to pay. A retailer cannot purchase goods from a supplier at list price, since that would leave no income to pay operating expenses, nor would there be any profit. A retailer needs a **discount,** or a reduction from a manufacturer's suggested list price. A **trade discount** is a discount offered to provide the retailer the opportunity to cover operating expenses and make a profit. Some suppliers will provide the list price and trade discount in their price information to retailers, and the retailer must be able to compute his cost from the information provided. (Some suppliers will provide cost information directly, especially if there is no suggested list price available.)

In their simplest form, trade discounts are simply percent decrease problems. For this particular type of problem, complements of the percents can be used very effectively in finding dealer costs, since the given list price is the base of the percent problem.

EXAMPLE 1

A vacuum cleaner is nationally advertised for $279. One of the suppliers of Teri's Vacuum Sales offers this machine at 40% trade discount. What will the vacuum cleaner cost Teri?

SOLUTION

Since Teri receives a 40% discount, she pays 60% of the list price. Therefore,

$$279 \times 0.60 = 167.40$$

Teri's cost for the vacuum cleaner will be $167.40.

When the trade discount problem does not provide the list price, then a complement cannot be used, as the base of the percent is not known. For those times, we can use our percent change diagram.

EXAMPLE 2

Value Market paid $93.39 for a particular model of ceiling fan, after their 45% trade discount. What was the suggested list price?

SOLUTION

The percent change diagram is:

100%	*Old*	____
45%	*– Change*	____
____%	*New*	93.39

Subtracting the percents, we find the new percent is 55%. Then we can solve the proportion.

$$93.39 \times 100 \div 55 = 169.80$$

The suggested list price of the ceiling fan was $169.80.

Two or more trade discounts can be combined into a **series discount,** or **chain discount.** For instance, if a supplier offers a 25/15 series discount, that means a 25% trade discount will be taken from list price, and a 15% trade discount will be taken from the discounted price. Complements can also be used very effectively on this type of problem.

EXAMPLE 3

A vacuum cleaner is nationally advertised for $279. Another supplier of Teri's Vacuum Sales offers a 25/15 series discount. What would the vacuum cleaner cost Teri from this supplier?

SOLUTION

A 25/15 series discount means the first discounted price will be 75% of the original list price, and Teri's cost will be 85% of the discounted price. The computation is:

$$279 \times 0.75 \times 0.85 = 177.8625$$

Teri's cost for the vacuum cleaner, which must be rounded to the nearest penny, would be $177.86.

If you compare Example 1 with Example 3, you will see that a 25/15 trade discount is not the same as a 40% trade discount. If you remembered the discussion of compounding from an earlier chapter, you probably expected that the answers would not be the same. The discounts in a series discount should never be added.

So if a 25/15 series discount is not equivalent to 40% off, just how big is a 25/15 trade discount? This can be expressed as a single number. We could set up the percent change problem to find the change needed to decrease $279 to $177.86, and get the answer. But there is another way, since the dollar amounts are actually irrelevant. Here is the computation we did in example 3.

$$279 \times 0.75 \times 0.85 = 177.8625$$

This computation involves only multiplication, and multiplication can be done in any order. You might recall from an earlier math class that our ability to choose which pair of numbers to multiply first is due to the associative property of multiplication. The percents which appear in this problem, complements of the original discount percents, can be multiplied. We get:

$$0.75 \times 0.85 = 0.6375$$

This result, 63.75%, is the percent of the list price paid by the retailer, and is called the **net cost equivalent** of the 25/15 series discount. The cost to the retailer of any item having a 25/15 series discount can be found simply by multiplying the list price by 0.6375. If a retailer deals frequently with a specific series discount, then he can avoid repetitive calculations by using the net cost equivalent in place of the separate discounts of the series. But never round a net cost equivalent. If you do, the answer will lose its ability to find the cost to the retailer.

We can proceed one step further and produce the **single equivalent discount,** or the percent discount from the list price offered by the supplier, by subtracting the net cost equivalent from 100% (in decimal form, 100% = 1).

$$1 - 0.6375 = 0.3625 = 36.25\%$$

Any item having a 25/15 series discount has been discounted 36.25%. Single equivalent discounts should never be rounded, for the same reason as that given for net cost equivalents.

EXAMPLE 4

Find the single equivalent discount for a 30/20/5 series discount.

SOLUTION

We first multiply the complements of the given percent discounts, which gives the net cost equivalent.

$$0.70 \times 0.80 \times 0.95 = 0.532$$

To get the single equivalent discount, we find the complement of the net cost equivalent.

$$1 - 0.532 = 0.468 = 46.8\%$$

Therefore, a 30/20/5 series discount is equivalent to a 46.8% trade discount.

If a supplier offered a retailer a $1,200 item with a 30/20/5 series discount, we could find the cost to the retailer by simply multiplying by the net cost equivalent we found in Example 4. That is

$$1200 \times 0.532 = 638.40$$

EXAMPLE 5

Find the list price of an item whose cost was $600 after a 25/10 series discount.

SOLUTION

Since we do not have the list price, we cannot simply multiply. We will change the 25/10 series discount into a single percent, then use the percent change diagram to obtain the list price. The net cost equivalent is:

$$0.75 \times 0.90 = 0.675 = 67.5\%$$

Therefore, the percent change diagram is:

100.0%	*Old*	_____
_____%	*– Change*	_____
67.5%	*New*	600.00

Solving the proportion, we get:

$$600 \times 100 \div 67.5 \approx 888.89$$

The list price of the item was $888.89 (rounded to the nearest penny).

EXAMPLE 6

Swiss Time is offering a wall clock to their retailers at $59 less 55%. Beaver State Clocks, a competitor, has a similar model priced at $62 less 40%. What additional percent discount is needed for Beaver State to match Swiss Time's price?

SOLUTION

First, it would be useful to know exactly what the cost of each clock is. Swiss Time's clock costs:

$$59 \times 0.45 = 26.55$$

Beaver State's clock costs:

$$62 \times 0.60 = 37.20$$

Therefore, we need to find out what discount would decrease $37.20 to $26.55. The percent change diagram is:

100%	*Old*	37.20
_____%	*– Change*	_____
_____%	*New*	26.55

We are looking for the percent change. The dollar amount of the change is $10.65, which we can then use in a proportion formed by the first two rows. The computation becomes:

$$10.65 \times 100 \div 37.20 \approx 28.62903$$

Therefore, Beaver State needs to offer approximately an additional 29%. Actually, 29% would be a little larger discount than necessary, and 28% would have been too small, but using 28.63%

would involve too much extra time on the part of the supplier to make it worthwhile. Most likely, the supplier would simply offer an additional 30% off, as long as his profit level is still acceptable. That is, Beaver State would now offer (possibly for a limited time) a 40/30 series discount.

Suppliers may offer retailers **volume discounts** in order to encourage their retailers to purchase larger quantities. Consider the following example.

EXAMPLE 7

Carter Electronics offers retailers a portable DVD player for $129 each, plus a trade discount of 35%. If a retailer orders at least 12 DVD players, an additional 5% volume discount is available. How much will 18 DVD players cost a retailer?

SOLUTION

The trade and volume discounts together act just like a series discount, so we will use their complements. Also, we need to remember to find the cost for all 18 DVD players. So our computation is:

$$18 \times 129 \times 0.65 \times 0.95 \approx 1433.835$$

Since the final answer must be rounded to the nearest penny, we find that the 18 DVD players will cost $1,433.84.

4.3 Cash Discounts

There is another type of discount retailers may receive from their suppliers. When a retailer receives merchandise from a supplier, an invoice is included. In addition to information about items and quantity purchased, the invoice provided by the supplier will also include terms that describe when payment is due, and possibly additional discounts. A **cash discount** may be offered by the supplier to encourage a retailer to make prompt payment on the invoice.

An example of a typical cash discount is 2/10. Although it looks just like the series discounts of the last section, this cash discount is interpreted differently. This example means a 2% discount is available if the invoice is paid by the tenth day after the invoice date. The cash discount is computed in the same fashion as the trade discount, and the use of complements is very effective in most situations.

If the invoice is not paid within the cash discount period, then the cash discount cannot be taken. In that case, the retailer must pay the **net** amount, the amount remaining after trade discounts are taken, by the net due date. This information often appears in the form net/20 or n/20. Each of these examples specifies that the net due date is 20 days after the invoice date. If the net due date is not specified by the invoice, then (with ordinary dating) the net due date is 30 days after the invoice date.

Shipping information is also provided in an invoice. The **FOB,** or **Free on Board,** specifies the destinations for which the seller will provide free shipping. For all other destinations, a shipping charge should be added. Shipping charges should never be discounted, so they are the last item to be considered when finding the total due on an invoice.

EXAMPLE 1

Complete the following invoice. Then find the last date the cash discount is available, the net due date, and the amounts due from the retailer for each date.

From: Mack's Computer Warehouse, Palo Alto, California
Date: May 17, 2012
Terms: 3/5, n/20
FOB: California

To: The Byte Shack, McCall, Idaho

Quantity	Item	Unit Price	Gross	Trade Discount	Net
5	Notebook computers	995.00 each	______	55%	______
2 dozen	CD-RW drives	59.00 each	______	40/10	______
3 gross	DVD+R discs	0.30 each	______	35/15/5	______
				Shipping:	50.00
				Total:	______

SOLUTION

The gross amounts are found by simply multiplying the quantity purchased by the unit price. We must also remember that there are 12 items in a **dozen,** and 144 items in a **gross.** The computations are:

$$5 \times 995 = 4975$$

$$2 \times 12 \times 59 = 1416$$

$$3 \times 144 \times 0.30 = 129.60$$

The net column is found by applying the trade discounts to the gross amounts. We shall use the complements of the trade discounts. The computations are:

$$4975 \times 0.45 = 2238.75$$

$$1416 \times 0.60 \times 0.90 = 764.64$$

$$129.60 \times 0.65 \times 0.85 \times 0.95 \approx 68.02$$

Since the FOB information (California) does not match the destination (Idaho), there is a shipping charge. We then add the net amounts in the last column to the $50 shipping charge.

$$2238.75 + 764.64 + 68.02 + 50.00 = 3121.41$$

Therefore, our completed invoice is:

From:	Mack's Computer Warehouse Palo Alto, California		Date: May 17, 2012 Terms: 3/5, n/20 FOB: California		
To:	The Byte Shack McCall, Idaho				
Quantity	Item	Unit Price	Gross	Trade Discount	Net
5	Notebook computers	995.00 each	4975.00	55%	2238.75
2 dozen	CD-RW drives	59.00 each	1416.00	40/10	764.64
3 gross	DVD+R discs	0.30 each	129.60	35/15/5	68.02
				Shipping:	50.00
				Total:	3121.41

The terms specify that the 3% cash discount expires 5 days after May 17. Therefore, the last date the cash discount is available is May 22. But the cash discount applies only to the merchandise, not the shipping. So we must remove the shipping first, then apply the 3% discount, and then add the shipping back on.

$$3121.41 - 50.00 = 3071.41$$

$$3071.41 \times 0.97 \approx 2979.27$$

$$2979.27 + 50.00 = 3029.27$$

If paid by May 22, a total of $3,029.27 would be sufficient to pay the invoice in full.

If not paid by May 22, then the net amount is due. As specified in the terms, the net due date occurs 20 days after the invoice date. Therefore, $3,121.41 is due on or before June 8.

Invoices from most suppliers will include the shipping charges in the total. As we did in Example 1, to deduct cash discounts in these cases, the shipping charge must be subtracted before computing the cash discount, then added back onto the result.

EXAMPLE 2

Ann receives an invoice dated August 15 for $3,850.45, and the total includes a $174.50 shipping charge. The terms of the invoice are 2/10, n/25, and a 5% penalty for late payments. How much should she pay on the following dates: August 23, September 3, September 13?

SOLUTION

The last day of the cash discount is August 25. If Ann pays on August 23, she is entitled to the 2% discount off of her merchandise, but not off of her shipping. The computation is:

$$3850.45 - 174.50 = 3675.95$$

$$3675.95 \times 0.98 \approx 3602.43$$

$$3602.43 + 174.50 = 3776.93$$

Therefore, if Ann pays the invoice on August 23, she should pay $3,776.93.

September 3 is nineteen days after the invoice, and on that day Ann should pay the net amount of $3,850.45.

The net amount is due 25 days after the invoice date, which is September 9. If Ann pays on September 13, she is paying late, and must pay the 5% late penalty. The late penalty applies to the shipping charge as well as the merchandise, since both are being paid late. We can compute the total paid by using an augmented percent.

$$3850.45 \times 1.05 = 4042.97$$

If Ann pays the invoice on September 13, she should pay $4042.97.

Day counting is important when dealing with invoices and payment terms. Although short periods of time are easy to handle (as in the previous example), longer periods can cause some difficulty due to the varying number of days in each month. One of the most efficient methods for counting days when dealing with longer periods of time is to use a **Table of Days,** which gives the day number of the year for each date of the year. A Table of Days is included in the appendix. We shall demonstrate the use of the Table of Days as we consider the following cash discount examples.

EXAMPLE 3

An invoice for $755, dated October 24, has terms of 2/50, n/90. Find the last date for the cash discount, the net due date, and the amounts due from the retailer for each date.

Solution

The terms specify that the 2% cash discount expires 50 days after October 24. The Table of Days identifies October 24 as day 297 of the year. Adding 50 days will bring us to day 347, or December 13. On or before that day, the retailer should pay:

$$755 \times 0.98 = 739.90$$

The net due date is 90 days after October 24. Adding 90 days to day 297 is day 387. But a year only has 365 days, so the net due date falls in the following year. Subtracting 365 from 387, we find it falls on the 22nd day of the following year, or January 22. On or before that date, the retailer should pay the net amount, $755.

The Table of Days is made for a typical year. However, every fourth year is a leap year having 366 days, due to the inclusion of February 29. Specifically, leap years are those years which are divisible by 4, namely 2012, 2016, 2020, 2024, and so on. (Actually, there are exceptions to this rule, but the next exception occurs in the year 2100, when few of us will be around to care.) When using the Table of Days during a leap year, a correction must be made when the time period being found starts before February 29 and ends after February 29. For dates on or after March 1 in those situations, you must add 1 to the day number given by the table.

EXAMPLE 4

An invoice for $386 has terms of 3/5, 1/15, and is dated February 21, 2012. Find the last date for each cash discount, the net due date, and the amounts due on each date.

Solution

When multiple cash discounts are offered, only one discount may be taken. The first discount expires 5 days after February 21, which is February 26. (We didn't need the Table of Days for that computation.) On or before February 26, the retailer should pay:

$$386 \times 0.97 = 374.42$$

The second discount expires 15 days after February 21. The table of days identifies February 21 as day 52. Adding 15 days brings us to day 67, which occurs in March. But since this is a leap year and our time period will include February 29, the day numbers in the table for March are one off. We look for day 66 (which would be day 67 after one is added), and find March 7. On or before March 7, the retailer should pay:

$$386 \times 0.99 = 382.14$$

The net due date is not specified, so we count 30 days from February 21 (or 15 days from March 7, the last cash discount date). The net amount, $386, is due on or before March 22.

In addition to the ordinary cash discount methods described above, there are several other methods in use, which modify the ordinary method by the use of suffixes. We shall consider three such variations.

End-of-month, or **EOM,** dating modifies the cash discount period so the last day of the cash discount period is the specified number of days after the end of a month. For instance, 2/10 EOM indicates that a 2% cash discount is available if the invoice is paid by the tenth day after the end of the month of the invoice date. If, however, the invoice was dated on the 26th of the month or later, standard practice is to allow an additional month for the cash discount period. Sometimes, the suffix **prox** may be used instead of EOM. This suffix comes from the Latin word **proximo,** which means "into the next month". The effect is identical. EOM or prox dating is useful for the supplier who desires all of his accounts to be on the same billing cycle.

With EOM dating, if the net due date is not specified, then it is typically assumed to be 20 days after the cash discount expired.

EXAMPLE 5

An invoice is dated April 14, with terms of 2/10 EOM. Find the last day of the cash discount period, and the net due date.

SOLUTION

The cash discount period ends 10 days after the end of the month of April. In other words, it ends May 10. The net due date will be 20 days later, on May 30.

EXAMPLE 6

An invoice is dated June 29, and has terms of 1/15 prox. Find the last day of the cash discount period, and the net due date.

SOLUTION

Since the invoice is dated after the 25th, we skip a month. The cash discount period ends 15 days into the next month after July. That is, it ends August 15. The net due date is September 4.

A supplier can offer additional time for a cash discount through the use of **extra,** or **X,** dating. An example is 2/20–50X, which means that a 2% cash discount is available until 70 days (the original 20 days plus an extra 50 days) after the invoice date. This example is also commonly abbreviated 2/20–50 ex, and has the same meaning. This style of dating is useful for the supplier who deals in seasonal merchandise, and wants to encourage the retailer to order early.

The net due date default rule for extra dating is the same as for EOM dating. Add 20 days to the last day of the cash discount period to get the net due date.

EXAMPLE 7

An invoice is dated November 20, with terms of 2/30–80X. Find the last date for the cash discount, and the net due date.

SOLUTION

The cash discount period ends 110 days after November 20. The Table of Days indicates that November 20 is day 324. Adding 110 days, we get day 434. Since this date is in the next year, we subtract 365 to get day 69. Therefore, the last discount date is March 10, and the net due date is March 30. (However, if the due date occurs in a leap year, then the last discount date would occur on March 9, and the net due date would be March 29.)

In every one of the above examples and methods, the cash discount is computed from the date of the invoice. A retailer will probably not receive the merchandise on the same day that the invoice was dated, but normally the difference is small enough to avoid being a problem. However, if a supplier back orders merchandise, they may still wish to provide the retailer an invoice, but not require payment until the merchandise is received by the retailer. **Receipt-of-goods,** or **ROG,** dating will accomplish this purpose. For example, the terms 2/10 ROG specify that the 2% cash discount is available if the invoice is paid by the tenth day after the retailer has received the goods. ROG dating is the only time when the date a retailer receives his order is relevant.

As with the other two alternate methods, the net due date for ROG dating is also 20 days after the cash discount expires.

EXAMPLE 8

An invoice was dated March 5, with terms of 1/10 ROG. The retailer received the merchandise on April 28. When does the cash discount expire? When is the net amount due?

SOLUTION

The cash discount period ends ten days after April 28. Adding ten days to day 118 (April 28), we get day 128, which is May 8. If the invoice is paid after May 8, no cash discount applies, and the invoice amount is due May 28.

4.4 Markups

As we mentioned in a previous section, a retailer cannot stay in business by selling merchandise at the same price he paid for it. The retailer must have a **markup,** or increase over the price he paid. The purpose of the markup is to cover operating expenses and provide a net profit. You may further recall that the gross profit also consisted of operating expenses and net profit. That is, the dollar value of the gross profit and the markup are the same. Markup typically views operating expenses and net profit as an increase over a cost, whereas gross profit views these same two items as a portion of the selling price. The markup can also be displayed on the number line diagram.

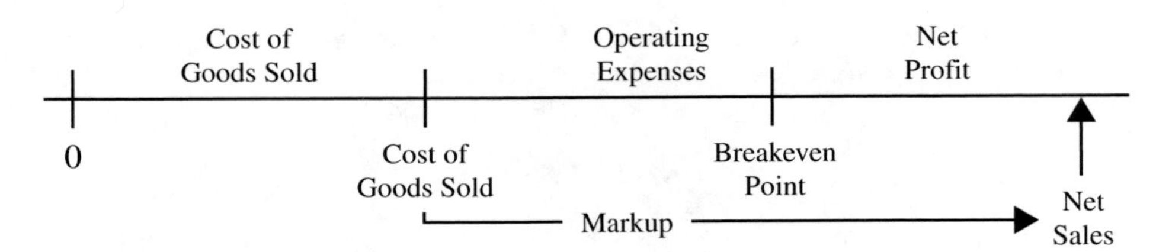

Markup amounts must be proportional to the cost of the merchandise. To see why, imagine a general store that sells both ballpoint pens and dining room tables. Although a dining room table might be marked up from $150 to $250 for customer purchase, no customer would buy a ballpoint pen that has been marked up by $100.

Once we recognize that markups are proportional to the cost of the merchandise, we need to identify the base of the percent. Should the base be the dealer cost, from which the markup is increased to obtain a selling price? Or should the base be the selling price, from which a certain amount is earmarked for operating expenses and net profit? These two possibilities reflect the two views of markup stated in the first paragraph of this section. In fact, both methods are used (but not simultaneously), since different businesses have different needs.

When we want to use the cost as the base in a markup problem, we shall refer to the percent as a **markup on cost.** If we want the selling price to be the base of the percent markup, we shall refer to the percent as a **markup on selling price.** We will use a **markup diagram,** which is a variation of the percent change diagram. (We use this variation in order to avoid problems of interpretation regarding the base, the old quantity, and the placement of the 100%.) The form of our markup diagram is:

____%	*Cost*	$____
____%	*+ Markup*	$____
____%	*Selling Price*	$____

We shall abbreviate the markup diagram as:

____%	C	$____
____%	$+M$	$____
____%	S	$____

The 100% will be placed to identify the base, so it could appear either next to the cost or next to the selling price. The proportion is solved in the same fashion as the percent change diagram was solved. Notice that the markup is always added to the cost in the markup diagram. Only the placement of the 100% changes in the two methods, as it identifies the base.

EXAMPLE 1

A retailer purchases wicker baskets for $14 each, and uses a 70% markup on cost. Find the retail price of these baskets.

Solution

The markup diagram will be:

100%	C	$14.00
70%	$+M$	$____
____%	S	$____

Adding the cost and markup percents, we find that the selling price percent will be 170%. Solving the proportion, we obtain:

$$170 \times 14.00 \div 100 = 23.80$$

The wicker baskets will sell for $23.80 each.

You should notice that a markup on cost problem is simply a standard percent increase problem. You should recognize the 170% selling price percent as the augmented percent of 70%, which occurs in every percent increase problem.

EXAMPLE 2

All-Sports purchases basketballs at $18.50 each, to which they apply a markup on selling price of 40% to cover their operating expenses. Find the selling price of the basketballs.

SOLUTION

The markup diagram is:

____%	C	$18.50
40%	$+M$	$____
100%	S	$____

The cost and markup percents must add to the selling price percent. Therefore, we subtract 40% from 100% to obtain the cost percent of 60%. Then we solve the proportion for the selling price.

$$18.50 \times 100 \div 60 \approx 30.8333$$

Rounding to the nearest penny, we find that the selling price of a basketball would be $30.83.

Notice that a markup on selling price is not a standard percent increase problem. The augmented percent of 40% did not occur in this problem. In fact, the complement of 40% appeared, which occurs both in percent decrease problems and in problems where the percent is part of a total. Although a markup on selling price can be described as the inverse to a percent decrease problem, it is actually most easily understood as a quantity that is a part of the total sales. You should find it much easier to use a markup diagram rather than any other approach, since you would be able to avoid the difficulty of remembering which approach to use.

The next two examples demonstrate that the markup diagram can also be used when the cost is not the given information.

EXAMPLE 3

After a 75% markup on cost, a cartoon character lunch box sells for $12.95. What was the cost?

SOLUTION

The markup diagram is:

100%	C	____
75%	$+M$	____
____%	S	12.95

We can add the cost and markup percents to get the selling price percent, 175%. Then we set up and solve the proportion.

$$12.95 \times 100 \div 175 = 7.40$$

The lunch box originally cost the retailer $7.40.

EXAMPLE 4

Coffee Beans wants to sell a coffee maker for $49.95, in order to meet a competitor's price. If they need a markup of 30% on selling price, what can they afford to pay for this coffee maker?

SOLUTION

The markup diagram for this problem is:

____%	C	____
30%	$+M$	____
100%	S	49.95

We then subtract to obtain the cost percent of 70%. Using this in a proportion, we find:

$$49.95 \times 70 \div 100 \approx 34.965$$

The cost of the coffee maker to the retailer should be about $34.97. That is, if Coffee Beans has a supplier who will sell them a coffee maker at less than $34.97, they can beat their competitor's price and retain their profit too.

EXAMPLE 5

A music store purchases an electric guitar for $450 and sells it for $799. What was the markup on selling price?

SOLUTION

By asking for the markup on selling price, the answer will not be just the dollar amount, but rather a percent, because a base (selling price) was given. The markup diagram would be:

____%	C	450
____%	$+M$	____
100%	S	799

Subtracting the cost from the selling price gives a markup of $349. The computation is:

$$349 \times 100 \div 799 \approx 43.68$$

The guitar was marked up by 43.68% on selling price.

Having two different systems of markup is like having two different currencies. Although we may be used to thinking in terms of dollars rather than euros, both work equally well in placing value on different items. So it is with the two types of markups.

EXAMPLE 6

Which is the larger markup, 40% on cost or 35% on selling price?

SOLUTION

If the two markups were of the same type, we could simply compare the rates. But because the bases are different, the rates alone are not sufficient to determine the answer. Since cost is always smaller than selling price, in this problem we see that the larger rate has the smaller base, and the smaller rate has the larger base. Which is more important, the base or the rate? It depends on the numbers.

A conceptually easy way to determine which markup is larger is to choose a dollar amount for cost, and apply (separately) both markups to that cost. The dollar amount used for the cost is irrelevant, so we shall arbitrarily choose $500. We set up two markup diagrams. The first is for the 40% markup on cost, and the second is for the 35% markup on selling price.

100%	C	500.00	____%	C	500.00
40%	$+M$	____	35%	$+M$	____
____%	S	____	100%	S	____

Completing both diagrams, we get:

100%	C	500.00	65%	C	500.00
40%	$+M$	200.00	35%	$+M$	269.23
140%	S	700.00	100%	S	769.23

Comparing the results, we see that the 35% markup on selling price provided a larger dollar markup, and a larger selling price.

4.5 Shrinkage

Retailers often cannot sell all of the merchandise they place in stock. Some of the reasons for this inability include shoplifting, employee theft, spoilage, or breakage. **Shrinkage** is the general term used to describe the occurrence of unsaleable merchandise.

Retailers often refer to shrinkage as a loss. In this context, a loss means a decrease in the merchandise available for sale. When considering a single item of unsaleable merchandise, since the costs of the item were not covered by income from its sale, a dollar loss also occurred. When considering a retailer's sales for an entire year, the income received will normally be greater than the costs (in spite of shrinkage), so a retailer will not show a dollar loss on his income tax return. Shrinkage losses, therefore, refer to the loss of the ability to sell individual items of merchandise.

It is possible for a retailer to experience too much shrinkage in his merchandise and sustain a dollar loss for the year. Such losses are unacceptable in order for a retailer to remain in business. Therefore, retailers must pass on the costs due to shrinkage to their customers. When the cost due to shrinkage, or **adjustment,** is added to the net cost, the result is called the **adjusted cost.** In order to insure a profit, a retailer must use the adjusted cost in place of the net cost in his computations.

Shrinkage may be expressed as a percent decrease or as a quantity decrease in the merchandise available. The fact that shrinkage is a decrease means the adjustment needed must reverse the effect of the decrease. A markup on selling price has the necessary characteristics to perform the adjustment. Here is the general appearance of a shrinkage problem.

____%	C	$ Cost
____%	$+M$	$ Adjustment
100%	S	$ Adjusted Cost

Note that in the same fashion as markup problems, the adjustment is added to the cost.

EXAMPLE 1

Kenny's Discount Store purchases calculators at a cost of $17.67 each. If Kenny typically experiences shrinkage of 7% of his merchandise, what is the amount of the adjusted cost and the adjustment due to shrinkage?

Solution

First, we set up the markup diagram.

____%	C	17.67
7%	$+M$	____
100%	S	____

We can find the cost percent by subtracting, and it is 93%. This value has meaning in the context of this problem, since a 7% loss of merchandise means that Kenny will have 93% of his merchandise remaining to sell. Then we can complete the markup diagram, using proportions as before.

93%	C	17.67
7%	$+M$	1.33
100%	S	19.00

The adjusted cost of each calculator is $19.00. The adjustment due to shrinkage was $1.33. Kenny must still markup up his merchandise to cover operating expenses and make a profit. In doing so, he must use the adjusted cost of $19.00 in these computations, not the net cost of $17.67.

It is tempting to try to cover a 7% shrinkage loss with a 7% increase in costs. In the first example, this would produce an adjusted cost of approximately $18.91. Obviously, this approach gives a smaller answer, but more importantly, this answer would not be sufficient to cover the costs. Imagine, for a moment, that Kenny purchased 100 calculators at $17.67 each, for a total cost of $1767. After 7% shrinkage, an adjusted cost of $18.91 for the 93 remaining calculators would cover a total cost of:

$$93 \times 18.91 = 1758.63$$

This leaves $8.37 of the total cost unaccounted for. But an adjusted cost of $19.00 for the 93 remaining calculators gives:

$$93 \times 19.00 = 1767.00$$

An adjustment for shrinkage that uses a markup on selling price will allow all of the costs of shrinkage to be covered. A markup on net cost will always fall short.

EXAMPLE 2

Tina's Produce buys bananas at $42 per hundred pounds, and she expects 15% to spoil. Tina needs a 20% markup on selling price to cover operating expenses. What should the selling price of the bananas be, per pound?

SOLUTION

First, we take shrinkage into account and find the adjusted cost. The markup diagram is:

____%	C	42.00
15%	$+M$	____
100%	S	____

The cost percent will be 85%. To find the adjusted cost, we use proportions.

$$42 \times 100 \div 85 \approx 49.4118$$

That is, the adjusted cost of 100 pounds of bananas is approximately $49.41. (Actually, since we are in the middle of the problem, we will try to minimize possible rounding errors at this point by keeping two additional decimal places.) Now we will add a markup of 20% on the selling price.

____%	C	49.4118
20%	$+M$	____
100%	S	____

For this markup, the cost percent is 80%. Solving this proportion, we get:

$$49.4118 \times 100 \div 80 \approx 61.76$$

Therefore, 100 pounds of bananas would sell for $61.76. Dividing by 100, we find that the selling price per pound would be about 62 cents.

Although the adjustment due to shrinkage is always handled by a markup on selling price, the markup for operating expenses could be either on cost or on selling price. Therefore, when finding selling prices in problems that involve shrinkage, pay close attention to the type of markup for the second half of the problem.

Some shrinkage problems are given as quantity decreases rather than percent decreases. The next example illustrates this situation.

EXAMPLE 3

Mirror Central purchases 36 mirrors for a total cost of $540. They all arrive at the store in good condition, but two are broken when placing them on the shelf. The retailer needs an 80% markup on cost. What should the selling price of each mirror be?

SOLUTION

The first step is to determine the adjusted cost. We could determine the rate of shrinkage, but it is easier to simply spread the total cost over the remaining 34 mirrors.

$$540 \div 34 \approx 15.8824$$

The adjusted cost of each mirror is approximately $15.88. To cover operating expenses, the markup diagram is:

100%	C	15.8824
80%	$+M$	____
____%	S	____

The selling price percent in the markup diagram will be 180%. Solving the proportion, we get:

$$15.8824 \times 180 \div 100 \approx 28.59$$

The selling price of each mirror should be approximately $28.59.

Sometimes the costs of shrinkage for merchandise cannot be passed on to the consumer, because either the selling price is either nationally advertised, or the merchandise comes with a preprinted selling price. In such cases, the retailer must determine the consequences of possible shrinkage to his profit, and the possible consequences of not carrying an item demanded by his customers if the loss would be too great.

EXAMPLE 4

The bookstore at Spring River College sells a particular textbook for $129.95. They receive a 40% trade discount from their supplier, and their operating expenses are 25% of cost. They also expect 5% shrinkage due to theft. How much profit can the bookstore expect from the sale of this textbook?

SOLUTION

Using the complement of the 40% trade discount, we find the net cost is:

$$129.95 \times 0.60 = 77.97$$

The markup diagram used to counteract the shrinkage is:

_____%	C	77.97
5%	$+M$	_____
100%	S	_____

The cost percent will be 95%. Solving the proportion, we get:

$$77.97 \times 100 \div 95 \approx 82.0737$$

The adjusted cost is approximately $82.07. Operating expenses will be based on this amount, not on the net cost, because it is only the adjusted cost which can account for the total costs. Since operating expenses are 25% of cost, we get:

$$82.07 \times 0.25 \approx 20.52$$

Therefore, it is intended that this textbook also cover approximately $20.52 in operating expenses. We can set up a number line diagram to sort out the details. The completed number line diagram is:

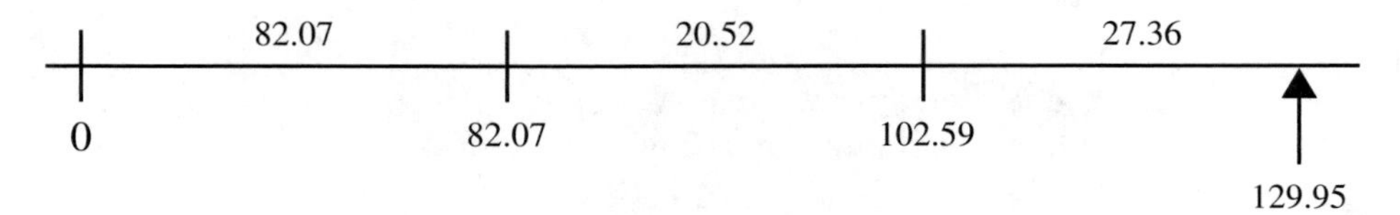

The store has a breakeven point of $102.59 per textbook. In spite of the loss due to shrinkage, they will still have a profit of $27.36 per textbook.

4.6 Markdowns

Price reductions are a common feature of retailing. In earlier sections we studied discounts, or price reductions offered by suppliers to the retailers. Price reductions offered by retailers to the general public are called **markdowns.** Markdowns are standard percent decrease problems, and the first three examples are typical markdown problems.

EXAMPLE 1

Benson Office Furniture is offering 20% off of all merchandise. If a desk regularly sells for $350, what is its sale price?

SOLUTION

The quickest way to find the sale price is to use the complement of 20%. We get:

$$350 \times 0.80 = 280$$

The sale price of the desk is $280.

EXAMPLE 2

Kathy's Kitchenware has a dinnerware set regularly priced at $139.95. This week she offers it at $\frac{1}{3}$ off. What is the sale price?

SOLUTION

The markdown in this problem is expressed as a fraction rather than a percent. We could change it to a percent in order to get a complement, but it is also possible to use the complement of a fraction. If a customer does not pay $\frac{1}{3}$ of the price, then they do pay $\frac{2}{3}$ of the price. Therefore,

$$139.95 \times \frac{2}{3} = 93.30$$

The sale price of the dinnerware set is $93.30.

EXAMPLE 3

A jewelry box has been marked down from $75 to $62. What percent markdown can the retailer advertise?

SOLUTION

We can use the percent change diagram to find markdown rates. The initial diagram is:

100%	*Old*	75.00
____%	*– Change*	____
____%	*New*	62.00

We first subtract $62 from $75 to get the dollar amount of the markdown, $13. Then we can solve the proportion.

$$13 \times 100 \div 75 \approx 17.33$$

A 17.33% markdown on the price of the jewelry box can be advertised.

When a markdown is offered, a retailer's profit will be reduced. Care must be taken so that the retailer does not wipe out his entire profit and incur a loss instead. The examples which follow are more concerned about the retailer's position after the markdown.

EXAMPLE 4

Valley Furnishings purchases a sofa for $450, which they mark up 40% on selling price. The sofa is sold during a storewide 15% off sale. What was the selling price of the sofa, and what percent markup (on the sale price) did Valley Furnishings finally get on the sale of the sofa?

SOLUTION

We use a markup diagram to find the original selling price.

____%	C	450.00
40%	$+M$	____
100%	S	____

We find the cost percent is 60%, and the selling price is:

$$450 \times 100 \div 60 = 750$$

For the 15% off sale, we use the complement to find the sale price.

$$750 \times 0.85 = 637.50$$

It may be tempting to expect that the 40% markup would be reduced to 25% by the 15% markdown. After all, both the 40% markup and the 15% markdown had the same base, namely the $750 selling price. But the markup we need will have the sale price as the base. The markup diagram is:

____%	C	450.00
____%	$+M$	____
100%	S	637.50

Subtracting the dollar amounts, we find the final markup was $187.50. The percent markup is found by computing:

$$187.50 \times 100 \div 637.50 \approx 29.41$$

Therefore, Valley Furnishings will have had a 29.41% markup on selling price for the sale of its sofa.

The result of the previous example is actually independent of the dollar amount involved. That is, whenever a 40% markup on selling price is followed by a 15% markdown, the result is equivalent to a 29.41% markup on the (reduced) selling price. As always, care must be taken when dealing with rates, as they cannot generally be added or subtracted.

EXAMPLE 5

Fannie's Fragrant Fantasies purchases perfume from their supplier for $20 per bottle. They mark up the price 250% on cost, and later have a 60% off sale. Operating expenses are 65% of cost. Does Fannie's incur a net profit or an operating loss for a bottle sold at the sale price? How much?

Solution

The markup diagram for a bottle of perfume is:

100%	C	$20
250%	$+M$	_____
_____%	S	_____

The selling price percent will be 350%, and the regular selling price can be found by solving a proportion.

$$20 \times 350 \div 100 = 70$$

The regular selling price will be $70 per bottle. The sale price is found by multiplying the selling price by the complement of the markdown.

$$70 \times 0.40 = 28$$

Operating expenses are:

$$20 \times 0.65 = 13$$

This information can be arranged on a number line diagram. The completed number line diagram is:

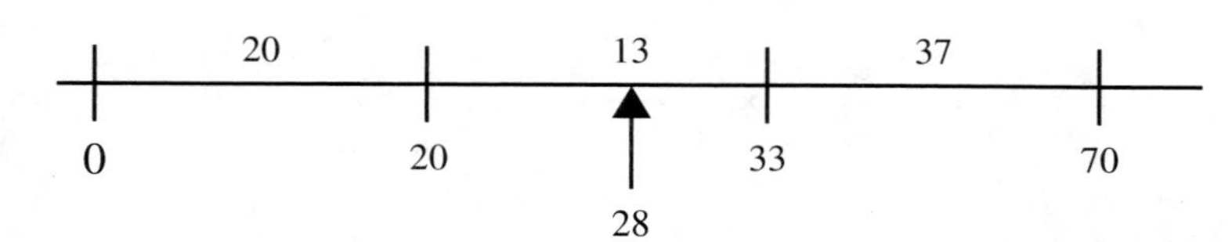

From the number line diagram, we see that the $28 sale price is below the $33 breakeven point, and subtracting will find the value of that operating loss:

$$33 - 28 = 5$$

Fannie's Fragrant Fantasies will incur a $5 operating loss when they sell the perfume at a price $5 below their breakeven point.

EXAMPLE 6

A sports store purchases an exercise machine for $169. They markup the machine 75% on cost, and operating expenses are 40% of cost. What is the largest possible markdown they can offer without incurring any loss?

Solution

The markup diagram for the exercise machine is:

100%	C	169.00
75%	$\underline{+M}$	_____
_____%	S	_____

The selling price percent is 175%, and the regular selling price can be obtained by solving the resulting proportion.

$$169 \times 175 \div 100 = 295.75$$

Operating expenses are found as a percent of the cost.

$$169.00 \times 0.40 = 67.60$$

This information is placed on a number line diagram. The completed diagram is:

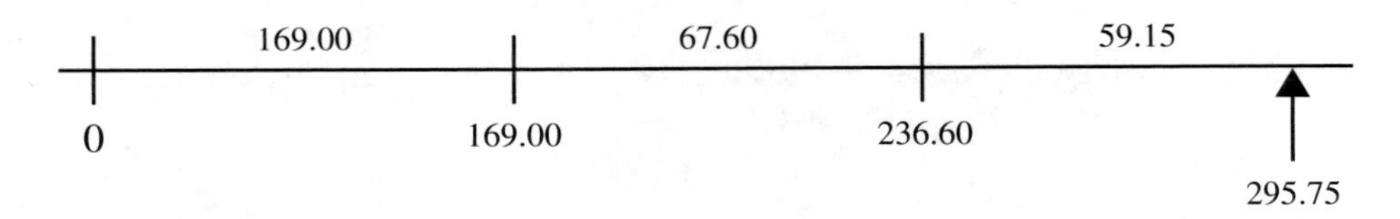

The largest dollar markdown that can be offered without incurring any loss is $59.15, which is the amount of the net profit if the machine is not put on sale. To convert this to a percent markdown, we use a percent change diagram.

100%	*Old*	295.75
_____%	*– Change*	59.15
_____%	*New*	236.60

This diagram leads us to the following computation:

$$59.15 \times 100 \div 295.75 = 20$$

The sports store can offer a 20% markdown without incurring any loss.

Once again, because of the different bases, we find that the rates cannot be subtracted. Also, once again, the dollar amounts were actually irrelevant. Anytime a retailer uses a 75% markup on cost, and operating expenses are 40% of cost, the largest possible markdown without incurring a loss will be 20%.

4.7 Sales Taxes

Taxes are imposed by federal, state, and local governments for the collection of revenue and for discouraging certain behaviors in the marketplace. Taxes which are imposed on the sale of goods or services are known as **sales taxes.** Both the retail sales tax and the excise tax are commonly used in the United States. We shall see how each of these types of sales tax operates.

As of 2012, all but four states in the U.S.A. collected **retail sales taxes,** taxes on the sale of goods or services to the final customer. There is much variety on the way the retail sales taxes are imposed. In some states, services are not taxed, and in others, food and prescription drugs may be excluded, or taxed at a lower rate than other goods. In those states which collect a retail sales tax, rates vary from approximately 3% to 8%. In some states, local jurisdictions, such as cities or counties, also collect retail sales taxes. The tax rate in these locations may be up to 7% higher.

Sales tax problems are percent increase problems. Often, they may be handled efficiently by the use of an augmented percent.

EXAMPLE 1

Rita purchases a music CD for $15.95, plus 6.25% sales tax. What is the total amount she must pay?

SOLUTION

When the sales tax is included, Rita must pay 106.25% of the retail price of the CD. The computation is:

$$15.95 \times 1.0625 \approx 16.95$$

Rita's total must be rounded to the nearest penny. Her total is $16.95.

EXAMPLE 2

On Monday, Norton's Bookstore collected $14,287.55 for both purchases and sales tax. If the sales tax rate was 5.875%, find the amount of sales tax collected.

SOLUTION

We cannot take 5.875% of $14,287.55, since the amount collected is not the base. Instead, we shall set up a percent increase diagram.

100.000%	*Old*	______
5.875%	*+ Change*	______
____%	*New*	14287.55

The new percent is 105.875%, the augmented percent of the tax rate. Solving the diagram, we find:

$$14287.55 \times 5.875 \div 105.875 \approx 792.82$$

Norton's Bookstore collected $792.82 in sales tax on Monday.

The federal government of the United States does not collect a retail sales tax, but they do collect excise taxes, as do all states. An **excise tax** is a retail sales tax on a specific commodity. Excise tax rates may be percents, or amounts per item purchased. For example, as of 2012, pistols are taxed at 10%, and gasoline is taxed at 18.4 cents per gallon. States and local governments often impose additional excise taxes. In attempts to reduce consumption, excise taxes are often levied on cigarettes and alcohol.

When both excise taxes and sales taxes are computed on the same item, the base of the percents in both cases is, in most states, the retail price before any tax. In such situations, the rates can be added. If the excise tax is built into the retail price and not separately itemized, then the sales tax is also automatically assessed on the excise tax.

EXAMPLE 3

Steve purchased two round trip airline tickets from Kansas City to London for $789 each. Taxes included a federal air transportation excise tax at 7.5%, an international air travel excise tax of $16.70 per person, and sales tax of 6.5%. Find the total amount due.

SOLUTION

The total tax is 14% of the ticket price, plus $16.70 per person. The total tax computation is:

$$789 \times 0.14 + 16.70 = 127.16$$

Then we find the total cost per ticket, and multiply by the number of tickets.

$$789 + 127.16 = 916.16$$

$$916.16 \times 2 = 1832.32$$

The total amount due for the airline tickets was $1,832.32.

4.8 Income Statements

Businesses use financial statements to provide summaries of a company's financial health. An **income statement,** also called a **profit-and-loss statement** or an **operating statement,** gives a summary of income, expenses, and profit for a period of time. An income statement has a specific format, and its major sections are related to the sections of our number line diagram. In section 4.1 we introduced a very simplified income statement. Figure 4.2 contains a more complete income statement for the Chicken Cafe. For comparison purposes, the related number line diagram is given in Figure 4.3.

The **Net Sales** section of the income statement appears first. Here we see the **sales returns,** or refunds received by customers, subtracted from the **gross sales,** or total income received by the retailer from his customers. The result of this section, net sales, corresponds to the length of the entire number line diagram. When accounting for a company's income, net sales is always used, since the returns are actually sales which were undone.

The **Cost of Goods Sold** section of the income statement appears next. Here we see the computation which produces the price paid to the supplier by the retailer for the goods which were sold that year. The goods in inventory at the beginning of the year are added to the purchases to produce the **goods available for sale.** Note that these goods were not all available for sale simultaneously at some time during the year, since both sales and purchases are made continuously throughout the year. But goods available for sale is the total value of all goods which need to be accounted for during that year by the retailer. The value of the ending inventory is subtracted from the goods available for sale to produce the cost of goods sold. This result corresponds to the first section of the number line diagram. We will discuss the details of how these numbers are produced in the next chapter.

The third section on the income statement is the **Gross Profit.** This is the income remaining after subtracting the cost of the merchandise, but before operating expenses are considered. This operation corresponds to the removal of the first section of the number line diagram, leaving only the second and third sections. Note that the value of the gross profit does not explicitly appear on the number line diagram.

The **Operating Expenses** section of the income statement appears next. Here we find a list of the different types of overhead expenses which this retailer incurred. The amounts in the section are added to obtain the total operating expenses. The middle section of the number line diagram contains this value.

Chicken Cafe Income Statement For the Year Ended December 31, 2012		
Net Sales:		
Gross Sales	$885,395	
Returns	$ 5,233	
Net Sales		$880,162
Cost of Goods Sold:		
Beginning Inventory	$ 18,690	
Purchases	$371,024	
Goods Available for Sale	$389,714	
Ending Inventory	$ 19,255	
Cost of Goods Sold		$370,459
Gross Profit		$509,703
Operating Expenses:		
Advertising	$ 14,259	
Insurance	$ 8,322	
Taxes	$ 40,871	
Rent	$ 86,400	
Salaries	$260,355	
Supplies	$ 27,538	
Utilities	$ 22,472	
Total Operating Expenses		$460,217
Net Profit		$ 49,486

Figure 4.2

Figure 4.3 Number line diagram for Chicken Cafe's Income Statement

The **Net Profit** is the bottom line of the income statement. It is obtained by subtracting the total operating expenses from the gross profit. This operation is equivalent to removing the second section from the (already shortened) number line diagram, leaving only the third section.

Notice that most of the operations on the income statement were subtractions. There were two exceptions, both when finding totals. Both goods available for sale and total operating expenses were totals, and for those two items additions were performed.

EXAMPLE 1

Using Figure 4.4, complete the income statement for Charlie's Music Shop.

Solution

To find net sales, we subtract returns from gross sales.

$$385762 - 3416 = 382346$$

Charlie's Music Shop Income Statement For the Year Ended December 31, 2013		
Net Sales:		
Gross Sales	$385,762	
Returns	$ 3,416	
Net Sales		$_______
Cost of Goods Sold:		
Beginning Inventory	$ 39,715	
Purchases	$249,290	
Goods Available for Sale	$_______	
Ending Inventory	$ 42,400	
Cost of Goods Sold		$_______
Gross Profit		$_______
Operating Expenses:		
Advertising	$ 6,570	
Insurance	$ 2,650	
Taxes	$ 12,125	
Rent	$ 26,200	
Salaries	$ 47,652	
Supplies	$ 1,390	
Utilities	$ 2,822	
Total Operating Expenses		$_______
Net Profit		$_______

Figure 4.4

To find goods available for sale, we add beginning inventory and purchases.

$$39715 + 249290 = 289005$$

To find cost of goods sold, we subtract ending inventory from goods available for sale.

$$289005 - 42400 = 246605$$

To find gross profit, we subtract cost of goods sold from net sales.

$$382346 - 246605 = 135741$$

To find total operating expenses, we add all of the items in that section.

$$6570 + 2650 + 12125 + 26200 + 47652 + 1390 + 2822 = 99409$$

To find the net profit, we subtract the total operating expenses from the gross profit.

$$135741 - 99409 = 36332$$

These values can be entered in the appropriate positions on the income statement.

In addition to the actual dollar amounts for each category, financial analysts also find percentages useful. A **vertical analysis** of an income statement computes a percentage for each item. For an income statement, these are based on the net sales, which is the total dollar amount being accounted for in the statement. The analysis is called vertical because the two dollar amounts being compared appear vertically, one above another, in the income statement.

EXAMPLE 2

Using Figure 4.2, perform a vertical analysis on Chicken Cafe's income statement.

SOLUTION

Each of the amounts is turned into a percent by using the net sales as the base. For example, the net profit $49,486 is turned into a percent by solving the proportion:

$$\frac{R}{100} = \frac{49486}{880162}$$

The completed vertical analysis for the Chicken Cafe is shown in Figure 4.5.

Chicken Cafe
Income Statement
For the Year Ended December 31, 2012

Net Sales:		
Gross Sales	$885,395	100.59%
Returns	$ 5,233	0.59%
Net Sales	$880,162	100.00%
Cost of Goods Sold:		
Beginning Inventory	$ 18,690	2.12%
Purchases	$371,024	42.15%
Goods Available for Sale	$389,714	44.28%
Ending Inventory	$ 19,255	2.19%
Cost of Goods Sold	$370,459	42.09%
Gross Profit	$509,703	57.91%
Operating Expenses:		
Advertising	$ 14,259	1.62%
Insurance	$ 8,322	0.95%
Taxes	$ 40,871	4.64%
Rent	$ 86,400	9.82%
Salaries	$260,355	29.58%
Supplies	$ 27,538	3.13%
Utilities	$ 22,472	2.55%
Total Operating Expenses	$460,217	52.29%
Net Profit	$ 49,486	5.62%

Figure 4.5

Some Typical Income Statement Ratios				
Retail Business	Cost	Gross Profit	Operating Expenses	Net Profit
Autos	86.9%	13.1%	12.6%	0.5%
Books	59.6%	40.4%	38.7%	1.7%
Computers	61.6%	38.4%	34.9%	3.5%
Clothing	56.9%	43.1%	40.8%	2.3%
Furniture	59.0%	41.0%	38.9%	2.1%
Gasoline	83.8%	16.2%	15.5%	0.7%
Grocery	76.0%	24.0%	23.0%	1.0%
Hardware	63.9%	36.1%	33.9%	2.2%
Pharmacy	73.4%	26.6%	23.3%	3.3%
Restaurant	40.9%	59.1%	56.2%	2.9%

Figure 4.6

Each of the percents is referred to as the ratio of that item. For example, 5.62% is called the **net profit ratio.** Similarly, the **cost ratio** (or **cost of goods sold ratio**) is 42.09%, the **operating expenses ratio** is 52.29%, the **advertising ratio** is 1.62%, and so on. Any of the amounts in the income statement can be turned into a ratio (normally expressed as a percent) by using net sales as the base.

If you look at the amounts closely, you may notice that whenever two amounts are added (or subtracted) to obtain a third amount, the rates also add (or subtract) to obtain the third rate. This situation is probably most obvious in the subtraction of sales returns from gross sales to produce net sales, but it also occurs elsewhere.

Occasionally, though, the percents won't quite add (or subtract), due to the prior rounding of the rates being added (or subtracted). One such example appears when purchases are added to beginning inventory to produce the goods available for sale. If we used only the rates, we would add 2.12% and 42.15% and obtain 44.27%. However, both 2.12% and 42.15% were rounded amounts, and using them to find the goods available for sale ratio would allow a rounding error to occur. The correct answer is 44.28%, found by solving the proportion.

The results of a vertical analysis are often compared with tables of operating ratios typical for that type of business. Data of this type can be found in various business publications. A few typical operating ratios are given in Figure 4.6.

A typical retail business spends about two-thirds of its income to purchase merchandise, and usually less than 5% of its income is net profit. The Chicken Cafe's cost ratio, 42.09%, is much smaller than the ratio for a typical retail business, but it is similar to a typical restaurant's cost ratio. In the same fashion, their operating expense ratio, 52.29%, and their net profit ratio, 5.62%, are different than the ratios of a typical retail business, but fairly similar to typical restaurant ratios.

EXAMPLE 3

Using the income statement information for Charlie's Music Shop from Example 1, find the cost ratio, the gross profit ratio, and the net profit ratio.

SOLUTION

We show the relevant portion of Charlie's income statement, with the previously missing quantities included, in Figure 4.7.

To find the ratios, we use proportions. The proportion which finds the cost ratio is:

$$\frac{R}{100} = \frac{246605}{382346}$$

Charlie's Music Shop Income Statement For the Year Ended December 31, 2013	
Net Sales:	$382,346
Cost of Goods Sold	$246,605
Gross Profit	$135,741
Total Operating Expenses	$ 99,409
Net Profit	$ 36,332

Figure 4.7

When solving this proportion, we get a cost ratio of approximately 64.50%. Similarly,

$$\frac{R}{100} = \frac{135741}{382346}$$

gives a gross profit ratio of approximately 35.50%, and:

$$\frac{R}{100} = \frac{36332}{382346}$$

gives a net profit ratio of approximately 9.50%. When compared to an average business, the cost ratio is typical and the net profit ratio is somewhat higher.

Businesses can also perform a **horizontal analysis** of an income statement, looking for changes in a current statement from a previous statement. Bad trends can be identified and addressed before serious problems result. Policies and decisions which resulted in good trends can be maintained and rewarded.

Figure 4.8 provides a horizontal analysis of a portion of the income statement for Chicken Cafe. In the horizontal analysis, the columns for the current period and the previous period are placed side by side. The current period is placed first so that quick glances at the statement will provide the most current information. The change column shows the dollar amount of the change from the previous period to the current period. Amounts which decreased are enclosed in parentheses. The last column shows the percent change, using the previous period as the base, which is the procedure in all percent change problems.

The percents in the last column will not add or subtract, even when the dollar amounts do, because the base of each percent is a different number. Each percent must be computed separately, using either a percent change diagram or a simple proportion.

Chicken Cafe
Income Statement
For the Year Ended December 31, 2012

	2012	2011	Change	Percent
Net Sales:	$880,162	$862,334	$17,828	2.07%
Cost of Goods Sold	$370,459	$345,231	$25,228	7.31%
Gross Profit	$509,703	$517,103	($ 7,400)	(1.43%)
Operating Expenses	$460,217	$455,408	$ 4,809	1.06%
Net Profit	$ 49,486	$ 61,695	($12,209)	(19.79%)

Figure 4.8

EXAMPLE 4

Using Figure 4.9, complete the horizontal analysis of the income statement for Charlie's Music Shop.

Charlie's Music Shop
Income Statement
For the Year Ended December 31, 2013

	2013	2012	Change	Percent
Net Sales:	$382,346	$355,411	$_____	_____%
Cost of Goods Sold	$246,605	$239,310	$_____	_____%
Gross Profit	$135,741	$116,101	$_____	_____%
Operating Expenses	$ 99,409	$102,340	$_____	_____%
Net Profit	$ 36,332	$ 13,761	$_____	_____%

Figure 4.9

Solution

We shall demonstrate both methods of completing the horizontal analysis. For net sales, here is the percent change diagram.

100.00%	*Old*	355411
_____%	*+ Change*	_____
_____%	*New*	382346

Solving the diagram, we get:

100.00%	*Old*	355411
7.58%	*+ Change*	26935
107.58%	*New*	382346

Therefore, net sales experienced a 7.58% increase.

To find the percent change in the cost of goods sold, we shall use the other method. First, the amount of the change is found, by subtracting the old amount from the new.

$$246605 - 239310 = 7295$$

Then, we set up a proportion, using the old value as the base, and the amount of the change as the part.

$$\frac{R}{100} = \frac{7295}{239310}$$

After solving the proportion, we find that the cost of goods sold had a 3.05% increase.

Other percent change diagrams proceed similarly, using one of the two methods described. Note that operating expenses decreased. If a percent change diagram is used, the change will be subtracted. Whichever method is used, the decreasing aspect of the answer must be indicated. The completed horizontal analysis is given in Figure 4.10.

Charlie's Music Shop
Income Statement
For the Year Ended December 31, 2013

	2013	2012	Change	Percent
Net Sales:	$382,346	$355,411	$26,935	7.58%
Cost of Goods Sold	$246,605	$239,310	$ 7,295	3.05%
Gross Profit	$135,741	$116,101	$19,640	16.92%
Operating Expenses	$ 99,409	$102,340	($ 2,931)	(2.86%)
Net Profit	$ 36,332	$ 13,761	$22,571	164.02%

Figure 4.10

Name: ______________________________ Date: __________

Exercises 4.1

* Complete each number line diagram.

1.

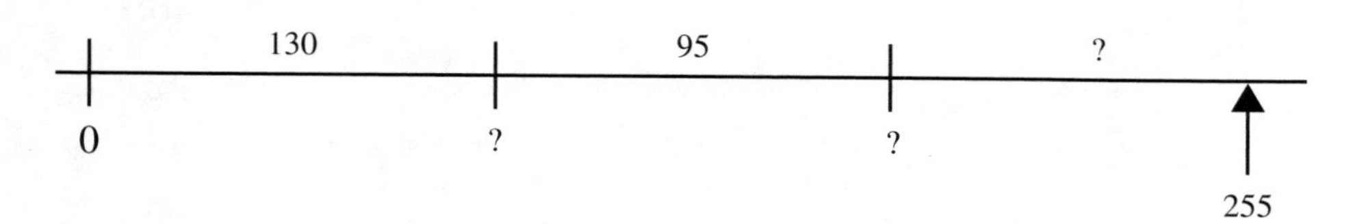

2.

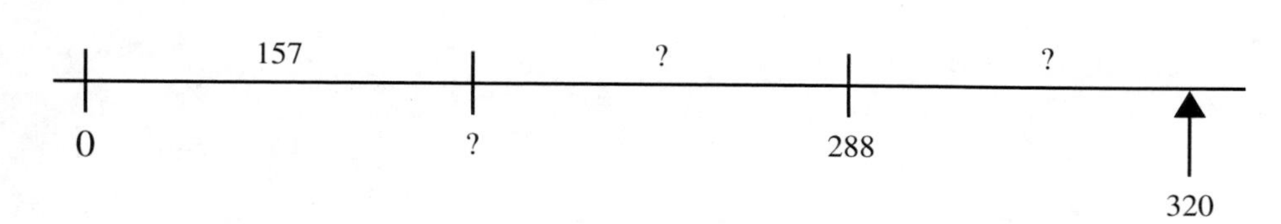

3.

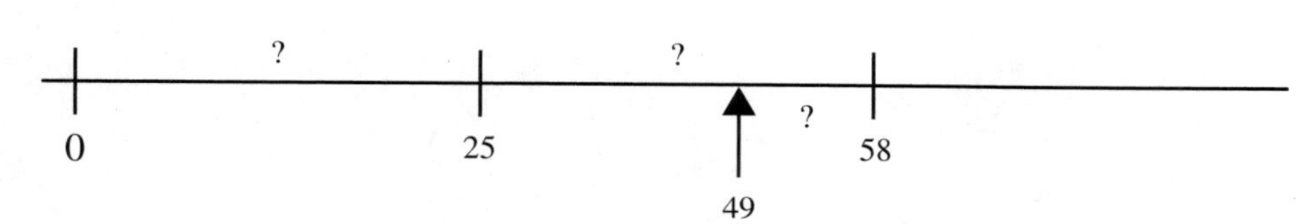

4.

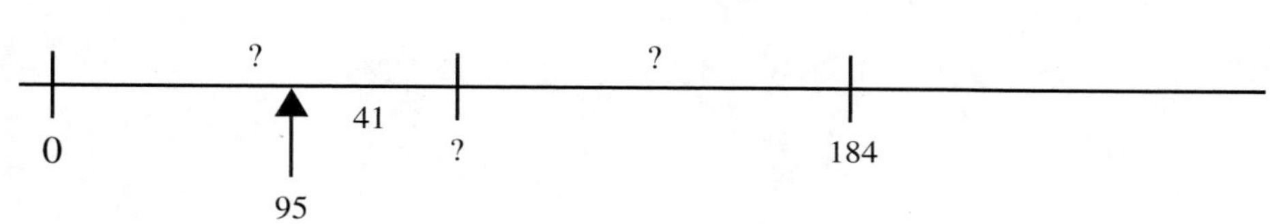

Complete each table.

	Net Cost	Operating Expenses	Breakeven Point	Net Profit	Selling Price
5.	$75	$44	_____	$18	_____
6.	$94.25	$73.22	_____	_____	$194.95
7.	$179	_____	$286	$29	_____
8.	$850	_____	_____	$155	$1,695
9.	_____	$242	$390	$41	_____
10.	_____	$91	_____	$16	$235
11.	_____	$16	$29	_____	$31.50
12.	$400	_____	$725	_____	$780

	Net Cost	Operating Expenses	Breakeven Point	Operating Loss	Selling Price
13.	$217	$135	_____	_____	$319
14.	$195	_____	$325	$98	_____
15.	$664	_____	_____	$120	$840
16.	_____	$310	$595	$52	_____
17.	_____	$261	_____	$14	$685
18.	_____	$29	$49	_____	$43
19.	$345	_____	$640	_____	$595
20.	$68	$47	_____	$22	_____

	Net Cost	Operating Expenses	Breakeven Point	Operating Loss	Absolute Loss	Selling Price
21.	$479	$233	_____	_____	_____	$389
22.	$23	$48	_____	_____	_____	$19
23.	$718	_____	_____	$220	$40	_____
24.	$229	_____	_____	$52	$17	_____
25.	_____	$561	$925	$140	_____	_____
26.	_____	$290	$490	_____	_____	$565

** 27. Carole's Boutique had net sales of $850,000 last year. Her cost of goods sold was $525,000, and her operating expenses were $270,000. Find her breakeven point and her net profit.

28. Simon's Software had net sales of $3.27 million last year. Their merchandise costs were $1.94 million, and operating expenses were $1.02 million. Find their breakeven point and net profit.

29. Wilson's Grocery buys apples at 60 cents per pound, and sells them for 99 cents per pound. If they make 11 cents per pound in net profit, find the amount set aside for operating expenses, and the breakeven point.

30. The Bicycle Haven buys a certain model of bicycle for $85, and sells it for $165. If they make a net profit of $22, find the amount set aside for operating expenses, and the breakeven point.

31. Red Springs Door Company sells a certain door for $395. Their net cost was $220, and operating expenses are approximately 57% of net cost. Find their operating expenses, breakeven point, and net profit.

32. Toby's Flowers sells a dozen roses for $22. Their net cost was $14, and operating expenses are 39% of cost. Find their operating expenses, breakeven point, and net profit.

33. Graceful Reflections bought a mirror for $45, and is trying to sell it at $59. Their operating expenses are 40% of cost. Find their operating expenses, breakeven point, and operating loss.

34. Save-More put bath towels on sale for $7.95 each. Their cost was $6.50, and operating expenses are 30% of cost. Find their operating expenses, breakeven point, and operating loss.

35. To clear out last season's clothing line, Bailey's marked some blouses down to $19 each. Their cost was $24.50, and operating expenses are 80% of cost. Find their operating expenses, breakeven point, operating loss, and absolute loss.

36. Linda's Lawn Sculptures bought a gargoyle sculpture some time ago for $85. It hasn't sold at its original price of $195, so they marked it down to $75. Operating expenses are 90% of cost. Find their operating expenses, breakeven point, operating loss, and absolute loss.

Name: ______________________________ Date: __________

Exercises 4.2

∗ Complete the table.

	List Price	Trade Discount	Net Cost
1.	$125	45%	_____
2.	$275	35%	_____
3.	_____	27%	$125
4.	_____	52%	$388
5.	$520	_____	$295
6.	$790	_____	$380
7.	$600	30/20	_____
8.	$475	40/10	_____
9.	$18.95	30/20/10	_____
10.	$49.40	25/20/5	_____

For each series discount, find the single equivalent discount, and the net cost equivalent. (Be sure to distinguish between your two answers.)

11. 40/10

12. 35/20

13. 30/10

14. 15/10

15. 25/5/5

16. 50/10/5

** 17. A discount store buys a piece of luggage whose list price is $80. They receive a 40% trade discount. What is their net cost?

18. An electronics store purchases a DVD recorder, obtaining a 30% trade discount off of the list price of $270. What is their net cost?

19. A garden store bought some rakes for $7 each, after the trade discount of 60%. What was the list price of the rakes?

20. A furniture store bought some bookcases at $79 each, after a trade discount of 55%. What was the list price of the bookcases?

21. A mattress is discounted from $149 to $59. What trade discount rate does the retailer receive?

22. An electric train set is discounted from $39 to $22. What trade discount rate does the retailer receive?

23. Tommy's Music orders some music books which list for $9.95. What is their cost, after a 20/10 trade discount?

24. Wall Art orders some posters which list for $16.95. What is their cost, after a 40/20 trade discount?

25. After the 30/20 trade discount, a department store paid $152 for a lawnmower. What was the list price?

26. After a 35/20 trade discount, a kitchen appliance store paid $40. What was the list price?

27. A retailer can obtain a board game from one supplier for $29 less 40%, while a second supplier has it listed for $33 less 50%. From which supplier should the retailer order?

28. A folding table is listed for $22 less 45% from one supplier, and for $25 less 55% from a second supplier. Which supplier offers the folding table at a lower price?

*** 29. Acme Corporation offers a set of the complete symphonies of Beethoven for $75 with a 40% trade discount. Beta Corporation offers the same set for $40.50.

a. What additional discount must Acme offer to match Beta's price?

b. What is the single equivalent discount for Acme in order to meet Beta's price?

30. Best Suppliers sells CDs for $12 with a 20/15 discount. Quality Suppliers sells CDs for $7.50.

    a. What additional discount must Best offer to meet Quality's price?

    b. What is the single equivalent discount for Best in order to meet Quality's price?

31. Midwest Auto Distributors offers a car battery for $79 less 40%. Missouri Motors offers the same battery for $89 less 50%.

    a. What additional discount is needed for Midwest to match Missouri's price?

    b. Find a single equivalent discount for Midwest which matches Missouri's price.

32. Louisiana Lighting sells a lamp for $125 less 55%. Southern Expressions sells the same lamp for $110 less 40%.

    a. What additional discount is needed for Southern Expressions to match Louisiana Lighting's price?

    b. Find a single equivalent discount for Southern which matches Louisiana's price.

33. Is a 30/20 discount twice as large as a 15/10 discount? Explain.

Name: ______________________________ Date: __________

Exercises 4.3

* Find the date using the table of days.

1. 240 days from March 13.
2. 270 days from March 9.
3. 120 days from January 13, 2012.
4. 150 days from February 3, 2016.
5. 180 days from September 16, 2013.
6. 210 days from October 3, 2014.
7. 150 days from December 17, 2015.
8. 180 days from December 3, 2015.

Find the last date the cash discount is available, and the date on which the net amount is due.

	Invoice Date	Terms	Date Goods Received
9.	April 14	2/10, n/30	April 16
10.	March 27	3/10, n/20	March 29
11.	May 29	1/15	June 1
12.	June 17	2/20	June 21
13.	October 11	3/10, 2/20	October 12
14.	August 14	3/5, 1/15	August 16
15.	January 7	2/10 EOM	January 9
16.	July 16	3/10 EOM	July 17
17.	September 12	2/10 prox	September 14
18.	December 14	1/10 prox	December 16
19.	November 26	2/10 EOM	November 28
20.	February 26	2/10 EOM	February 28
21.	June 16	1/20-70 X	June 19
22.	August 18	3/10-90 X	August 22
23.	March 16	2/10 ROG	March 21
24.	October 11	3/15 ROG	November 16

A Nebraska retailer purchases goods from a Michigan supplier. For each of the following, should shipping charges be added to the invoice?

25. FOB Michigan

26. FOB Alabama

27. FOB Nebraska

28. FOB Detroit

** Find the amount that should be paid on the invoice for the given due date. Assume a 1.5% late charge.

	Invoice Date	Terms	Date Goods Received	Invoice Amount	Date Paid
29.	August 3	1/5, n/30	August 7	$21,380	August 10
30.	October 6	1/10, n/30	October 9	$17,600	October 12
31.	April 18	2/5 ROG	May 19	$11,880	May 23
32.	July 16	2/10 EOM	July 17	$7,300	August 3
33.	December 6	1/5-30 X	December 20	$3,500	February 23
34.	November 30	2/10 ROG	December 11	$29,400	January 15

Complete each invoice. Then find the last date for which a cash discount is available, the day on which the net amount is due, and the amounts to be paid on each of those dates. If a shipping charge applies, add $50.

35.

From: Anita's Wholesale Supply
Chicago, IL 60637

Date: Feb. 5, 2015
Terms: 2/5, 1/15
FOB: Chicago

To: Jack's Discount Stationery
Overland Park, KS 66210

Quantity	Item	Unit Price	Gross	Trade Discount	Net
15 gross	Bic blue medium pens	41.00/gross	_____	15/10	_____
10 gross	Trusty #2 pencils	1.95/dozen	_____	10/10	_____
8 dozen	Pink Pearl erasers	3.00/dozen	_____	25	_____
2 dozen	Acme pencil sharpeners	8.95 each	_____	30/10	_____
10	Boston electric sharpeners	19.95 each	_____	30/5/5	_____
		Total:	_____	Total:	_____

36.

From:	Kaw River Electronics Boner Springs, KS	Date: July 15, 2014 Terms: 1/10 e.o.m. FOB: Bonner Springs			
To:	Electronics Hut Olathe, KS				
Quantity	Item	Unit Price	Gross	Trade Discount	Net
2	Televisions	217.00 each	_____	30%	_____
1 dozen	Radios	36.98 each	_____	20/10	_____
1 gross	9 volt batteries	3.00 each	_____	40/20/5	_____
		Total:	_____	Total:	_____

37.

From:	Accuview Microscopics Raytown, MO	Date: July 26, 2013 Terms: 1/5 ROG FOB: Missouri			
To:	Peters Science Supply Laurel, MT				
Quantity	Item	Unit Price	Gross	Trade Discount	Net
8	Microscopes	179.00 each	_____	45%	_____
9 dozen	Assorted prepared slides	3.50 each	_____	30/20	_____
2 gross	Blank slides	3.00/dozen	_____	20/10	_____
2 gallons	Formaldehyde	4.70/gallon	_____	30/15/5	_____
		Total:	_____	Total:	_____

38.

From:	Zeppelin Musical Supplier Lakewood, NJ	Date: April 10, 2012 Terms: 2/10-50 X FOB: Houston			
To:	Apollo Music Houston, TX				
Quantity	Item	Unit Price	Gross	Trade Discount	Net
3 dozen	Clarinets	459.00 each	_____	50	_____
2 dozen	Flutes	489.00 each	_____	50	_____
16	Guitars	229.00 each	_____	40	_____
2	Tubas	1,995.00 each	_____	40	_____
2 gross	Medium clarinet reeds	1.89 each	_____	35/20	_____
3 gross	Guitar picks	0.80/dozen	_____	35/30	_____
		Total:	_____	Total:	_____

Name: ______________________________ Date: __________

Exercises 4.4

∗ Complete the table.

	Cost	Markup	Selling Price
1.	$250	70% on cost	_____
2.	$375	55% on cost	_____
3.	$480	40% on selling price	_____
4.	$675	35% on selling price	_____
5.	_____	55% on selling price	$299
6.	_____	45% on selling price	$559
7.	_____	65% on cost	$729
8.	_____	90% on cost	$995
9.	$300	_____ on cost	$559
10.	$645	_____ on cost	$1,139
11.	$48	_____ on selling price	$98.50
12.	$0.89	_____ on selling price	$1.98

∗∗ 13. A retailer buys a backpack for $15, and marks it up 80% on cost. How much is the selling price?

14. A retailer buys a cordless phone for $40, and marks it up 95% on cost. How much is the selling price?

15. The Computer Outlet buys a printer for $239, and marks it up 30% on selling price. How much is the selling price?

16. Kansas Furniture Sales buys a swivel chair for $43, and marks it up 55% on selling price. How much is the selling price?

17. Springfield Garden sells a hedge trimmer for $39.99, after a markup of 85% on cost. How much was their cost?

18. Canopy Hardware sells an extension ladder for $89.95, after a markup of 90% on cost. How much was their cost?

19. Eastside Hardware sells a pair of pliers for $5.59, after a markup of 60% on selling price. How much was their cost?

20. Jack's Emporium sells a hammer for $8.95, after a markup of 65% on selling price. How much was their cost?

21. Savings Mart buys a vacuum cleaner for $169, and sells it for $299. How much was their markup on cost?

22. Kitchen Stuff buys a toaster for $13.00, and sells it for $29.99. How much was their markup on cost?

23. The Tool Shed buys an extension cord for $2.25, and sells it for $4.99. How much was their markup on selling price?

24. Kerwin Electronics buys a television for $199, and sells it for $369. How much was their markup on selling price?

25. Which is the larger markup, 35% on cost or 25% on selling price? Explain.

26. Which is the larger markup, 55% on cost or 45% on selling price? Explain.

Name: ______________________________ Date: __________

Exercises 4.5

✳ Find the adjusted cost and the adjustment due to shrinkage.

1. $85 net cost, 3% shrinkage

2. $124 net cost, 5% shrinkage

3. $4.95 net cost, 8% shrinkage

4. $0.59 net cost, 14% shrinkage

✳✳ 5. Linens and Such buys towels at $3.50 each, and expects 3% shrinkage. What is their adjusted cost?

6. The Downtown Grocery buys bags of cookies at $2.59 each, and expects 5% shrinkage. What is their adjusted cost?

7. Big Buys buys a bag of pens for 97 cents, and expects 2% shrinkage. If they need a markup of 25% on cost, what should their selling price be?

8. Merle's buys pairs of pants at $15.99, expecting 4% shrinkage. If they need a markup of 96% of cost, what should their selling price be?

9. Forsyth Shoes buys a pair of shoes for $45, and expects 3% shrinkage. If they need a markup of 55% on selling price, what should their selling price be?

10. Aroma Heaven buys candles at $1.25, and expects 7% shrinkage. If they need a markup of 65% on selling price, what should their selling price be?

11. Quigley's buys 36 lamps for a total cost of $1,440. The manager assumes two will be broken while on display, and also needs a 75% markup on cost. What is the minimum selling price of each lamp?

12. Felicia's Fabrics buys an 18-yard bolt of cloth for $87. Due to flaws and short ends, they expect to sell 16 yards of it. If they need a markup of 70% on selling price, what should be the selling price of the fabric, per yard?

***13. Coddington's sells prepriced packages of nylons for $8.99. They receive a 40% trade discount from their supplier, and expect 3% shrinkage. Their operating expenses are 55% of cost. How much net profit can they expect from the sale of each package of nylons?

14. Charlie's sells prepriced packages of tortilla chips for $3.19. They receive a 20% trade discount from their supplier, and expect 2% shrinkage. Their operating expenses are 19% of cost. How much net profit can they expect from the sale of each package of chips?

Name: ______________________________ Date: __________

Exercises 4.6

✳ Complete the table.

	Original Price	Markdown	Sale Price
1.	$495	25%	______
2.	$189	30%	______
3.	______	40%	$300
4.	______	35%	$175
5.	$255	_____	$185
6.	$18.88	_____	$13.88
7.	$45.59	1/3	_____
8.	$62.40	2/3	_____

✳✳ 9. A living room suite regularly priced at $1,495, is marked off 30% for a sale. Find the sale price.

10. A set of vertical blinds is advertised at 55% off of the regular price of $59.99. What is the sale price?

11. A dinnerware set is marked down from $89.99 to $74.99. What percent markdown can be advertised?

12. A bath towel is marked down from $16 to $11.99. What is the percent markdown?

13. A quilt was marked down 60% to $64.99. What was the original price?

14. A set of earrings was marked down 55% to $17.99. What was the original price?

15. Missy's Clothing purchases sweaters for $11.50 each, which they markup 55% on selling price. Some of the sweaters were sold during a storewide 20% off sale. What was the sale price, and what percent markup on selling price did the sweaters actually bring?

16. Baby Furnishings purchases strollers for $60 each, and marks them up 80% on cost. They later sell them at 35% off. What was the sale price, and what percent markup on cost did the strollers actually bring?

17. A craft store purchases Halloween scarecrows for $4 each. They mark them up 120% on cost, and operating expenses are 74% of cost. What is the largest possible markdown they can offer without incurring any loss?

18. Phoebe's purchases large holiday wreaths at $25, and marks them up 145% on cost. Operating expenses are 92% of cost. What is the largest possible markdown they can offer without incurring any loss?

∗∗∗19. Carter's standard markup is 75% on cost, and operating expenses are 44% of cost. What is the largest possible markdown they can offer without incurring any loss?

20. Dilley's standard markup is 55% on selling price, and operating expenses are 65% of cost. What is the largest possible markdown they can offer without incurring any loss?

Name: ______________________________ Date: __________

Exercises 4.7

✳ Complete the table.

	Subtotal	Sales Tax Rate	Sales Tax	Total
1.	$39.27	5.25%	_____	_____
2.	$85.44	6.85%	_____	_____
3.	_____	7.25%	_____	$192.55
4.	_____	5.9%	_____	$38.78
5.	_____	4.2%	$12.44	_____
6.	_____	9.6%	$8.55	_____
7.	$38.22	_____	$2.29	_____
8.	$614.55	_____	$48.24	_____
9.	$12.50	_____	_____	$12.94
10.	$13.21	_____	_____	$14.30
11.	_____	_____	$0.54	$10.42
12.	_____	_____	$52.50	$927.50

✳✳ 13. Robin's grocery subtotal was $141.36. If sales tax is 4%, what is her total?

14. Tom bought a $39.99 computer game. If sales tax is 7.5%, what is his total?

15. Pamela paid a total of $39.42 for various items from the local discount store. If the tax rate was 6.5%, what was the amount of the tax?

16. Corey paid a total of $28.44 for various items from the hardware store. If the tax rate was 5.25%, what was the amount of the tax?

17. While on vacation, Sherman bought a $6.50 guidebook. If he paid $6.97, what was the sales tax rate?

18. David rented a $85.00 motel room, for which he paid $94.69. What was the tax rate?

19. Suppose gasoline is selling for $3.639 per gallon. If the sales tax rate is 5% and the built-in excise taxes are 24 cents per gallon, find the price before tax.

20. Suppose Mike pays $3.99 for a pack of cigarettes. If the sales tax rate was 8% and the built-in excise taxes are $1.50 per pack, find the amount of the taxes.

Name: ______________________________ Date: __________

Exercises 4.8

* Complete the following income statements.

1.

Penney's Hardware
Income Statement
For the Month Ended October 31, 2013

Net Sales:		
Gross Sales	$342,661	
Returns	$ 2,737	
Net Sales		$_______
Cost of Goods Sold:		
Beginning Inventory	$ 74,310	
Purchases	$158,511	
Goods Available for Sale	$_______	
Ending Inventory	$ 79,685	
Cost of Goods Sold		$_______
Gross Profit		$_______
Operating Expenses:		
Advertising	$ 12,429	
Insurance	$ 2,922	
Taxes	$ 17,871	
Rent	$ 9,500	
Salaries	$ 52,727	
Supplies	$ 8,152	
Utilities	$ 5,324	
Total Operating Expenses		$_______
Net Profit		$_______

2.

Midtown Autos
Income Statement
For the Year Ended October 31, 2012

Net Sales:		
Gross Sales	$676,477	
Returns	$ 6,144	
Net Sales		$_______
Cost of Goods Sold:		
Beginning Inventory	$118,211	
Purchases	$603,416	
Goods Available for Sale	$______	
Ending Inventory	$127,309	
Cost of Goods Sold		$_______
Gross Profit		$_______
Operating Expenses:		
Advertising	$ 5,463	
Insurance	$ 4,322	
Taxes	$ 9,800	
Rent	$ 5,471	
Salaries	$ 42,120	
Supplies	$ 2,425	
Utilities	$ 3,359	
Total Operating Expenses		$_______
Net Profit		$_______

* Perform a vertical analysis on the following income statements.

3.

Marie's Restaurant
Income Statement
For the Year Ended December 31, 2014

Net Sales:		
Gross Sales	$855,458	
Returns	$ 1,233	
Net Sales		$854,225
Cost of Goods Sold:		
Beginning Inventory	$ 16,859	
Purchases	$323,801	
Goods Available for Sale	$340,660	
Ending Inventory	$ 17,455	
Cost of Goods Sold		$323,205
Gross Profit		$531,020
Operating Expenses:		
Advertising	$ 11,259	
Insurance	$ 12,483	
Taxes	$ 87,442	
Rent	$ 38,455	
Salaries	$271,008	
Supplies	$ 67,425	
Utilities	$ 25,472	
Total Operating Expenses		$513,543
Net Profit		$ 17,477

4.

Rick's Service Station
Income Statement
For the Year Ended December 31, 2013

Net Sales:		
Gross Sales	$524,443	
Returns	$ 2,476	
Net Sales		$521,967
Cost of Goods Sold:		
Beginning Inventory	$ 16,292	
Purchases	$438,349	
Goods Available for Sale	$454,641	
Ending Inventory	$ 14,816	
Cost of Goods Sold		$439,825
Gross Profit		$ 82,142
Operating Expenses:		
Advertising	$ 1,529	
Insurance	$ 4,240	
Taxes	$ 10,250	
Rent	$ 6,354	
Salaries	$ 50,322	
Supplies	$ 3,466	
Utilities	$ 4,456	
Total Operating Expenses		$ 80,617
Net Profit		$ 1,525

Using the income statement for Marie's Restaurant (in problem #3), find the following:

5. cost ratio

6. net profit ratio

7. gross profit ratio

8. advertising ratio

Perform a horizontal analysis on the following income statements.

9.

Marie's Restaurant
Income Statement

	2014	2013
Net Sales:		
Gross Sales	$855,458	$822,319
Returns	$ 1,233	$ 1,142
Net Sales	$854,225	$821,177
Cost of Goods Sold:		
Beginning Inventory	$ 16,859	$ 15,899
Purchases	$323,801	$306,454
Goods Available for Sale	$340,660	$322,353
Ending Inventory	$ 17,455	$ 16,859
Cost of Goods Sold	$323,205	$305,494
Gross Profit	$531,020	$515,683
Operating Expenses:		
Advertising	$ 11,259	$ 11,484
Insurance	$ 12,483	$ 11,525
Taxes	$ 87,442	$ 84,328
Rent	$38,455	$ 34,524
Salaries	$271,008	$262,455
Supplies	$ 67,425	$ 61,663
Utilities	$ 25,472	$ 24,966
Total Operating Expenses	$513,543	$490,013
Net Profit	$ 17,477	$25,670

10.

Rick's Service Station
Income Statement

	2013	2012
Net Sales:		
Gross Sales	$524,443	$575,629
Returns	$ 2,476	$ 2,541
Net Sales	$521,967	$573,088
Cost of Goods Sold:		
Beginning Inventory	$ 16,292	$ 17,351
Purchases	$438,349	$452,616
Goods Available for Sale	$454,641	$469,967
Ending Inventory	$ 14,816	$ 16,292
Cost of Goods Sold	$439,825	$453,675
Gross Profit	$ 82,142	$119,413
Operating Expenses:		
Advertising	$ 1,529	$ 2,290
Insurance	$ 4,240	$ 4,100
Taxes	$ 10,250	$ 14,683
Rent	$ 6,354	$ 6,255
Salaries	$ 50,322	$ 49,785
Supplies	$ 3,466	$ 5,217
Utilities	$ 4,456	$ 4,188
Total Operating Expenses	$ 80,617	$ 86,518
Net Profit	$ 1,525	$ 32,895

Name: ______________________________ Date: __________

Chapter 4 Review

Summary of Important Concepts

- ▲ Profit, operating loss, absolute loss, breakeven point
- ▲ Trade discounts, series discounts, equivalents
- ▲ Cash discounts, EOM, ROG, X
- ▲ Invoices, shipping charges
- ▲ Markups on cost, markups on selling price
- ▲ Shrinkage
- ▲ Markdowns
- ▲ Sales taxes
- ▲ Income statements

Exercises

1. A refrigerator is marked up from $575 to $995. Operating expenses are 38% of cost. What is the breakeven point?

2. If the suggested list price is $275, and the dealer receives a 25/20 trade discount, what is the dealer's cost?

3. What is the single equivalent discount for a 20/15/10 series discount?

4. What is the net cost equivalent for a 30/25/15 series discount?

5. If an invoice is dated May 19 and offers terms of 3/10-45X, what is the last day on which the cash discount may be taken?

6. What is the net due date for an invoice dated May 19 with terms of 1/10 e.o.m.?

7. Complete the following markup diagram for a markup based on selling price.

_____ %	*C*	_____
30%	+ *M*	_____
_____ %	*S*	72.33

8. What is the cost, if the selling price is $419 and the markup on cost is 55%?

9. What is the selling price, if the cost is $95 and the markup on selling price is 35%?

10. Which is the larger markup, a 35% markup on cost, or a 30% markup on selling price? Give an explanation for your choice.

11. A merchant can buy berries at 63 cents per pound, but he knows that about 15% of the berries will spoil. If he needs a 30% markup on cost, what should the selling price be, per pound?

12. An item normally selling for $27.45 is marked 20% off for a sale. What is the sale price?

13. A store buys a lawnmower for $339 and marks it up 55% on cost. The mower did not sell during the summer, so in their fall sale they marked it down 35%. The store's operating expenses are about 20% of cost. Does the store experience a net profit or a net loss? How much?

14. A furniture store purchases bedroom suites for $940 each. They normally mark up merchandise 55% on selling price, and operating costs are equal to 32% of cost. What is the largest percent markdown the store can offer without incurring any loss?

15. Sarah's groceries subtotalled $84.36. If sales tax is 5.75%, what is her total?

16. Complete the following simplified income statement, and perform a vertical analysis.

Toby's
Income Statement
For the Year Ended December 31, 2013

Net Sales:		
Gross Sales	$475,662	______%
Returns	$ 1,441	______%
Net Sales	______	______%
Cost of Goods Sold:		
Beginning Inventory	$125,959	______%
Purchases	$288,434	______%
Goods Available for Sale	______	______%
Ending Inventory	$142,604	______%
Cost of Goods Sold	______	______%
Gross Profit	______	______%
Operating Expenses:		
Total Operating Expenses:	$192,441	______%
Net Profit	______	______%

5 Asset Values

5.1 Balance Sheets

In the previous chapter, we looked at a retailer's cash flow, or income and expenses, in his business. These were summarized in an income statement.

In this chapter, we shall turn our attention to another aspect of a business, its value or worth. The items of value which a business owns are called its **assets.** Businesses also usually have debts, or **liabilities,** which need to be paid to their creditors. The **net worth,** or **owner's equity,** is the amount by which the assets exceed the liabilities. The **balance sheet** is the financial statement which summarizes a company's assets, liabilities, and owner's equity, at some particular point in time.

Chicken Cafe
Balance Sheet
December 31, 2012

Current Assets:		Current Liabilities:	
Cash	$ 14,750	Accts. Payable	$ 24,335
Securities	$ 39,075	Notes Payable	$ 33,200
Accts. Receivable	$ 12,410	Salaries	$ 9,500
Inventory	$ 19,255	Total	$ 67,035
Total	$ 85,490		
		Long-Term Liabilities:	
Fixed Assets:		Mortgage	$ 49,200
Building	$ 29,000	Total	$ 49,200
Land	$ 29,020		
Equipment	$ 18,200	Total Liabilities	$116,235
Fixtures	$ 14,300		
Total	$ 90,520	Owner's Equity	$ 59,775
Total Assets	$176,010	Total Liabilities & Equity	$176,010

Figure 5.1

Figure 5.1 provides an example of a balance sheet for the Chicken Cafe. Notice that the assets are all placed in the left column, and the liabilities in the right column. (In some balance sheets, there is only one column, with assets first and liabilities second.) The assets are grouped into two types, current assets and fixed assets. Similarly, liabilities are also grouped into two types, current liabilities and long-term liabilities.

Current assets are those assets which can be expected, within one year, to be turned into cash during the normal course of business. Cash refers to the cash on hand and is, of course, already cash. **Securities** includes stocks and bonds that the owner of the business may have purchased, so that some of the owner's unspent cash can earn a return. These can be easily sold in the market when additional cash is needed. **Accounts receivables** represent those sales which the business made, but has not yet received payment. Most purchasers will pay these accounts within thirty to ninety days. **Inventory** includes all of the merchandise the retailer has available to sell. Depending on the type of business and the current state of the economy, the inventory may or may not move quickly. The methods by which a value is placed on inventory will be studied in the next section of this chapter.

Fixed assets are those assets which are necessary to maintain while operating the business, and are not expected to be turned into cash. Fixed assets is not a perfect opposite of current assets, but normally most assets will fall into one category or the other. At Chicken Cafe, the building and land are needed to accommodate customers. Fixtures would include the tables and chairs, and equipment would include the appliances needed to cook meals. The value of fixed assets can change over time, due to normal wear and tear during use. We will study how to account for these changes in a later section of this chapter.

Current liabilities are those debts for which payment is due within one year. (This definition is consistent with the definition of current assets, since both specify a one-year time period.) **Accounts payable** represent those purchases the business has made from its suppliers, but has not yet made payment. **Notes payable** are those purchases made for which a short-term loan or promissory note was given. To be included with the current liabilities, the due date on the loan has to be for one year or less. A business may take out such a loan for major expenses or improvements, expecting that the increase in business will pay for the loan when it is due. Salaries are included in accounts payable when some workers have earned wages, but the payday for those wages has not yet arrived.

Long-term liabilities are those debts for which payment is not due within one year. Chicken Cafe has only one long-term liability, the mortgage for their building and land. The amount of the mortgage is the current balance, not the original balance.

If the company were sold, and all of the proceeds from the sale of the assets were used to pay the liabilities, the amount left over is the net worth, or owner's equity, of the company. That amount would be distributed to the owner or owners after the sale. Owner's equity is computed by subtracting the total liabilities from the total assets. On some balance sheets, owner's equity will be listed as **stockholder's equity,** since stockholders are the owners of any company that issues stocks.

If a company's liabilities are greater than its assets, then the company is **insolvent**, or unable to pay its debts. **Bankruptcy,** the legal declaration of an insolvent company, may provide some protections against creditors who want to shut a company down and liquidate all of its assets.

The essence of the balance sheet is to summarize all assets and liabilities. When the company is viewed as a separate entity from the owners, then the owner's equity is one of the company's liabilities. In that sense, owner's equity belongs in the liability column, and the balance between assets and liabilities in the balance sheet is obtained. However, the owner's equity does not consist of the amount which was invested by the owners. The owners assume a risk when they invest in a company, and in return for their investment, the difference between the assets and liabilities is their portion.

EXAMPLE 1

Complete the balance sheet for Charlie's Music Shop, found in Figure 5.2.

Charlie's Music Shop
Balance Sheet
December 31, 2013

Current Assets:		Current Liabilities:	
Cash	$ 13,320	Accts. Payable	$ 4,130
Accts. Receivable	$ 8,370	Notes Payable	$ 30,405
Inventory	$ 42,400	Salaries	$ 2,500
Total	$_______	Total	$_______
		Long-Term Liabilities:	
Fixed Assets:		Loan	$ 8,800
Delivery Van	$ 9,300	Total	$_______
Equipment	$ 12,520		
Fixtures	$ 5,200	Total Liabilities	$_______
Total	$_______		
		Owner's Equity	$_______
Total Assets	$_______		
		Total Liabilities & Equity	$_______

Figure 5.2

SOLUTION

Every total in the balance sheet is found by adding. Only one of the entries needed is not a total, namely owner's equity, and it is found by subtracting the total liabilities from the total assets. The completed balance sheet is found in Figure 5.3.

Charlie's Music Shop
Balance Sheet
December 31, 2013

Current Assets:		Current Liabilities:	
Cash	$ 13,320	Accts. Payable	$ 4,130
Accts. Receivable	$ 8,370	Notes Payable	$ 30,405
Inventory	$ 42,400	Salaries	$ 2,500
Total	$ 64,090	Total	$ 37,035
		Long-Term Liabilities:	
Fixed Assets:		Loan	$ 8,800
Delivery Van	$ 9,300	Total	$ 8,800
Equipment	$ 12,520		
Fixtures	$ 5,200	Total Liabilities	$ 45,835
Total	$ 27,020		
		Owner's Equity	$ 45,275
Total Assets	$ 91,110		
		Total Liabilities & Equity	$ 91,110

Figure 5.3

Both vertical and horizontal analyses can be performed on balance sheets. The approach in each analysis is the same as was done with an income statement in the previous chapter. When performing a vertical analysis on a balance sheet, the base is total assets. All assets are a part of total assets, and all liabilities are paid out of total assets.

EXAMPLE 2

Perform a vertical analysis of Charlie's Music Shop's balance sheet.

SOLUTION

Each of the amounts needs to be turned into a percent, using the total assets, $91,110, as the base. As an example, the $13,320 cash is turned into a percent by solving the proportion:

$$\frac{R}{100} = \frac{13320}{91110}$$

The result, 14.62%, is the portion of the total assets of Charlie's Music Shop that is currently in the form of cash. All other amounts are turned into percents in the same way. The completed vertical analysis is given in Figure 5.4.

Charlie's Music Shop
Balance Sheet
December 31, 2013

Current Assets:			Current Liabilities:		
Cash	$ 13,320	14.62%	Accts. Payable	$ 4,130	4.53%
Accts. Receivable	$ 8,370	9.19%	Notes Payable	$ 30,405	33.37%
Inventory	$ 42,400	46.54%	Salaries	$ 2,500	2.74%
Total	$ 64,090	70.34%	Total	$ 37,035	40.65%
Fixed Assets:			Long-Term Liabilities:		
Delivery Van	$ 9,300	10.21%	Loan	$ 8,800	9.66%
Equipment	$ 12,520	13.72%	Total	$ 8,800	9.66%
Fixtures	$ 5,200	5.71%			
Total	$ 27,020	29.66%	Total Liabilities	$ 45,835	50.31%
Total Assets	$ 91,110	100.00%	Owner's Equity	$ 45,275	49.69%
			Total Liabilities & Equity	$ 91,110	100.00%

Figure 5.4

Typical ratios on a horizontal analysis of a balance sheet are also available in annual business publications. Some of these ratios are given in Figure 5.5.

Some Typical Balance Sheet Ratios					
Retail Business	Inventory	Current Assets	Fixed Assets	Current Liabilities	Long-Term Liabilities
Autos	64.1%	84.2%	9.5%	71.1%	6.7%
Books	46.9%	69.0%	21.1%	46.9%	14.1%
Computers	19.9%	74.7%	15.5%	57.8%	10.1%
Clothing	52.7%	69.3%	21.3%	47.1%	15.1%
Furniture	50.4%	74.0%	18.4%	50.5%	13.6%
Gasoline	21.0%	40.0%	46.6%	31.2%	37.2%
Grocery	29.0%	49.6%	37.1%	38.2%	28.3%
Hardware	50.1%	71.9%	16.7%	34.9%	20.6%
Pharmacy	37.4%	75.2%	13.8%	45.8%	13.9%
Restaurant	6.4%	25.3%	54.6%	40.5%	37.5%

Figure 5.5

EXAMPLE 3

Using Figure 5.6, perform a horizontal analysis on Chicken Cafe's simplified balance sheet.

Chicken Cafe
Balance Sheet
October 31, 2012

	2012	2011	Change	Percent
Current Assets	$ 85,490	$ 82,700	$______	______%
Fixed Assets	$ 90,520	$ 84,600	$______	______%
Total Assets	$176,010	$167,300	$______	______%
Current Liabilities	$ 67,035	$ 61,580	$______	______%
Long-Term Liabilities	$ 49,200	$ 62,300	$______	______%
Total Liabilities	$116,235	$123,880	$______	______%
Owner's Equity	$ 59,775	$ 43,420	$______	______%

Figure 5.6

SOLUTION

We can use the percent change diagram to find the missing amounts. For example, the values for current assets produces the diagram:

100.00%	*Old*	82700
3.37%	+ *Change*	2790
103.37%	*New*	85490

Or, as we demonstrated in the last section of chapter 4, we can solve these with simple proportions. The completed statement is given in Figure 5.7.

Chicken Cafe
Balance Sheet
October 31, 2012

	2012	2011	Change	Percent
Current Assets	$ 85,490	$ 82,700	$ 2,790	3.37%
Fixed Assets	$ 90,520	$ 84,600	$ 5,920	7.00%
Total Assets	$176,010	$167,300	$ 8,710	5.21%
Current Liabilities	$ 67,035	$ 61,580	$ 5,455	8.86%
Long-Term Liabilities	$ 49,200	$ 62,300	($ 13,100)	(21.03%)
Total Liabilities	$116,235	$123,880	($ 7,645)	(6.17%)
Owner's Equity	$ 59,775	$ 43,420	$ 16,355	37.67%

Figure 5.7

5.2 Inventory

Inventory values appeared on both types of financial statements we discussed, on income statements and on balance sheets. On an income statement, the inventory value is a necessary step to computing the cost of the goods sold, and eventually the net profit of the business. On a balance sheet, the inventory forms part of the total assets of the business. The inventory value may affect the taxes imposed upon a company, since both profit and assets can be taxed.

We will often speak of beginning and ending inventories. **Beginning inventory** is the value of the merchandise in a retailer's stock at the beginning of some period of time, usually a year. **Ending inventory** is the value of the merchandise at the end of that period of time. Normally, a retailer is interested in finding an ending inventory for the time period just passed. The beginning inventory will be the same as the ending inventory of the previous period.

Conceptually, the inventory value may seem very easy to compute. Just add up the values of every item in the store. In fact, you may have seen people doing this very thing. But what value do we put on each item? Should we use retail prices, those prices at which the retailer hopes to sell his merchandise? Or should we use costs, those amounts which the retailer paid to his suppliers for his merchandise? It turns out both values are important.

An **inventory value at retail** is the value of all of the merchandise in a retail store at some point in time, using retail values for each item. Since retail prices are displayed with each item on a store's shelf, inventory values at retail are simply computed as an employee counts the items on the shelf. Although this can be a sizable task, it is conceptually simple, but not as accurate as it might first appear. Will all of the goods be sold at the retail price displayed? Or will markdowns be offered on any items? Will others spoil, break, or be lost in other ways? Each of these situations will cause the inventory value at retail to be different from the dollar value the inventory will actually generate.

An **inventory value at cost** is the value of all of the merchandise in a retail store at some point in time, using the costs paid by the retailer for each item. On an income statement, cost values are used for the beginning and ending inventory values when the cost of goods sold is being computed. On a balance sheet, the inventory value is the cost of the merchandise to the retailer.

In order to compute an inventory value at cost directly, a retailer must know the price paid for each item. With today's technology, this is possible by using a **perpetual inventory** system. Every item can be individually tagged when received from the supplier. Details about that item, including its cost and retail price, are stored in the computer. When the item is purchased by a customer, the checker scans the tag, and the computer records the sale of that particular item. In this way, in addition to having both a retail and cost inventory value available on command, the computer can also quickly reveal which items need to be restocked. A perpetual inventory system is the most accurate inventory method available, but it is not always perfectly accurate. Shoplifters, for example, bypass the checkout scanner.

Without a computer, inventory values at cost must be estimated. Exact values are rarely possible, since the cost paid for two identical items may be not be the same, especially if they were purchased at different times or from different suppliers. There are three standard inventory methods which deal with this situation. Each method is based on a particular way in which a retailer may place his merchandise on the shelf. Because of the differing tax implications, a retailer must prepare his tax returns with a specific inventory method in mind, which may or may not match the method the retailer actually uses to stock the shelves. The three methods are FIFO, LIFO, and weighted average.

When dealing with questions about inventory, both the inventory value at the beginning of the year and a record of purchases throughout the year are needed. When the dollar values of the beginning inventory and the purchases are added, we obtain the **goods available for sale**. Each of those goods were on a retailer's shelf at some time during the year, but since sales and purchases are made throughout the year, those goods were not all available at the same time during the year. At the end of the year, every one of those goods is either part of the ending inventory, or part of the goods that were sold. Therefore, the sum of the ending inventory and the cost of goods sold is also equal to the goods available for sale. As a result, for every question dealing with inventory, there is a corresponding question about the cost of goods sold.

The **First In First Out (FIFO)** method of evaluating ending inventory assumes that the first items in the store (purchased from the supplier) will be the first items out (bought by the customer). With this assumption, items that have already been sold will have been purchased earlier, and any items remaining on the shelves will have been purchased later. Grocery stores, for example, have a strong incentive to sell their older items first. If customers only bought the newest items, their older merchandise could spoil and cause a loss, so grocery stores rotate their stock. In a grocery store, FIFO is often put into practice (although it may or may not be their accounting method). Other stores may achieve the same result by not placing the newer items on the shelf until needed.

EXAMPLE 1

Sportstown carries two-person pup tents in its inventory. Their beginning inventory at cost, and purchases of this item were:

Beginning inventory:	January 1	7 tents at $30 each
Purchases:	March 12	20 tents at $33 each
	July 15	15 tents at $37 each
	October 10	5 tents at $43 each

On December 31, there were eight tents in stock. Using the FIFO method, find the value of the ending inventory and the cost of goods sold.

SOLUTION

According to the FIFO method, the eight tents in stock were the last eight purchased. Since only five tents were purchased on October 10, we must assume that the other three in stock were purchased on July 15. The inventory value calculation is:

$$\begin{array}{rr} 5 \times 43 = & 215 \\ 3 \times 37 = & \underline{111} \\ & 326 \end{array}$$

The cost of goods sold is determined by the values of the items not in inventory. For this example, that includes all of the items in beginning inventory, all of the purchases on March 12, and all but three items purchased on July 15. The cost of goods sold calculation is:

$$\begin{aligned} 7 \times 30 &= 210 \\ 20 \times 33 &= 660 \\ 12 \times 37 &= \underline{444} \\ & \quad 1314 \end{aligned}$$

The FIFO method estimates the cost of the eight tents remaining in stock to be $326, and the cost of goods sold to be $1314.

The **Last In First Out (LIFO)** method of evaluating ending inventory assumes that the last items in the store (purchased from the supplier) will be the first items out (bought by the customer). With this assumption, items that have already been sold will have been purchased last, and any items remaining on the shelves will have been purchased first. If a retailer does not rotate his stock, but pushes the old merchandise to the back when placing the new merchandise on the shelf, then he will be using the LIFO method in his stock (whether or not he uses it in his accounting). Then customers who grab the items in front will be purchasing the newer items first.

EXAMPLE 2

Using the LIFO method, recompute the ending inventory and the cost of goods sold for Sportstown's two-person pup tents, as given in example 1.

Solution

According to the LIFO method, the eight tents in stock were the first eight purchased. Since only seven appear in beginning inventory, the last of the eight tents in stock must have come from the purchase on March 12. The inventory calculation is:

$$\begin{aligned} 7 \times 30 &= 210 \\ 1 \times 33 &= \underline{\ \ 33} \\ & \quad 243 \end{aligned}$$

The cost of goods sold is determined by the values of the items not in inventory. For this example, that includes all but one of the items from the purchase on March 12, and all of the items purchased on July 15 and October 10. The cost of goods sold calculation is:

$$\begin{aligned} 19 \times 33 &= 627 \\ 15 \times 37 &= 555 \\ 5 \times 43 &= \underline{215} \\ & \quad 1397 \end{aligned}$$

Using the LIFO method, the cost of the eight tents would be estimated at $243, and the cost of goods sold to be $1397.

The FIFO and LIFO methods are easily confused with each other. Probably the most important observation to make about the names of these two methods is that they specify which items were sold, not which remain in stock. The FIFO method says that the first items are part of the cost of goods sold, and the LIFO method says that the last items are part of the cost of goods sold. When computing inventory values, we do not want to know which items were sold, but which were *not* sold.

The **Weighted Average,** or **Average Cost,** method of evaluating ending inventory assumes that the items remaining in ending inventory will be a representative sample of all items that were available during the year. If a retailer mixes his new merchandise in with the old merchandise in a bin on the display floor, (or his customers do the mixing on his shelves), then some items from each of the retailer's purchases may remain at the end of the year. To compute the weighted average value of the inventory, we assume that each item's cost is the average cost of all items purchased.

EXAMPLE 3

Using the Weighted Average method, recompute the ending inventory and the cost of goods sold for Sportstown's two-person pup tents, as given in example 1.

SOLUTION

We first compute the total value of all merchandise available for sale at some point in time during the year. This consists of the beginning inventory plus all purchases.

$$\begin{array}{rr} 7 \times 30 = & 210 \\ 20 \times 33 = & 660 \\ 15 \times 37 = & 555 \\ 5 \times 43 = & 215 \\ \hline 47 \qquad & 1640 \end{array}$$

The goods available for sale for the year was $1640. Since 47 items were purchased the average cost was:

$$\text{Average Cost} = \frac{1640}{47} \approx 34.8936$$

The average cost during the year was approximately $34.89 per pup tent, but since we are still in the middle of the problem, we will use the unrounded value above. There were eight tents in inventory at the end of the year, and their value was:

$$8 \times 34.8936 \approx 279.15$$

Since there was $1,640 worth of goods available for sale during the year, we can subtract to find the cost of goods sold:

$$1640.00 - 279.15 = 1360.85$$

Alternatively, we could have found the cost of goods sold by first determining that 39 items remained in stock, and multiplied that quantity by the average cost of $34.8936. Nevertheless, we found that the Weighted Average method estimated the ending inventory at $279.15, and the cost of goods sold at $1,360.85.

Note that the average cost was not found by simply averaging the prices $30, $33, $37, and $43. Averaging the prices will not work if different quantities were purchased at those different prices.

The tax implications of the different inventory methods can be examined by looking back at the three results we obtained for Sportstown's ending inventory of pup tents. You should see that LIFO gave the lowest estimate for ending inventory, and FIFO gave the highest estimate. On the other hand, the LIFO estimate for the cost of goods sold was higher than the FIFO estimate. Since costs are subtracted from total sales to obtain the net profit, a higher value for costs would mean a lower value for net profit, and vice versa. Therefore, the LIFO estimate for net profit would be lower than the FIFO estimate. And since income taxes are based on net profit, the LIFO method would (in this example) produce a smaller income tax bill. But don't jump to a too hasty conclusion. In this example, the LIFO method would produce the lower tax bill only because the costs to the retailer were increasing over time. The other methods can sometimes produce the smaller tax bill if the costs either decrease or vary in both directions over time.

5.3 Basic Depreciation

Fixed assets, those assets which are used in the production of income, are not turned into cash under normal circumstances. Normally, a business will hold its fixed assets for a number of years. Purchases of new equipment, fixtures, or land will change the total value of the fixed assets. Deterioration of equipment and fixtures can also change the value of the fixed assets. Businesses must be able to estimate the current value of their fixed assets, taking into account the depreciation, or decline in value of the assets, that might be due to deterioration. You may already be familiar with this type of depreciation if you have owned a car. A new car may be fairly expensive, but it does not hold its value. As a car gets older, its value drops.

Businesses are able to deduct their costs of doing business from their gross income or sales, so income tax is paid on their net profit. For example, when a business purchases an expensive new piece of equipment, the cost of the equipment affects their ability to show a profit. For tax purposes, however, the cost of the equipment is usually not deductible in the year of purchase. Essentially, the purchase is a transformation of cash into equipment, with no change in value of the total assets of the company. During each year that the equipment is used, the value of the equipment will decline, and that decline will be deducted from the income. In this way, depreciation can be described as the spreading of the cost of an asset over the years of the asset's useful life.

To summarize, **depreciation** has two different, but related, definitions. The primary definition, that depreciation is a decline in value, is the meaning desired when a balance sheet is being prepared, since a balance sheet must provide information about the true value of the assets of a company. The secondary definition, that depreciation is a spreading of the cost over several years, is the meaning needed when the tax returns of a business are being prepared. The second definition is actually an instance of the first definition as it applies to taxation.

However, differences can appear between the two definitions of depreciation for several reasons. Ambiguities must be removed from the process of taxation, so that taxpayers will know what is expected of them and not be subject to arbitrary rulings. Since the primary use of depreciation is to estimate the value of an asset, many arguments could easily arise over the value of an asset which is not currently for sale. Specific rules are needed to assign values, which hopefully mirror the actual values involved. Governments also implement policies through the use of specific taxes or exemptions from taxation. For example, business investments can be encouraged by providing tax deductions for depreciation more quickly than the actual deterioration of the equipment.

When an asset is to be depreciated, a business needs to know the **basis,** or total original value, of the asset. Usually, the basis is the cost, but may be adjusted due to improvements made to the asset. As the years go by, the **book value,** or current value, of the asset will change. Eventually, when the asset is no longer useful, its only value will be **scrap value,** or **salvage value.** The **depreciable amount** is the total amount of depreciation over all years of the asset's useful life. Usually, the depreciable amount is the difference between cost and scrap value. A **depreciation schedule** is a table which shows the amount of depreciation and book value for each year of an asset's useful life. By this definition of depreciation schedule, the table will have at least three columns, namely year, depreciation, and book value. Often, the **accumulated depreciation,** or the total depreciation from the beginning through the current year, is included.

Depreciation schedules are usually prepared at the time of purchase of an asset, and predictions of the asset's future book values are made. There are several methods by which the book values can be determined. The most commonly used depreciation methods are straight line, units of production, and declining balance. In this section, our focus will be on the first two methods. At times, we will use unrealistically short lifetimes for some of the assets. We do this to avoid having to produce lengthy depreciation schedules as examples.

The **Straight Line Method** of depreciation assumes that an asset's value will decline by equal amounts each year. This method is both the easiest to understand and the easiest to implement. Since each year's depreciation is the same as every other year, we only need to determine this **annual depreciation.** To obtain it, we simply divide the depreciable amount by the estimated number of years of the asset's useful life.

$$\text{Annual Depreciation} = \frac{\text{Depreciable Amount}}{\text{Life in Years}}$$

To prepare a depreciation schedule, we must identify the current depreciation, the accumulated depreciation, and the book value for each year. In a straight line schedule, the amount of current depreciation each year is the annual depreciation. The accumulated depreciation column is a running subtotal of the depreciation claimed so far. Each year, the current depreciation is added to the previous year's accumulated depreciation to obtain the new accumulated depreciation. The original book value, the cost, can be placed in year zero. Each year, the book value declines by the amount of current depreciation. The new book value is found by subtracting the current depreciation from the old book value. In a straight line schedule, if done properly, the last year's accumulated depreciation will be the depreciable amount, and the last year's book value will be the scrap value.

EXAMPLE 1

Johnson Hog Farms buys a new farm tractor at a cost of $120,000. The tractor is to be depreciated over four years, and afterwards have a scrap value of $10,000. Prepare a straight line depreciation schedule.

SOLUTION

The difference between cost and scrap value is the depreciable amount. The annual depreciation is:

$$\text{Annual Depreciation} = \frac{120000 - 10000}{4} = \frac{110000}{4} = 27500$$

The original cost, $120,000, will be the book value in year zero. The current depreciation will be $27,500 each year. The accumulated depreciation is found by adding, and the book value is found by subtracting. The final result is:

Year	Current Depreciation	Accumulated Depreciation	Book Value
0			$120,000
1	$27,500	$ 27,500	$ 92,500
2	$27,500	$ 55,000	$ 65,000
3	$27,500	$ 82,500	$ 37,500
4	$27,500	$110,000	$ 10,000

We note that the depreciable amount and the scrap value do appear in the last year. If these values had not appeared, then we would suspect that arithmetic errors had occurred.

In the example above, we implicitly assumed that the tractor was used the entire first year (since January 1), and not purchased later in the year. In any depreciation method where lifetimes are measured in years (as is the case with the Straight Line Method), the year of service and the calendar year (or the tax year) may not actually coincide. In such cases, a partial year adjustment is needed.

To understand the need for a partial year adjustment, consider a business owner who purchased a vehicle on November 1 for use in his business. At the end of the year, the vehicle will have had two months of service in the business, and should have experienced a two-month decline in value. It would be incorrect to claim a full year's depreciation on the vehicle for only two months of use. The correct partial year depreciation amount in this example would be $\frac{2}{12}$ of a first year's full depreciation.

Partial year depreciation always affects the first year of a depreciation schedule when lifetimes are measured in years. The first year must be prorated in some fashion, according to the asset's actual time of service or use in the business. Although different conventions for prorating this depreciation are available, we shall concentrate our attention primarily on one standard convention.

Partial year depreciation also affects the number of years in a depreciation schedule. Suppose, for example, that an asset will be depreciated over three years. If the asset is placed into service during the middle of some first calendar year, then the third anniversary of that date is during the fourth calendar year. Depreciation schedules with partial year adjustments will always have one more year than the lifetime of the asset.

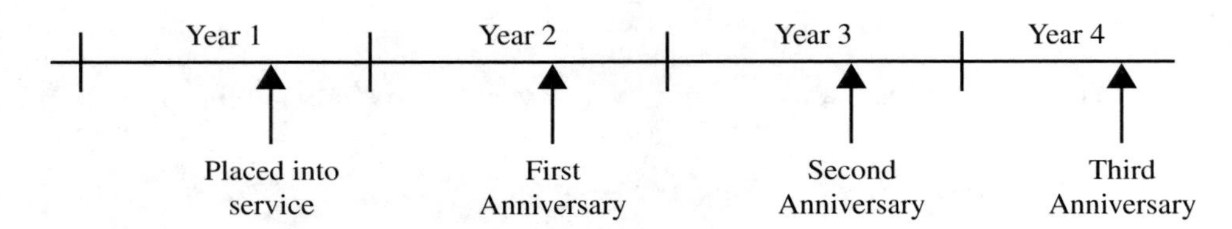

Partial year depreciation may or may not affect the depreciation amounts for the years after the first year, depending on the depreciation method used. It will affect all of the book values, since the first year's book value will have changed.

The **standard convention** for partial year depreciation counts the number of months of service of an asset during the partial year, rounded to the nearest whole number of months. (If an asset is placed into service on or before the 15th, that month will be counted as a month of service. If the asset is placed into service on the 16th or later, then that month is not counted.) The count is then divided by 12, giving an approximate fraction of the year for which the asset was used in business. The first year's depreciation is adjusted by multiplying by this fraction.

EXAMPLE 2

Sunnyfield Dance Studio purchases a copier for business use on September 22, 2012. It cost $3,600, has an estimated scrap value of $300, and will be depreciated over four years. Prepare a straight line depreciation schedule using the standard convention.

SOLUTION

For the straight line method, we find the annual depreciation.

$$\text{Annual Depreciation} = \frac{3600 - 300}{4} = \frac{3300}{4} = 825$$

Each calendar year after the first, the copier will experience $825 depreciation. With an original service date of September 22, the first calendar year will have only 3 months of service. Therefore, the first year depreciation is:

$$\frac{3}{12}\times 825 = 206.25$$

In the context of depreciation, answers are estimates and typically rounded to the nearest dollar. Therefore the first year's depreciation will be $206. The depreciation amount for the last (fifth) year of this four year schedule is found by subtracting the scrap value from the previous year's book value. The schedule is:

Year	Current Depreciation	Accumulated Depreciation	Book Value
			$ 3,600
2012	$ 206	$ 206	$ 3,394
2013	$ 825	$ 1,031	$ 2,569
2014	$ 825	$ 1,856	$ 1,744
2015	$ 825	$ 2,681	$ 919
2016	$ 619	$ 3,300	$ 300

Straight line depreciation is the easiest method to adjust for partial years. As you can see in the previous example, only the first and last year's depreciation amounts changed. The essential character of straight line depreciation, where equal amounts of depreciation occur each year, remains unchanged, and is still visible in the middle years of the schedule.

Another method of depreciation with similar characteristics to the straight line method exists, but where the calendar is relatively unimportant. The **Units of Production Method** of depreciation assumes that an asset's value will decline by equal amounts per unit produced. Machines on assembly lines may be equipped with counters, and can report the number of items produced by that machine. Alternatively, the number of hours a machine is in operation can be used. The more a machine is used, the more its value will decline. Vehicles are another example where units of production depreciation can be applied. As a vehicle is used in business, the odometer counts the number of miles produced.

To obtain the **unit depreciation**, or decline in value per unit produced, we simply divide the depreciable amount by the estimated number of units produced during the asset's useful life.

$$\text{Unit Depreciation} = \frac{\text{Depreciable Amount}}{\text{Life in Units}}$$

Since the life is measured in units, not years, we will also need information about the number of units produced each year in order to prepare a depreciation schedule. This information cannot be obtained at the time of purchase, so a depreciation schedule cannot be completed at that time. It must be continued each year.

EXAMPLE 3

Herman's Floral Shop purchases a delivery van for $24,000. Depreciation will be taken over 80,000 miles, and the scrap value is estimated at $4,000. Prepare a units of production depreciation schedule, given that the van was used 14,340 miles during the first year, 22,600 miles in the second year, 18,280 miles during the third year, 19,500 miles during the fourth year, and 16,320 miles during the fifth year.

SOLUTION

The unit depreciation is:

$$\text{Unit Depreciation} = \frac{24000 - 4000}{80000} = \frac{20000}{80000} = 0.25$$

Therefore, the van will experience depreciation of 25 cents per mile. We shall show the work of producing the values in the current depreciation column in the schedule itself. The schedule is:

Year	Usage	Current Depreciation	Accumulated Depreciation	Book Value
0				$ 24,000
1	14,340	$0.25 \times 14340 = 3585$	$ 3,585	$ 20,415
2	22,600	$0.25 \times 22600 = 5650$	$ 9,235	$ 14,765
3	18,280	$0.25 \times 18280 = 4570$	$13,805	$ 10,195
4	19,500	$0.25 \times 19500 = 4875$	$18,680	$ 5,320
5	5,280	$0.25 \times 5280 = 1320$	$20,000	$ 4,000

Notice that the fifth year's usage is for 5,280 miles, not the 16,320 miles originally given. The van was to be depreciated over 80,000 miles, and after the first four years, 74,720 miles of depreciation had already occurred. Only 5,280 miles of depreciation were left.

Lifetimes in a units of production schedule are not based on time, so no partial year adjustment is ever needed. Usage is the sole determinant of the amount of depreciation in a particular year.

5.4 Accelerated Depreciation

Some assets, like new cars, will experience larger declines in value at the beginning of their useful life than toward the end. An **accelerated depreciation** method, giving larger amounts of depreciation in earlier years, is needed for these types of assets. Neither the straight line method nor the units of production method provide the earlier large decline in value.

One class of accelerated depreciation methods are the **declining balance** methods. These methods assume that values of an asset decline by a constant annual rate, or percent. The initial decline in value is stated as an approximate percentage of the straight line depreciation. Common initial declines in value are 200% (often called double), 150%, and 125%. All are greater than 100% in order to provide larger amounts of depreciation in earlier years. This initial decline is built into the name of the method. Therefore, we have the **200% Declining Balance Method** (often called the **Double Declining Balance Method**), the **150% Declining Balance Method,** and the **125% Declining Balance Method.**

The **method rate,** the initial percent decline in value built into the name of the method, is not the annual rate of depreciation. The annual rate is found by dividing the method rate by the estimated life of the asset, measured in years.

$$\text{Annual Depreciation Rate} = \frac{\text{Method Rate}}{\text{Life in Years}}$$

This rate is a percent of the book value of the previous year. Each year, the value of an asset will experience the percent decrease given by the annual depreciation rate.

Unlike the straight line method, declining balance methods may or may not (and usually do not) produce scrap value in the last year of an asset's useful life. To remedy this defect, the last year of a depreciation schedule is usually modified so that scrap value appears.

EXAMPLE 1

Sunnyside Memorial Park builds a new road at a cost of $37,000. For tax purposes, it has an expected life of 5 years and a scrap value of $7,500. Prepare a 150% declining balance depreciation schedule.

SOLUTION

The annual rate of depreciation is:

$$\text{Annual Depreciation Rate} = \frac{150\%}{5} = 30\%$$

Each year, the road will lose 30% of the previous year's book value. Each current depreciation amount is obtained by multiplying the previous book value by 30%. Since the values are estimates, all answers are rounded to the nearest dollar. The last year of the schedule is modified to produce scrap value. We find the fifth year current depreciation by subtracting scrap value from the fourth year book value. The final result is:

Year	Current Depreciation	Accumulated Depreciation	Book Value
0			$ 37,000
1	$37000 \times 0.30 = 11100$	$ 11,100	$ 25,900
2	$25900 \times 0.30 = 7770$	$ 18,870	$ 18,130
3	$18130 \times 0.30 = 5439$	$ 24,309	$ 12,691
4	$12691 \times 0.30 \approx 3807$	$ 28,116	$ 8,884
5	$8884 - 7500 = 1384$	$ 29,500	$ 7,500

The major drawback of the declining balance methods is their inability to produce a previously determined scrap value. Without a modification in the last year's calculations, the final book value could be either larger or smaller than the scrap value. More interestingly, even if a schedule is continued for hundreds of years, the declining balance methods will never produce a zero book value. When a percentage reduction in value is based on the previous year's book value, there will always be some percentage remaining.

Partial year considerations must also be made when using the declining balance methods. Consider the following example.

EXAMPLE 2

Clearbrook Art Supply purchases three computers for business use on May 14, 2012. They cost $4,200, have an estimated scrap value of $300, and will be depreciated over five years. Prepare a double declining balance depreciation schedule using the standard convention.

SOLUTION

For a declining balance method of depreciation, we need to find the depreciation rate.

$$\text{Annual Depreciation Rate} = \frac{200\%}{5} = 40\%$$

Since a partial year adjustment will be made, six calendar years will be needed to depreciate five years of service. Each calendar year after the first, there will be a 40% decline in the value of the computers. The first year, because of the original service date of May 14, will experience only $\frac{8}{12}$ of that 40% decline. Each of these percents has the previous year's book value as its base. The schedule is:

Year	Current Depreciation	Accumulated Depreciation	Book Value
			$4,200
2012	$4200 \times 0.40 \times \frac{8}{12} = \$1{,}120$	$1,120	$3,080
2013	$3080 \times 0.40 = \$1{,}232$	$2,352	$1,848
2014	$1848 \times 0.40 \approx \$739$	$3,091	$1,109
2015	$1109 \times 0.40 \approx \$444$	$3,535	$ 665
2016	$665 \times 0.40 = \$266$	$3,801	$ 399
2017	$399 - 300 = \$99$	$3,900	$ 300

The last year's depreciation of this schedule was computed by subtracting, so that the book value of the computers would not dip below their scrap value.

The standard method of depreciation for federal income tax purposes is called the **Modified Accelerated Cost Recovery System**, or **MACRS**. The MACRS method was introduced in 1986, and generally property placed into service after that date will be depreciated according to the MACRS method. It is a modification of the **Accelerated Cost Recovery System**, or **ACRS**, which was in use from 1981 to 1986. Essentially, a MACRS depreciation schedule will begin with a declining balance method, and then switch to a straight line method to finish the schedule. This approach will give accelerated depreciation, and at the end of an asset's lifetime obtain a zero scrap value. The details, though, are beyond the scope of this course.

5.5 Ratio Analysis

In addition to horizontal and vertical analyses, analysts often use financial ratios to examine financial statements. There are many different financial ratios which measure different aspects of a company's health. They can be grouped according to their function.

Profitability ratios measure the return generated by a company's sales, assets, or equity. Some specific examples are:

$$\textbf{Net Profit Ratio} = \frac{\text{Net Profit}}{\text{Net Sales}}$$

$$\textbf{Gross Profit Ratio} = \frac{\text{Gross Profit}}{\text{Net Sales}}$$

$$\textbf{Return On Assets} = \frac{\text{Net Profit}}{\text{Total Assets}}$$

$$\textbf{Return On Equity} = \frac{\text{Net Profit}}{\text{Owner's Equity}}$$

Each of the profitability ratios measures the profit against some other aspect of value of a company. You should recognize the net profit ratio and the gross profit ratio. Both can be found in a vertical analysis of an income statement. To determine the other two ratios, both an income statement and a balance sheet are required.

EXAMPLE 1

Using Chicken Cafe's income statement and balance sheet in Figure 5.8, determine their net profit ratio and their return on equity.

SOLUTION

Chicken Cafe's net profit was $49,486, their net sales was $880,162, and their owner's equity was $59,775. The ratios are:

$$\text{Net Profit Ratio} = \frac{49486}{880162} \approx 0.0562$$

$$\text{Return on equity} = \frac{49486}{59775} \approx 0.8279$$

Since net profit ratios often fall below 5%, the 5.62% net profit ratio seems reasonable. The 82.79% return on equity would be very attractive to an investor, when typical rates of return on stock investments might only be 20% in a good year.

Chicken Cafe
Income Statement
For the Year Ended December 31, 2012

Net Sales:		
Gross Sales	$885,395	
Returns	$ 5,233	
Net Sales		$880,162
Cost of Goods Sold:		
Beginning Inventory	$ 18,690	
Purchases	$371,024	
Goods Available for Sale	$389,714	
Ending Inventory	$ 19,255	
Cost of Goods Sold		$370,459
Gross Profit		$509,703
Operating Expenses:		
Advertising	$ 14,259	
Insurance	$ 8,322	
Taxes	$ 40,871	
Rent	$ 86,400	
Salaries	$260,355	
Supplies	$ 27,538	
Utilities	$ 22,472	
Total Operating Expenses		$460,217
Net Profit		$ 49,486

Chicken Cafe
Balance Sheet
December 31, 2012

Current Assets:		
Cash	$ 14,750	
Securities	$ 39,075	
Accts. Receivable	$ 12,410	
Inventory	$ 19,255	
Total		$ 85,490
Fixed Assets:		
Building	$ 29,000	
Land	$ 29,020	
Equipment	$ 18,200	
Fixtures	$ 14,300	
Total		$ 90,520
Total Assets		$176,010
Current Liabilities:		
Accts. Payable	$ 24,335	
Notes Payable	$ 33,200	
Salaries	$ 9,500	
Total		$ 67,035
Long-Term Liabilities:		
Mortgage	$ 49,200	
Total		$ 49,200
Total Liabilities		$116,235
Owner's Equity		$ 59,775
Total Liabilities & Equity		$176,010

Figure 5.8

Some typical values of return on equity, as well as other financial ratios introduced in this section, are included in Figure 5.9. A table of typical income statement ratios appeared in section 4.8, and a table of typical balance sheet ratios appeared in section 5.1.

Liquidity ratios measure a company's ability to pay its short term debt. For example,

$$\textbf{Current Ratio} = \frac{\text{Current Assets}}{\text{Current Liabilities}}$$

$$\textbf{Acid Test Ratio} = \frac{\text{Current Assets} - \text{Inventory}}{\text{Current Liabilities}}$$

The current ratio is also known as the **working capital ratio,** and the acid test ratio is also called the **quick ratio.** (Those current assets which are not inventory are sometimes called the **quick assets.**) Each of the liquidity ratios measures some aspect of value of a company against their current liabilities, or short term debt. These ratios can be found from a balance sheet.

Some Other Typical Financial Ratios							
Retail Business	Return on Assets	Return on Equity	Current Ratio	Acid Test	Total Asset Turnover	Inventory Turnover	Debt to Equity
Autos	3.0%	19.8%	1.2	0.2	3.7	5.0	5.2
Books	2.5%	9.6%	1.5	0.3	2.8	3.6	1.8
Computers	6.2%	20.3%	1.3	1.0	3.8	17.6	2.6
Clothing	6.0%	17.9%	1.7	0.2	2.5	2.8	1.3
Furniture	3.7%	13.1%	1.6	0.3	2.8	3.3	2.1
Gasoline	3.9%	18.7%	1.3	0.5	5.3	35.4	3.9
Grocery	5.5%	20.0%	1.4	0.4	5.1	15.7	2.7
Hardware	4.5%	12.3%	2.4	0.6	2.4	3.0	1.5
Pharmacy	9.8%	28.2%	1.8	0.7	4.8	10.2	2.0
Restaurant	4.8%	26.1%	0.6	0.3	3.1	35.8	6.5

Figure 5.9

EXAMPLE 2

Using Chicken Cafe's balance sheet from Figure 5.8, find their current ratio and their acid test ratio.

SOLUTION

Chicken Cafe's current assets were $85,490, their current liabilities were $67,035, and their inventory was $19,255. The ratios are:

$$\text{Current Ratio} = \frac{85490}{67035} = 1.28$$

$$\text{Acid Test Ratio} = \frac{85490 - 19255}{67035} = \frac{66235}{67035} = 0.99$$

The value of the current ratio is 1.28 (sometimes written 1.28:1). For every $1 of current liabilities, Chicken Cafe has $1.28 of current assets. In order to make this interpretation clearer, we can rephrase this statement using the definitions of current assets and current liabilities. For every $1 of debt payable within the year, Chicken Cafe should have $1.28 in cash with which to pay the debt. Similarly, Chicken Cafe's acid test ratio of 0.99 indicates that, without waiting for the sale of their inventory, they have 99 cents to pay each $1 of debt.

Where is the line between good and mediocre current ratios? It might be tempting to say that any current ratio greater than 1 is good, since the company would be able to pay its bills. But financial analysts often use a higher standard, sometimes about 2 for a typical company. This is because current assets are being used as a prediction of future income, and a company's income ought to be more than just enough to get by. (Too many of us have probably experienced just getting by, where our bills claim almost all of our paycheck. We don't like being strapped for cash, and neither does a business.)

On the other hand, some businesses turn over their inventory very quickly. In such situations, the current assets will not be a good prediction of future income. Businesses where inventory moves quickly can operate with smaller current ratios without a problem.

Unlike the current ratio, an acid test ratio of 1 or better is usually considered good. The purpose of the acid test ratio is to measure ability to pay short term debt if, for some reason, the inventory cannot be sold. That is, the acid test ratio helps measure a business's ability to weather an economic downturn or a sudden uninsured catastrophe. Many businesses, however, operate with acid test ratios much less than one, and therefore must sell their inventory in order to meet their current obligations.

Activity ratios measure the ability of a company to generate sales with its assets. For example,

$$\textbf{Total Asset Turnover} = \frac{\text{Net Sales}}{\text{Total Assets}}$$

$$\textbf{Inventory Turnover at Cost} = \frac{\text{Cost of Goods Sold}}{\text{Average Inventory at Cost}}$$

$$\textbf{Inventory Turnover at Retail} = \frac{\text{Net Sales}}{\text{Average Inventory at Retail}}$$

A typical activity ratio compares an income statement value against a balance sheet value. An income statement will be required, and a balance sheet may be required.

The two forms of the inventory turnover ratio are, in theory, equal. The relationship between the two forms of the average inventory is the markup. In the same way, net sales is related to cost of goods sold by the markup. But in practice, it is possible for the inventory turnover ratios to be slightly different, due to the fact that most of the quantities used in the formulas are actually estimates. Remember, inventory values at cost were estimated through assumptions such as LIFO and FIFO, while inventory values at retail assume you know exactly which items will be sold at a markdown, and for how much. Sometimes, the inventory turnover ratio is called **the stock turnover ratio.**

EXAMPLE 3

Using Chicken Cafe's income statement from Figure 5.8, determine their inventory turnover ratio.

SOLUTION

Chicken Cafe's cost of goods sold was $370,459, and their two consecutive inventory values were $18,690 and $19,255. Their average inventory was:

$$\text{Average Inventory} = \frac{18690 + 19255}{2} = 18972.50$$

Therefore, their inventory ratio is:

$$\text{Inventory Turnover at Cost} = \frac{370459}{18972.50} = 19.53$$

Chicken Cafe's inventory turnover of 19.53 means the business sells, each year, 19.53 times the average amount of merchandise it keeps on hand. Or, that Chicken Cafe restocks its inventory 19.53 times per year. Since Chicken Cafe deals in perishable food items, we can expect that it would restock its merchandise frequently.

In fact, we can use Chicken Cafe's inventory turnover to find how long merchandise remains in inventory. Simply divide the inventory turnover into one year, measured in your preferred time unit (days, weeks, or months). We get:

$$\frac{52 \text{ weeks}}{19.53} \approx 2.66$$

Chicken Cafe's merchandise remains in inventory an average of 2.66 weeks.

The quality of an inventory turnover ratio depends very much on the type of business being measured. A grocery store or restaurant will operate on a much higher turnover ratio than an antique shop.

Leverage ratios measure the company's amount of indebtedness. More specifically, **leveraging** is the use of borrowed money to obtain your goals, rather than using your own money. For example,

$$\textbf{Debt to Equity Ratio} = \frac{\text{Total Liabilities}}{\text{Owner's Equity}}$$

The debt to equity ratio is an example of a style of ratio where both quantities being compared occur in the name of the ratio. That is, an A to B ratio compares the quantities A and B, and always does so as $\frac{A}{B}$, never as $\frac{B}{A}$.

EXAMPLE 4

Using Chicken Cafe's balance sheet from Figure 5.8, determine their debt to equity ratio.

SOLUTION

Chicken Cafe's total liabilities was $116,235, and their owner's equity was $59,775. Therefore, the ratio is:

$$\text{Debt to Equity Ratio} = \frac{116235}{59775} \approx 1.94$$

Chicken Cafe's debt to equity ratio of 1.94 means that for every $1 of owner's equity, there is $1.94 of total liability. In more simple English, if the company was liquidated today, for each $1 the owners would get, the creditors would receive $1.94. (Note that this makes a total of $2.94.)

Different analysts have different opinions about debt. When debt is large, some analysts will see possible difficulties with future repayment. On the other hand, some analysts see a large debt as evidence of the leveraged use of one's funds, yielding a greater return on equity for investors.

Name: ______________________ Date: __________

Exercises 5.1

* Complete the following balance sheets.

1.

Penney's Hardware
Balance Sheet
October 31, 2013

Current Assets:		Current Liabilities:	
Cash	$12,942	Accts. Payable	$ 23,296
Securities	$12,300	Notes Payable	$ 24,000
Accts. Receivable	$4,688	Salaries	$ 11,014
Inventory	$79,685	Total	$______
Total	$______	Long-Term Liabilities:	
		Loan	$17,520
Fixed Assets:		Total	$______
Equipment	$23,276		
Fixtures	$18,755	Total Liabilities	$______
Total	$______		
		Owner's Equity	$______
Total Assets	$______		
		Total Liabilities & Equity	$______

2.

Midtown Autos
Balance Sheet
December 31, 2012

Current Assets:		Current Liabilities:	
Cash	$ 5,082	Accts. Payable	$ 3,167
Accts. Receivable	$ 2,595	Notes Payable	$99,950
Inventory	$127,309	Salaries	$ 1,133
Total	$______	Total	$______
		Long-Term Liabilities:	
Fixed Assets:		Loan	$22,000
Equipment	$ 7,389	Total	$______
Fixtures	$ 3,844		
Total	$______	Total Liabilities	$______
Total Assets	$______	Owner's Equity	$______
		Total Liabilities & Equity	$______

** Perform a vertical analysis on the following balance sheets.

3.

Marie's Restaurant
Balance Sheet
December 31, 2014

Current Assets:			Current Liabilities:		
Cash	$ 32,417	_____%	Accts. Payable	$ 12,655	_____%
Securities	$ 5,000	_____%	Notes Payable	$ 25,400	_____%
Accts. Receivable	$ 8,722	_____%	Salaries	$ 5,374	_____%
Inventory	$ 17,455	_____%	Total	$ 43,429	_____%
Total	$ 63,594	_____%			
			Long-Term Liabilities:		
Fixed Assets:			Mortgage	$ 75,000	_____%
Building	$107,320	_____%	Total	$ 75,000	_____%
Land	$ 12,500	_____%			
Equipment	$ 22,100	_____%	Total Liabilities	$118,429	_____%
Fixtures	$ 9,966	_____%			
Total	$151,886	_____%	Owner's Equity	$ 97,051	_____%
Total Assets	$215,480	_____%	Total Liabilities & Equity	$215,480	_____%

4.

Rick's Service Station
Balance Sheet
December 31, 2013

Current Assets:			Current Liabilities:		
Cash	$12,853	_____%	Accts. Payable	$ 4,681	_____%
Accts. Receivable	$ 3,572	_____%	Notes Payable	$21,890	_____%
Inventory	$14,816	_____%	Salaries	$ 746	_____%
Total	$31,241	_____%	Total	$27,317	_____%
			Long-Term Liabilities:		
Fixed Assets:			Mortgage	$38,605	_____%
Building	$42,000	_____%	Total	$38,605	_____%
Land	$12,000	_____%			
Equipment	$ 9,575	_____%			
Total	$63,575	_____%	Total Liabilities	$65,922	_____%
Total Assets	$94,816	_____%	Owner's Equity	$28,894	_____%
			Total Liabilities & Equity	$94,816	_____%

Perform a horizontal analysis on the following balance sheets.

5.

Marie's Restaurant
Balance Sheet

	2014	2013	Change	Percent
Current Assets	$ 63,594	$ 59,400	$_____	_____%
Fixed Assets	$151,886	$149,200	$_____	_____%
Total Assets	$215,480	$208,600	$_____	_____%
Current Liabilities	$ 43,429	$ 39,618	$_____	_____%
Long-Term Liabilities	$ 75,000	$ 82,000	$_____	_____%
Total Liabilities	$118,429	$121,618	$_____	_____%
Owner's Equity	$ 97,051	$ 86,982	$_____	_____%

6.

Rick's Service Station
Balance Sheet

	2013	2012	Change	Percent
Current Assets	$31,241	$29,477	$_____	_____%
Fixed Assets	$63,575	$65,394	$_____	_____%
Total Assets	$94,816	$94,871	$_____	_____%
Current Liabilities	$27,317	$24,301	$_____	_____%
Long-Term Liabilities	$38,605	$41,727	$_____	_____%
Total Liabilities	$65,922	$66,028	$_____	_____%
Owner's Equity	$28,894	$28,843	$_____	_____%

Name: ______________________________ Date: __________

Exercises 5.2

** Taylor Kitchenware carries dishwashers in its inventory. Their beginning inventory and purchases for the year, at cost, were

Beginning Inventory:	January 1	4 dishwashers at $199 each
Purchases:	March 10	2 dishwashers at $219 each
	June 5	2 dishwashers at $229 each
	October 11	3 dishwashers at $239 each

On December 31, there were 5 dishwashers in stock.

1. Find the value of the ending inventory, using the LIFO method.

2. Find the value of the cost of goods sold, using the LIFO method.

3. Find the value of the ending inventory, using the FIFO method.

4. Find the value of the cost of goods sold, using the FIFO method.

5. Find the value of the ending inventory, using the Weighted Average method.

6. Find the value of the cost of goods sold, using the Weighted Average method.

Jeff's Music keeps several inexpensive guitars in stock. Their beginning inventory and purchases, at cost, for this guitar were

Beginning Inventory:	January 1	5 guitars at $209 each
Purchases:	April 20	6 guitars at $219 each
	August 10	13 guitars at $197 each
	September 21	7 guitars at $222 each

On December 31, they had 6 guitars in stock.

7. Find the value of the ending inventory, using the LIFO method.

8. Find the value of the cost of goods sold, using the LIFO method.

9. Find the value of the ending inventory, using the FIFO method.

10. Find the value of the cost of goods sold, using the FIFO method.

11. Find the value of the ending inventory, using the Weighted Average method.

12. Find the value of the cost of goods sold, using the Weighted Average method.

Barney's Hardware had the following purchases of wrench sets (at cost) during the year 2013.

Beginning Inventory:	January 1	65 sets at $11 each
Purchases:	March	125 sets at $13 each
	June	135 sets at $14 each
	September	125 sets at $15 each
	November	105 sets at $14 each

At the end of the year 2013, there are 167 sets in inventory.

13. Find the value of the ending inventory using the FIFO method.

14. Find the value of the cost of goods sold using the FIFO method.

15. Find the value of the ending inventory using the LIFO method.

16. Find the value of the cost of goods sold using the LIFO method.

17. Find the value of the ending inventory using the Weighted Average method.

18. Find the value of the cost of goods sold using the Weighted Average method.

*** During the year 2014, Barney's Hardware makes the following purchases (at cost).

April	75 sets at $15 each
October	95 sets at $16 each

At the end of the year 2014, there are 192 sets in inventory. Use your results from problems #13–18 on the previous page for the following problems:

19. Find the value of the ending inventory using the FIFO method.

20. Find the value of the cost of goods sold using the FIFO method.

21. Find the value of the ending inventory using the LIFO method.

22. Find the value of the cost of goods sold using the LIFO method.

Name: ______________________________ Date: __________

Exercises 5.3

* Using the Straight Line Depreciation method, find the annual depreciation.

	Cost	Scrap Value	Lifetime
1.	$19,500	$700	6 years
2.	$82,400	$16,300	5 years
3.	$60,000	$0	8 years
4.	$75,000	$5,000	4 years

Using the Units of Production Depreciation method, find the depreciation.

	Cost	Scrap Value	Lifetime	Usage
5.	$83,500	$14,200	300,000 units	42,375 units
6.	$49,200	$7,300	600,000 units	88,000 units
7.	$33,000	$0	150,000 units	22,400 units
8.	$9,280	$500	75,000 units	7,300 units

Find the first year's depreciation, using the Straight Line method and the standard partial-year convention.

	Cost	Scrap Value	Lifetime	Service Date
9.	$145,000	$18,000	5 years	April 6
10.	$ 69,000	$ 5,000	7 years	January 17
11.	$ 85,000	$10,000	4 years	May 17
12.	$122,500	$ 0	10 years	September 2

** Prepare a depreciation schedule for each scenario.

13. Tyler and Johnson, a law firm, purchased $75,000 worth of office furniture. Assume that the furniture will have a life of seven years and a scrap value of $8,000. Prepare a depreciation schedule using the Straight Line method.

14. Bordner and Porter, an accounting firm, purchased $142,500 worth of computer equipment. Assume that the equipment will have a five-year life and no scrap value. Prepare a depreciation schedule using the Straight Line method.

15. On March 28, Parkinson Farms purchases a tractor for $65,000. Assume a lifetime of 3 years and a scrap value of $5,000. Prepare a Straight Line depreciation schedule using the standard convention.

16. Coronado Window Glass purchased a truck for $24,800. They are using the Units of Production method to depreciate the vehicle over a period of 80,000 miles. Assume that the scrap value of the truck will be $2,000. Prepare a depreciation schedule, showing annual usage of 7,900 miles, 14,250 miles, 17,300 miles, 16,200 miles, and 18,120 miles during the first five years. How many miles of depreciation remain?

Name: ______________________________ Date: __________

Exercises 5.4

Using a declining balance depreciation method, find the first year's depreciation.

	Cost	Scrap Value	Lifetime	Method
1.	$77,200	$11,300	5 years	Double
2.	$52,350	$8,000	20 years	125%
3.	$84,000	$0	10 years	150%
4.	$21,300	$800	9 years	200%

Find the first year's depreciation, using a Declining Balance method and the standard partial-year convention.

	Cost	Scrap Value	Lifetime	Service Date	Method
5.	$ 72,000	$ 4,000	8 years	August 14	200% DB
6.	$ 95,000	$ 3,000	6 years	October 7	125% DB
7.	$122,500	$ 0	10 years	September 2	150% DB
8.	$ 85,000	$10,000	4 years	May 17	Double DB

** Prepare a depreciation schedule for each scenario.

9. Tyler and Johnson, a law firm, purchased $75,000 worth of office furniture. Assume that the furniture will have a life of seven years and a scrap value of $8,000. Prepare a depreciation schedule using the Double Declining Balance method

10. Bordner and Porter, an accounting firm, purchased $142,500 worth of computer equipment. Assume that the equipment will have a five-year life and no scrap value. Prepare a depreciation schedule using the Double Declining Balance method.

11. On March 28, Gateway Marine purchases a $47,500 boat for use in its business. Assume a lifetime of 10 years and a scrap value of $6,500. Prepare a 200% Declining Balance depreciation schedule using the standard convention.

12. On February 17, Stevenson's Restaurant purchases $62,400 of dining room furniture. Assume a lifetime of 7 years and a scrap value of $2,000. Prepare a 150% Declining Balance depreciation schedule using the standard convention.

Name: ____ Date: __________

Exercises 5.5

∗ 1. Suppose the current assets of a company are $782,500, the current liabilities are $242,300, and the inventory (at cost) is $427,600.

   a. Find the current ratio.

   b. Find the acid test ratio.

2. Suppose the total assets of a company are $946,000, the total liabilities are $483,600, and the net profit last year was $39,250.

   a. Find the return on assets.

   b. Find the return on equity.

3. Suppose last year's net sales was $466,875, the net profit was $27,324, and the gross profit was $255,387.

   a. Find the net profit ratio.

   b. Find the gross profit ratio.

4. Suppose the total assets of a company were $457,300, and last year's net sales was $926,300. Find the total asset turnover.

5. Suppose the sales for the year was $275,000, and the average inventory at retail was $53,000.

   a. Find the inventory turnover at retail.

   b. Find the average length of time merchandise is staying in inventory.

6. Suppose the cost of goods sold for the month was $259,000, and the average inventory at cost was $113,000.

   a. Find the inventory turnover at cost.

   b. Find the average length of time merchandise is staying in inventory.

7. Suppose the total assets of a company is $524,300, and the total liabilities is $135,100. Find the debt to equity ratio.

Marie's Restaurant
Income Statement
For the Year Ended December 31, 2014

Net Sales:		
Gross Sales	$855,458	
Returns	$ 1,233	
Net Sales		$854,225
Cost of Goods Sold:		
Beginning Inventory	$ 16,859	
Purchases	$323,801	
Goods Available for Sale	$340,660	
Ending Inventory	$ 17,455	
Cost of Goods Sold		$323,205
Gross Profit		$531,020
Operating Expenses:		
Advertising	$ 11,259	
Insurance	$ 12,483	
Taxes	$ 87,442	
Rent	$ 38,455	
Salaries	$271,008	
Supplies	$ 67,425	
Utilities	$ 25,472	
Total Operating Expenses		$513,543
Net Profit		$ 17,477

Marie's Restaurant
Balance Sheet
December 31, 2014

Current Assets:		
Cash	$ 32,417	
Securities	$ 5,000	
Accts. Receivable	$ 8,722	
Inventory	$ 17,477	
Total		$ 63,594
Fixed Assets:		
Building	$107,320	
Land	$ 12,500	
Equipment	$ 22,100	
Fixtures	$ 9,966	
Total		$151,886
Total Assets		$215,480
Current Liabilities:		
Accts. Payable	$ 12,655	
Notes Payable	$ 25,400	
Salaries	$ 5,374	
Total		$ 43,429
Long-Term Liabilities:		
Mortgage	$ 75,000	
Total		$ 75,000
Total Liabilities		$118,429
Owner's Equity		$ 97,051
Total Liabilities & Equity		$215,480

** Use the financial statements shown above to determine the following ratios. Explain the meaning of each ratio in words. Compare each result with typical values.

8. Current Ratio

9. Return on Equity

10. Inventory Turnover

11. Acid Test Ratio

12. Debt to Equity Ratio

13. Net Profit Ratio

14. Gross Profit Ratio

15. Total Asset Turnover

Rick's Service Station Income Statement For the Year Ended December 31, 2013		
Net Sales:		
Gross Sales	$524,443	
Returns	$ 2,476	
Net Sales		$521,967
Cost of Goods Sold:		
Beginning Inventory	$ 16,292	
Purchases	$438,349	
Goods Available for Sale	$454,641	
Ending Inventory	$ 14,861	
Cost of Goods Sold		$439,825
Gross Profit		$ 82,142
Operating Expenses:		
Advertising	$ 1,529	
Insurance	$ 4,240	
Taxes	$ 10,250	
Rent	$ 6,354	
Salaries	$ 50,322	
Supplies	$ 3,466	
Utilities	$ 4,456	
Total Operating Expenses		$ 80,617
Net Profit		$ 1,525

Rick's Service Station Balance Sheet December 31, 2013		
Current Assets:		
Cash	$ 12,853	
Accts. Receivable	$ 3,572	
Inventory	$ 14,816	
Total		$ 31,241
Fixed Assets:		
Building	$ 42,000	
Land	$ 12,000	
Equipment	$ 9,575	
Total		$ 63,575
Total Assets		$ 94,816
Current Liabilities:		
Accts. Payable	$ 4,681	
Notes Payable	$ 21,890	
Salaries	$ 746	
Total		$ 27,317
Long-Term Liabilities:		
Mortgage	$ 38,605	
Total		$ 38,605
Total Liabilities		$ 65,922
Owner's Equity		$ 28,894
Total Liabilities & Equity		$ 94,816

Use the financial statements shown above to determine the following ratios. Explain the meaning of each ratio in words. Compare each result with typical values.

16. Current Ratio

17. Return on Equity

18. Inventory Turnover

19. Acid Test Ratio

20. Debt to Equity Ratio

21. Net Profit Ratio

22. Gross Profit Ratio

23. Total Asset Turnover

*** 24. Suppose the cost of goods sold for the month was $713,000, the average inventory at retail was $210,500, and the markup was 42% of cost.

a. Find the stock turnover at cost.

b. Find the average length of time merchandise is staying in inventory.

25. Suppose the sales for the year was $1,200,000, the average inventory at cost was $413,000, and the markup was 13% of selling price.

a. Find the stock turnover at retail.

b. Find the average length of time merchandise is staying in inventory.

Name: ______________________________ Date: __________

Chapter 5 Review

Summary of Important Concepts

- ▲ Balance sheets
- ▲ Inventory: LIFO, FIFO, Weighted average
- ▲ Depreciation: Straight Line, Units of Production, Declining Balance
- ▲ Partial year depreciation
- ▲ Financial ratios

Exercises

1. Complete the following simplified balance sheet, and perform a horizontal analysis.

Toby's
Balance Sheet
December 31, 2014

	2014	2013	Change	Percent
Current Assets	$ 154,680	$141,930	$______	______%
Fixed Assets	$ 72,130	$ 68,350	$______	______%
Total Assets	$______	$______	$______	______%
Current Liabilities	$ 69,424	$ 61,677	$______	______%
Long-Term Liabilities	$ 44,360	$ 57,240	$______	______%
Total Liabilities	$______	$______	$______	______%
Owner's Equity	$______	$______	$______	______%

Figure 5.10

A store had the following beginning inventory and purchases.

Beginning Inventory	January 1	24 @ $2.55 ea.
Purchases	May 7	43 @ $2.69 ea.
	August 14	21 @ $2.88 ea.

At the end of the year, there were 33 items in stock.

2. Find the ending inventory using FIFO.

3. Find the ending inventory using LIFO.

4. Find the ending inventory using the Weighted Average method.

5. Find the annual Straight Line depreciation for an asset valued at $27,800, having a scrap value of $2,300, and a life of 15 years.

6. Find the first year's 150% Declining Balance depreciation for an asset valued at $164,000, having a scrap value of $14,700, and a life of 10 years.

The original cost of an asset was $425,000, and after 4 years its scrap value is expected to be $30,000.

7. Prepare a depreciation schedule using the Straight Line method.

8. Prepare a depreciation schedule using the 150% Declining Balance method.

9. A copy machine cost $12,000. It is expected to produce 200,000 copies and have a scrap value of $1,000. Usage of the machine was 35,000 copies during the first year, 45,000 copies during the second year, and 58,000 copies during the third year. Prepare a Units of Production depreciation schedule.

10. On May 8, a business bought equipment for $290,000. It has a scrap value of $16,000 and an estimated life of 5 years. Construct a depreciation schedule using the Straight Line method with the standard convention.

11. Using Toby's financial statements in figures 5.10 and 5.11, find their current ratio, their inventory turnover ratio, and their return on equity.

Toby's
Income Statement
For the Year Ended December 31, 2014

Net Sales:		
Gross Sales	$475,662	____%
Returns	$ 1,441	____%
Net Sales	______	____%
Cost of Goods Sold:		
Beginning Inventory	$125,959	____%
Purchases	$288,434	____%
Goods Available for Sale	______	____%
Ending Inventory	$142,604	____%
Cost of Goods Sold	______	____%
Gross Profit	______	____%
Operating Expenses:		
Total Operating Expenses	$192,441	____%
Net Profit	______	____%

Figure 5.11

6 Simple Interest

6.1 The Interest Formula

In order for a business to be profitable, it must have a sufficient supply of money to be able to purchase necessary goods and services. Sometimes, a business will have more than enough money, and can bank or invest the surplus, so that it earns interest. Sometimes, a business will not have enough money, and will borrow and pay interest for the transaction. In both cases, **interest** is the fee paid for the use of another person's money.

Whether a particular transaction involves a loan or a savings deposit, interest is computed in exactly the same way. The interest formula is:

$$I = PRT$$

In this formula, I is the dollar amount of interest paid or received. P is the **principal,** or dollar amount on which the interest is computed. Usually, but not always, the principal is the amount borrowed for a loan, or the amount deposited for savings. R is the **rate** (percent) of interest per period. When the formula is used, R must be expressed in either decimal or fraction form. T is the **time,** measured using the same period as the rate.

Unless otherwise stated, the period used in an interest problem is a year. In other words, an interest rate of 6% actually means 6% per year. When another period is used, that period will be specifically identified when the rate is stated.

A single use of the $I = PRT$ formula will always produce **simple interest,** where interest is computed only on the original principal. You may also be familiar with **compound interest,** often used for savings accounts, where interest is computed on the original principal plus any previously earned interest. Compound interest is actually simple interest repeated over and over, on a changing principal. We will discuss compound interest in more detail in the next chapter. In this chapter, each savings deposit will earn simple interest.

EXAMPLE 1

Karen deposits $650 into a savings account earning 3% simple interest. How much interest will be earned in 4 years?

SOLUTION

The principal is $650, the rate is 3%, or 0.03 as a decimal, and the time is 4 years. The computation is:

$$I = PRT = 650 \times 0.03 \times 4 = 78$$

Karen's $650 account earned $78 interest after 4 years at 3% per year.

The $I = PRT$ formula can also be used to compute interest on loans. Consider the following example.

EXAMPLE 2

Caldwell Construction borrows $150,000 at 13% simple interest for eight years. Find the interest earned by the lender.

SOLUTION

The principal is $150,000, the decimal rate is 0.13, and the time is 8 years. The computation is:

$$I = PRT = 150000 \times 0.13 \times 8 = 156000$$

The simple interest on $150,000 for the given rate and time will be $156,000. At the end of the 8-year period, Caldwell Construction will have to repay both the $150,000 principal and the $156,000 interest to settle their loan.

The answer to the second example may have been a bit of a surprise. Interest amounts can be larger than their principals. The reason is the combination of rate and time. If the interest earned is 13% per year for 8 years, that makes a total change of 104%. Since this is greater than 100%, we can expect the dollar amount of interest to be greater than the principal.

EXAMPLE 3

Tony deposits $371.68 into a savings account earning $2\frac{1}{3}\%$ for five months. Find the simple interest earned.

SOLUTION

The principal is $371.68. Changing the rate to decimal form, we obtain 0.023333 . . . Since the period for the rate is not specified, it is an annual rate. Therefore, we must describe the time in years, which is $\frac{5}{12}$. The computation is:

$$I = PRT = 371.68 \times 0.023333\ldots \times \frac{5}{12} \approx 3.613555\ldots$$

Rounding to the nearest penny, we find that Tony's account earned $3.61 interest.

In the previous example, we encountered a rate whose decimal form did not terminate. Such rates must be handled carefully. If the rate is rounded too much, the final answer will be affected. In general, you should keep as many decimal places as possible until you have obtained the final answer. In some situations (especially when the answer will have seven or more digits) you should allow the calculator to turn the fractional rate into a decimal, rather than doing it in your head, in order to take advantage of the calculator's hidden memory. More decimals will be kept, which means less chance of rounding errors. In the previous example, that would mean *using a calculator* for the computation:

$$2\frac{1}{3}\% = 2\frac{1}{3} \times 0.01 = ((1 \div 3) + 2) \times 0.01 \approx 0.02333333\ldots$$

The calculator's answer may look the same, but your calculator will have retained more decimal places, and be capable of greater accuracy.

Loans actually come in two types, simple loans and fixed payment loans. A **simple loan** provides a borrower with a certain amount of proceeds, which will be repaid on the maturity date along with interest. No payments before the maturity date are necessary. The loan to Caldwell Construction in Example 2 was a simple loan. Typically, simple loans are short term loans.

A **fixed payment loan** provides a borrower with a certain amount of proceeds, which will be repaid, together with interest, by a certain number of equal partial payments made on a regular basis. Most long term loans are fixed payment loans. The details of the interest computations for fixed payment loans are much more complicated, and will be discussed in chapter 7.

EXAMPLE 4

Betty borrows $1,459 at 1.28% per month simple interest for two years. Find the interest earned.

SOLUTION

The principal is $1,459, the decimal rate is 0.0128, and the time (which must be expressed in months to match the period given by the rate) is 24 months. The computation is:

$$I = PRT = 1459 \times 0.0128 \times 24 = 448.2048$$

Rounded to the nearest penny, $448.20 interest was earned on Betty's loan.

In interest problems, when the time is given in days, we encounter a curious situation. The answer will depend on some further assumptions about the number of days in a year. When **exact interest** is used, then the year is assumed to have 365 days (or 366 days in a leap year). Computations can also be done using **ordinary interest,** where the year is assumed to have 360 days. Consider the following two examples.

EXAMPLE 5

Jean borrows $600 at 13% exact simple interest for 75 days. Find the interest.

SOLUTION

Exact interest assumes that the year has 365 days. The computation is:

$$I = PRT = 600 \times 0.13 \times \frac{75}{365} \approx 16.0274$$

Rounded to the nearest penny, Jean will owe $16.03 interest.

EXAMPLE 6

Jerry borrows $600 at 13% ordinary simple interest for 75 days. Find the interest.

SOLUTION

Ordinary interest assumes that the year has 360 days. The computation is:

$$I = PRT = 600 \times 0.13 \times \frac{75}{360} = 16.25$$

Jerry will owe $16.25 interest.

The two different assumptions give different answers, of course. Ordinary interest will always produce larger dollar amounts of interest than exact interest. You may find lenders using ordinary interest for the loans they offer, but you will not find banks offering ordinary interest on savings accounts.

Why should ordinary interest be encountered at all? Before the days of computers and calculators, interest computations by hand were labor intensive. If 360 days were used in one year, computations would often be easier, because fractions could usually be reduced to much simpler forms. Now, with today's computing power, both methods are easy, but ordinary interest still brings a bit more income to those lending institutions who use it.

The issue of whether to use exact interest or ordinary interest should arise only when days are involved. Do not try to use ordinary interest if the time is stated in years.

EXAMPLE 7

Tina deposits $8,000 into an account earning 3.5% exact simple interest on April 5, and withdraws it on July 11. How much interest was earned on the account from the day of deposit to the day of withdrawal?

SOLUTION

The principal is $8,000 and the decimal rate is 0.035. Using the Table of Days (in the Appendix), we find April 5 is day 95, and July 11 is day 192. That gives 97 days of interest, or a time of $\frac{97}{365}$. The computation is:

$$I = PRT = 8000 \times 0.035 \times \frac{97}{365} \approx 74.4110$$

Rounded to the nearest penny, the interest earned on Tina's deposit is $74.41.

EXAMPLE 8

Frost's Music borrows $35,000 at $7\frac{5}{8}$% ordinary simple interest on September 16, and repays the loan on May 12 of the next year. Find the interest earned.

SOLUTION

The principal is $35,000 and the decimal rate is 0.07625. Using the Table of Days, we find September 16 is day 259 and May 12 is day 132. Subtracting 259 from 365, we find that there are 106 days left in the current year. Adding this to the 132 days in the next year, we obtain a total of 238 days. Therefore, the time is $\frac{238}{360}$. The computation is:

$$I = PRT = 35000 \times 0.07625 \times \frac{238}{360} \approx 1764.3403$$

Rounded to the nearest penny, the interest earned on the loan to Frost's Music is $1,764.34.

When leap years are involved, a small adjustment in your computations will be required, (as we previously discussed in section 4.3. In the previous example, if the dates had been September 16, 2011, and May 12, 2012, then February 29, 2012 would have fallen between the two dates. In that case, the time period would contain 239 days, not 238.

6.2 Finding Principal, Rate, or Time

In the first section of this chapter, we used the formula $I = PRT$ to find the amount of interest. The formula can also be used to find any one of the variables, if the other three are known. One non-algebraic approach to doing this is to use the following **IPRT diagram.**

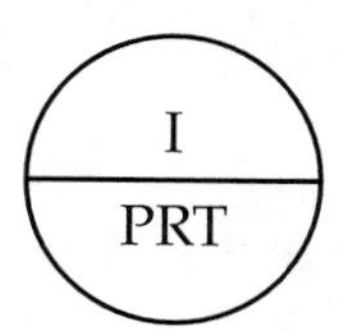

This diagram works the same way as the PBR diagram of an earlier chapter. Cover up the variable whose value you wish to find, and the portion that remains is the formula you need. If we do this for each of the variables, *I, P, R,* and *T,* we obtain the following four **IPRT formulas.**

$$I = PRT, \ P = \frac{I}{RT}, \ R = \frac{I}{PT}, \ T = \frac{I}{PR}$$

In each of the following examples, we will use the formula for the variable being sought. If, however, you do not remember the formula, then the IPRT diagram will produce it for you.

EXAMPLE 1

Jennifer received $360 interest over the last two years from a savings deposit earning 2.5% simple interest. Find the amount of Jennifer's deposit.

SOLUTION

We need to find the principal, given that the interest is $360, the time is 2 years, and the decimal form of the rate is 0.025. The computation is:

$$P = \frac{I}{RT} = \frac{360}{0.025 \times 2} = 7200$$

A deposit of $7,200 will produce $360 interest in two years at 2.5% per year.

Before continuing, make sure that you can obtain the correct answer to Example 1 on *your* calculator. Many people will set up the computation to this type of problem correctly, but still obtain the wrong answer, because they misinterpret the operations in the computation. It is tempting to look at the computation and use your calculator to obtain:

$$360 \div 0.025 \times 2 = 28800$$

However, this answer is not correct. Most calculators will not perform the multiplication of 0.025 and 2 before the division, when entered into the calculator in this fashion. If your calculator has parentheses, you may include them around the quantities in the denominator, as follows:

$$360 \div (0.025 \times 2) = 7200$$

If your calculator does not have parentheses, here is an alternative approach without them.

$$360 \div 0.025 \div 2 = 7200$$

In this approach, we have divided by each quantity in the denominator. The approach works because the answer from the first quotient must be divided (not multiplied) by the last value. If you remember that every quantity in the denominator of a computation must be divided, then you will be able to perform any computation of this type on your calculator without using parentheses.

EXAMPLE 2

Alan borrowed $700 and paid $336 simple interest in six years. Find the interest rate earned on the loan.

SOLUTION

The principal is $700, the dollar amount of the interest is $336, and the time is 6 years. The computation is:

$$R = \frac{I}{PT} = \frac{336}{700 \times 6} = 0.08 = 8\%$$

We find that an 8% annual rate of interest for a $700 principal will produce $336 interest in 6 years.

EXAMPLE 3

How long will it take for Tim's $1000 deposit to earn $120 at 4% interest?

SOLUTION

The principal is $1,000, the interest is $120, and the rate (in decimal form) is 0.04. The computation is:

$$T = \frac{I}{PR} = \frac{120}{1000 \times 0.04} = 3$$

Since rates of interest are (by default) annual rates, the time will also be in years. It will take three years for Tim's $1,000 deposit to earn $120 interest at an annual rate of 4%.

EXAMPLE 4

Ruth paid $500 exact interest on a 7.5% loan for 200 days. How much did she borrow?

SOLUTION

Since the rate is an annual rate, the time must also be expressed in years. For exact interest, we use 365 days in a year, and therefore the time is $\frac{200}{365}$ of a year. As a decimal, the rate is 0.075, and the interest is $500. The computation is:

$$P = \frac{I}{RT} = \frac{500}{0.075 \times \frac{200}{365}} = \frac{500}{0.075} \times \frac{365}{200} \approx 12166.6666\ldots$$

Rounded to the nearest penny, Ruth borrowed $12,166.67.

Notice that a fraction appeared in the denominator, and we must divide by each quantity in the denominator. Since dividing by a fraction is the same as multiplying by the reciprocal, we rewrote the computation before using our calculator. Without using parentheses, we must remember to divide by those quantities appearing in the denominator. Either of the following two approaches will work when evaluating the computation on your calculator.

$$500 \times 365 \div 0.075 \div 200 \approx 12166.6666\ldots$$

$$500 \div 0.075 \times 365 \div 200 \approx 12166.6666.\ldots$$

EXAMPLE 5

Gary was charged $22 ordinary interest on a $250, 18% loan. How many days was the loan outstanding?

SOLUTION

The principal is $250, the interest is $22, and the rate is 0.18. The computation is:

$$T = \frac{I}{PR} = \frac{22}{250 \times 0.18} \approx 0.488889$$

Since the rate was an annual rate, the answer for time is given in years. We need to find the number of days. Since ordinary interest is specified, we assume that there are 360 days in a year. Therefore,

$$0.488889 \times 360 = 176$$

For $250 to earn $22 at 18% ordinary interest, 176 days are needed. Gary borrowed the money for 176 days.

EXAMPLE 6

At 8% simple interest, how long will it take for an investment to double?

SOLUTION

The information desired is the time, and the given rate (in decimal form) is 0.08. But neither the principal nor the interest is stated.

Can this problem be solved? It is tempting to conclude that we do not have enough information, but in fact that is not the case. For some types of financial problems, the dollar amounts are irrelevant. When this happens, you may choose whatever dollar amount you wish for the principal, and proceed from that assumption. You should make sure, by examining the steps in your work, that the dollar amounts were really irrelevant.

Let us choose a principal of $100. If the investment doubles, then there will be a $200 total after some period of time. Of that $200, only $100 is interest. The computation is:

$$T = \frac{I}{PR} = \frac{100}{100 \times 0.08} = \frac{1}{0.08} = 12.5$$

It will take 12.5 years for the investment to double, at 8% simple interest per year. We notice that the principal and interest amounts did cancel, and so they were in fact irrelevant.

6.3 Adding Interest

In the previous two sections of this chapter, we discussed the interest formula, and how it is used to obtain the dollar amount of interest being earned in any situation. Typically, but not always, the interest is added to the principal. This is true whether interest is being computed for a loan or a savings account. We will address those situations in which interest is not added to the principal in the next section.

Though the basic ideas involved in the computation of interest are the same for both loans and savings, unfortunately, many of the terms used to describe the different dollar amounts often vary according to the situation. There are two terms whose use is general, both defined earlier, but are important enough to be restated. The **interest** is the fee paid for the use of another person's money, and the **principal** is the dollar amount on which the interest is computed.

When money is loaned to a borrower, interest is typically earned by the lender. That is, the borrower will pay back more money than was originally borrowed. The amount received by the borrower is called the **proceeds.** Usually, but not always, the proceeds is the principal. In a simple loan, the amount paid back is called the **maturity value.** The difference between the maturity value and the proceeds is the interest. In a fixed payment loan, the proceeds may be called the amount financed, and the amount paid back is usually called the total of payments. In this section, the loans we consider will all be simple loans.

If money is deposited in a savings account, interest is typically earned by the depositor. That is, the depositor will be able to withdraw more money than was originally deposited. The amount originally placed into an account is often called the **deposit,** or the **initial balance.** If a depositor makes no further deposits, then this amount is usually the principal. The amount that can be withdrawn at a future date is often called the (future) **balance** or, for savings bonds or certificates of deposit, the **maturity value.** The difference between the amount deposited and the maturity value is the interest.

So how do we know which amount is the principal, from which the interest is calculated? Typically, and for every problem in this section, the proceeds of a simple loan, or the original deposit into a savings account, is the principal. In other words, the principal is usually the amount before interest is added. We will discuss the other situation in the next section.

EXAMPLE 1

Sharon deposits $4,000 in a savings account earning 3.35% simple interest. What will the balance be in 3 months?

SOLUTION

The principal is the amount deposited, in this case $4,000. The rate, in decimal form, is 0.0335, and the time is $\frac{3}{12}$ of a year. Therefore,

$$I = PRT = 4000 \times 0.0335 \times \frac{3}{12} = 33.50$$

Adding the $33.50 interest to the $4,000 principal, we obtain a balance of $4,033.50.

EXAMPLE 2

Victor borrows $6,000 at 14% ordinary interest for 90 days. Find the maturity value of the loan.

Solution

The principal is \$6,000, the rate is 0.14, and the time is $\frac{90}{360}$. The computation for interest is:

$$I = PRT = 6000 \times 0.14 \times \frac{90}{360} = 210$$

Adding the \$210 interest to the \$6,000 principal, we find that the maturity value of Victor's loan, the amount he will pay back when the loan is due, is \$6,210.

One way in which a short term loan may be made, like that in Example 2, is by means of a note. A **simple interest note** is an instrument which specifies the terms of a loan, using simple interest, where the interest will be added to the principal to obtain the maturity value, and which is due and payable at some specific date in the (usually not too distant) future.

EXAMPLE 3

On July 31, Ashley signs a \$5,000 simple interest note earning 14% ordinary interest, which is due in sixty days. Find the due date, interest, proceeds, and maturity value.

Solution

Using the Table of Days, we find that July 31 is day 212. Adding 60 days, we obtain a due date of day 272, or September 29. The computation for interest is:

$$I = PRT = 5000 \times 0.14 \times \frac{60}{360} \approx 116.67$$

The proceeds of a simple interest note is the principal, which was \$5,000. The maturity value is obtained by adding the principal and the \$116.67 interest, which gives \$5,116.67. In other words, Ashley received \$5,000 on July 31, and has promised to pay back \$5,116.67 on September 29.

Time periods for notes can also be stated in months. A three-month note dated July 31 would be due on October 31. A two-month note dated July 31 would be due on September 30 (since there is no September 31). By comparing this situation with the previous example, we can also see that a two-month note is not the same as a 60-day note.

In each of the previous examples, the principal was given (as well as the rate and time), and we had to find the other dollar amounts. If the rate or time is the value sought, then two of the three dollar amounts should be given. Any of the three dollar amounts could be the missing amount, since the third dollar amount can always be found by adding or subtracting. Then an IPRT formula can find the missing value of rate or time.

EXAMPLE 4

Karen borrows \$4,000 for 150 days and pays back \$4,250. If ordinary interest was used, what was the rate of interest?

Solution

The principal is \$4,000 and the maturity value is \$4,250. Subtracting, we find that \$250 interest was earned. Using an IPRT formula, we obtain:

$$R = \frac{I}{PT} = \frac{250}{4000 \times \frac{150}{360}} = \frac{250}{4000} \times \frac{360}{150} = 0.15 = 15\%$$

Karen borrowed at a rate of 15% annual interest.

In the next example, the only dollar amount provided is the interest, and we shall find both the principal and the maturity value.

EXAMPLE 5

Peter earned $375 interest on his deposit, after 60 days of 12% ordinary interest. How much were the principal and the final balance?

SOLUTION

We use an IPRT formula to determine the principal.

$$P = \frac{I}{RT} = \frac{375}{0.12 \times \frac{60}{360}} = \frac{375}{0.12} \times \frac{360}{60} = 18750$$

Adding the $18,750 principal to the $375 interest, we obtain a maturity value of $19,125. Peter deposited $18,750, and had $19,125 in his account 60 days later.

Problems in which the only dollar amount provided is the maturity value (or future balance) cannot be solved by means of an IPRT formula, since we need the values of three of the four variables to use them. However, a percent change diagram will solve these types of problems. In typical situations (when the interest is added to the principal to produce the maturity value), the dollar amount of the principal will be the old quantity, the interest will be the change, and the maturity value will be the new quantity. Care must be taken on the percent side of the diagram, since the rate of interest is generally not the rate of change. This is because the rate of interest is stated annually, and the rate of change in a percent change diagram is for the entire time period in question. For example, if a problem involves a simple interest rate of 8% per year for 5 years, then the percent change is 40%.

EXAMPLE 6

After four years at 6% per year simple interest, the balance in Bill's account will be $3,410. Find the principal and the interest.

SOLUTION

The future balance, $3,410, is the new quantity. The old percent is 100%, and the change percent will be 6% per year times 4 years, or 24%. We have:

100%	*Old*	______
$6\% \times 4 = 24\%$	+ *Change*	______
______%	*New*	3410

We find the new percent will be 124%. We can cross-multiply to find the principal.

$$3410 \times 100 \div 124 = 2750$$

The principal is $2,750. Subtracting this from the future balance, we obtain a value of $660 for the interest. Bill's original deposit of $2,750 earned $660 interest after four years, producing a balance of $3,410.

EXAMPLE 7

An 80-day simple interest note earning 15% exact interest has a maturity value of $1,282.83. Find the proceeds and the interest.

SOLUTION

Since the maturity value is the only dollar amount given, we will set up a percent change diagram.

100.00000%	*Old*	______
$15\% \times \frac{80}{365} \approx 3.28767\%$	+ *Change*	______
______%	*New*	1282.83

The new percent is approximately 103.28767%. We shall solve the proportion to find the principal, or proceeds.

$$1282.83 \times 100 \div 103.28767 \approx 1241.9972$$

Rounding to the nearest penny, we get proceeds of $1,242.00. Subtracting this from the $1,282,83 maturity value gives $40.83 interest.

6.4 Discount Interest

As we mentioned in the previous section, interest is not always added to the principal. Sometimes, it is subtracted from the principal. Some situations where discount interest is used are Treasury bills, simple discount notes, and the sale of notes.

Interest which is subtracted from the principal is called **discount interest.** After subtracting the interest from the principal, we obtain the proceeds. When using discount interest, the principal and the proceeds are not the same. The principal is, in fact, the maturity value of the transaction, as it is the amount obtained when the interest is added back to the proceeds. The computation of the interest is exactly the same as before. Just use the $I = PRT$ formula.

EXAMPLE 1

Tom borrows $750 at 8% ordinary discount interest for ninety days. Find the interest and proceeds of the loan.

SOLUTION

The computation of interest is exactly the same as before, using the $I = PRT$ formula. We have:

$$I = PRT = 750 \times 0.08 \times \frac{90}{360} = 15$$

The $15 interest is subtracted from the $750 principal to obtain proceeds of $735. In other words, Tom received $735 from the transaction, and will repay the maturity value of $750.

A **simple discount note** is one instrument which describes the terms of a loan using discount interest, where the interest is subtracted from the principal to obtain the proceeds.

EXAMPLE 2

A simple discount note dated August 7 for $9,000 is payable in 90 days at 12% ordinary interest. Find the due date, interest, proceeds, and maturity value.

SOLUTION

Using the Table of Days, we find August 7 is day 219. Adding 90 days, we get a due date of day 309, or November 5. The interest computation is:

$$I = PRT = 9000 \times 0.12 \times \frac{90}{360} = 270$$

Subtracting the $270 interest from the $9,000 principal, we obtain proceeds of $8,730. The maturity value of the note is $9,000.

If the proceeds of a discount interest transaction are given, and the principal (or maturity value) is being sought, a percent change diagram will be necessary. Be sure to remember that discount interest is subtracted, and therefore we will need a percent decrease diagram.

EXAMPLE 3

Jan needs proceeds of $1,000. The bank is willing to accept a 60-day simple discount note from her at 15% ordinary interest. What will be the principal of the note?

SOLUTION

The proceeds of $1,000 are obtained after the interest is subtracted, so it is the new quantity. We have:

100.0%	*Old*	______
$15\% \times \frac{60}{360} = 2.5\%$	*– Change*	______
______%	*New*	1000

Subtracting, we find the new percent to be 97.5%. Then we can solve the proportion given by the diagram.

$$1000 \times 100 \div 97.5 \approx 1025.64$$

Jan's simple discount note will have a principal of $1,025.64. If we compute the interest using $I = PRT$ and subtract, proceeds of $1,000 will remain.

In the context of a consumer loan, discount interest may seem strange. The borrower seems to be receiving less than they borrowed. The lender will probably explain to the borrower that they are simply paying the interest up front, rather than at the time when the loan is due. More subtly, the borrower is paying interest on the amount to be paid back, rather than the amount received. That is, interest is being computed on the proceeds and the interest, and not just the proceeds.

Discount interest is commonly used in other types of transactions. For example, the sale of Treasury securities by the U.S. government involves discount interest. **Treasury bills,** or **T-bills,** are short-term (one year or less) loans sold by the government to investors with a minimum maturity value of \$10,000. **Treasury bonds,** or **T-bonds,** are long-term (10 years or more) loans available in amounts of \$1,000 or more. **Treasury notes,** or **T-notes,** are medium-term loans available in amounts of at least \$1,000. All of these government securities are sold to investors at a discount. Essentially, the federal government is borrowing money from the investors.

EXAMPLE 4

A 13-week \$10,000 T-bill is sold at a 3.28% discount rate. What was the sale price?

SOLUTION

The interest computation is:

$$I = PRT = 10000 \times 0.0328 \times \frac{13}{52} = 82$$

Subtracting the \$82 interest from the \$10,000 principal, we find proceeds of \$9,918. Investors were paying \$9,918 for each \$10,000 T-bill.

Simple interest notes and simple discount notes (as well as other types of debt instruments) can be sold in the financial marketplace. An original note is a contract entered into by the borrower, and establishes a specific maturity value for the note on a specific date. When a note is sold, the maturity value and due date cannot be changed, so the new lender must use discount interest. The new party to the transaction is essentially lending their money from the time of the new transaction to the due date of the note, a time period known as the **discount period**. The discount interest charged by the new lender is sometimes called the **bank discount**, or simply the **discount**. The following example is lengthy, but it should more clearly illustrate how the sale of notes occurs.

EXAMPLE 5

On June 7, Joe's Bar and Grill signs a \$12,000, 12% ordinary, 120-day simple interest note for supplies purchased from Anita's Restaurant Supply. Anita sold the note on June 25, at an 11% ordinary discount rate, to Tony's Financial Services. Tony sold the note to The Big Bank on July 1, at a 10.75% exact discount rate. Find the proceeds of each transaction.

SOLUTION

The original transaction involves Joe and Anita. The due date for the note will be 120 days after June 7. Using the Table of Days, we find the due date to be October 5. The interest computation for this transaction is:

$$I = PRT = 12000 \times 0.12 \times \frac{120}{360} = 480$$

Therefore, Joe received \$12,000 worth of supplies from Anita, in exchange for a note promising to pay principal and interest, \$12,480, on October 5.

The second transaction involves Anita and Tony. In essence, Tony is lending Anita money based on the income the note will bring on its due date. Therefore, Tony is lending money for the discount period of June 25 to October 5, or 102 days, in expectation of receiving $12,480 on October 5. The interest computation is:

$$I = 12480 \times 0.11 \times \frac{102}{360} = 388.96$$

This is a standard discount interest computation, where the principal was the maturity value of the note. The discount, $388.96, is subtracted from the $12,480 maturity value to obtain the proceeds, which is $12,091.04. In other words, Anita gave Tony the note in exchange for $12,091.04.

The third transaction involves Tony and The Big Bank. Another discount interest computation is performed. Note that the maturity value of the note is still $12,480, since Joe's promise to pay $12,480 cannot be changed by this transaction.

$$I = PRT = 12480 \times 0.1075 \times \frac{96}{365} \approx 352.86$$

Subtracting the $352.86 bank discount from the $12,480 principal, we find proceeds of $12,127.14. That is, Tony gave the note to The Big Bank in exchange for $12,127.14.

Whenever a note is sold in the marketplace, discount interest is the only appropriate means to effect the transaction. This is because the original borrower has contracted to pay a certain amount (the maturity value) on a certain date (the due date). These values cannot be changed in transactions which do not involve the original borrower. Therefore interest must be subtracted from what the borrower will pay, not added for the borrower to pay.

6.5 Rates

Whenever simple interest is computed, we have seen that the formula $I = PRT$ will produce the dollar amount of interest. All we need to know is the principal, rate, and time. This situation might lead one to think that a borrower should simply shop around for the lowest rate, thereby obtaining the lowest interest payments. Unfortunately, things are not that simple.

When the interest formula $I = PRT$ is used, lenders have the ability to specify how the principal and time are determined. We have already seen some possible variations for these values. Is the principal equal to the proceeds or the maturity value (i.e., is interest added to or subtracted from the principal)? Will we use ordinary or exact interest for the value for time? These choices affect the dollar amount of the interest obtained, even if the rate is always the same.

In order to make comparisons between rates whose principals and times are varied, a standardized method for reporting rates is needed. The **effective rate** of a loan is found by using the money available to the borrower as the principal, a true value for the time, and the total finance charges for interest. For a simple loan, the principal is the proceeds, and exact interest is used if days are counted. (For fixed payment loans, the principal is the amount the borrower still retains, which changes as payments are made. We will discuss this situation in chapter 8.) That is, an effective rate insists on truth in computation.

In 1969, Congress passed the Truth-in-Lending Act, which requires all lenders to state the **Annual Percentage Rate,** or **APR,** to their customers. The APR is the rate of interest charged, as computed from the actual money lent for the actual amount of time it was lent. The intent of the law was to provide a uniform means of reporting interest rates, so the customer could make accurate comparisons of different loan offers. The APR is usually equivalent to the effective rate.

Federal law requires that the APR of a loan be stated on most consumer loan contracts. By law, the APR must be stated with sufficient accuracy, often to the nearest $\frac{1}{8}$%. This window of accuracy was chosen to accommodate the use of tables for APR computations, to ensure that an APR was never more than off by more than $\frac{1}{16}$ of a percentage point. To obtain the necessary accuracy in the decimal representation provided by your calculator, round to the nearest hundredth of a percent.

EXAMPLE 1

Kelly borrows $7,000 for 120 days and pays back $7,250. What was the effective rate (APR) of the loan?

SOLUTION

The proceeds of the loan, $7,000, is the principal of an effective rate computation. Subtracting the dollar amounts, we find that Karen paid $250 interest. We need to use the exact time, so the time fraction is $\frac{120}{365}$. The rate is:

$$R = \frac{I}{PT} = \frac{250}{7000 \times \frac{120}{365}} = \frac{250}{7000} \times \frac{365}{120} \approx 0.1086 = 10.86\%$$

Karen's loan should report an effective rate of 10.86%.

Often the effective rate will not be the same as the **nominal rate,** or quoted rate, of a loan. Consider the following example.

EXAMPLE 2

A $940, 60-day simple interest note carries 12% ordinary interest. What is the effective rate of the note?

SOLUTION

To determine the effective rate, the amount of interest must be known. Therefore, we compute the interest first. The principal of the note is $940, the rate is 0.12, and the time is $\frac{60}{360}$. We obtain:

$$I = PRT = 940 \times 0.12 \times \frac{60}{360} = 18.80$$

Now, we find the effective rate. Since the proceeds is the principal of a simple interest note, we use $940 as the principal. We also have $18.80 interest, and an exact time of $\frac{60}{365}$. The computation is:

$$R = \frac{I}{PT} = \frac{18.80}{940 \times \frac{60}{365}} = \frac{18.80}{940} \times \frac{365}{60} \approx 0.1217 = 12.17\%$$

The effective rate of the $940, sixty-day, 12% ordinary simple interest note is 12.17%.

Whenever ordinary interest is used, as in the above example, the effective rate will not be the same as the nominal rate. Additionally, whenever discount interest is used, as in the following example, the effective rate of the loan will not be the same as the nominal rate.

EXAMPLE 3

A $7,800 simple discount note earning 17% exact interest is due in ninety days. Find the effective rate.

SOLUTION

First, we must find the actual amount of interest earned. For that computation, the principal (of the note) is $7,800, the rate is 0.17, and the time is $\frac{90}{365}$. We get:

$$I = PRT = 7800 \times 0.17 \times \frac{90}{365} \approx 326.96$$

We also need the proceeds of the note. Since this is a simple interest note, the $326.96 interest is subtracted from the $7,800 principal (of the note) to produce $7,473.04 proceeds.

Now we can find the effective rate. The proceeds of $7,473.04 is the principal (of the effective rate computation), $326.96 is the interest, and the time is $\frac{90}{365}$. The computation is:

$$R = \frac{I}{PT} = \frac{326.96}{7473.04 \times \frac{90}{365}} = \frac{326.96}{7473.04} \times \frac{365}{90} \approx 0.1774 = 17.74\%$$

The effective rate of the $7,800, 90-day, 17% simple discount note is 17.74%.

Is the effective rate ever the same as the nominal rate? Yes, if the following conditions are met: the loan is a simple loan, the loan does not require any fees (to be discussed later), the loan adds the interest to the principal, and the loan uses exact interest. See if you can construct an example to demonstrate this situation.

Effective rates of loans (in the absence of other fees) do not depend on the amount borrowed. Only the time and nominal rate are actually relevant. In essence, we can convert a nominal rate into an effective rate (or any other rate) if we also know the time involved. Consider the following example, which has the same time and rate as Example 3.

EXAMPLE 4

Find the effective rate of a 17% exact discount loan for ninety days.

SOLUTION

If the dollar amounts are irrelevant, we may begin with whatever principal we wish. So we shall choose a principal of $100. This gives an interest computation of:

$$I = PRT = 100 \times 0.17 \times \frac{90}{365} \approx 4.19$$

On a discount loan, interest is subtracted, so the proceeds are $95.81. The effective rate computation is:

$$R = \frac{I}{PT} = \frac{4.19}{95.81 \times \frac{90}{365}} = \frac{4.19}{95.81} \times \frac{365}{90} \approx 0.1774 = 17.74\%$$

The effective rate of a 17% exact discount loan for 90 days will be 17.74%, no matter what the principal might be. This is the same result that we found in Example 3.

How can we know for sure that the dollar amounts are irrelevant in a rate conversion? Suppose, for example, that the principal was twice as large. Then, because of the $I = PRT$ formula, the interest would be twice as large. When computing the effective rate, the extra factors of two present in both the interest and the principal would cancel. (If you round both the interest and proceeds to the nearest penny, the answer may be slightly different.)

It is possible, using formulas or algebra, to streamline (slightly) the process of a rate conversion. However, your author wishes to use approaches which emphasize some of the conceptual ideas involved. The rate conversion approach demonstrated in Example 4 is based on the ubiquitous simple interest formula, proceeds as principal in a discount note, and truth in computation for an effective rate.

Lenders often assess other fees when offering loans. From the point of view of the borrower, a fee will increase the cost of the loan, and is reflected in the loan's effective rate. The total value of all fees and interest is called the **finance charge.** The finance charge is used in place of the interest amount when computing effective rates. Fees paid by the borrower on the day a loan is made also reduce the amount of benefit provided by the proceeds. When computing the effective rate, the principal should be the proceeds minus the fees paid.

In problems involving fees, however, the APR may be different from the effective rate. The APR is not required to reflect every type of fee. For the most part, fees for services provided by third parties to establish that they are credit worthy are excluded from the APR, even though the services would not have been necessary had the loan not been needed.

EXAMPLE 5

Tom borrows $3,000 for 90 days at 13% ordinary discount interest, and pays a transaction fee of $50. What is the effective rate?

SOLUTION

First, we find the interest charged. The principal is $3,000, the rate is 0.13, and the time is $\frac{90}{360}$ of a year. We get:

$$I = PRT = 3000 \times 0.13 \times \frac{90}{360} = 97.50$$

This is a discount interest loan, so interest is subtracted from the principal to obtain proceeds of $2,902.50. But on the day that the loan is made, Tom pays a $50 transaction fee to obtain these proceeds, for a net gain of $2,852.50. And the finance charges on this loan include the $97.50 interest and the $50 transaction fee, for a total of $147.50.

Now we can find the effective rate. We use Tom's net gain, $2,852,50, as the principal, the $147.50 finance charge as the interest, and an exact time of $\frac{90}{365}$ of a year. The computation is:

$$R = \frac{I}{PT} = \frac{147.50}{2852.50 \times \frac{90}{365}} = \frac{147.50}{2852.50} \times \frac{365}{90} \approx 0.2097 = 20.97\%$$

The effective rate of Tom's 13% loan is 20.97%.

The previous example contained all three regular components that cause different effective rates, namely ordinary interest, discount interest, and fees. As you can see in that example, the effective rate can be very different than the nominal rate.

6.6 Applying Loan Payments

In the previous sections of this chapter, we have discussed simple loans, which by definition are paid back with a single payment on the maturity date. Many loans, however, require periodic payments, and even if they do not, a borrower may still make partial payments before the maturity date. In this section, we look at two common methods of applying partial payments on a loan balance.

A basic principle for most loans is that interest is earned and paid in **arrears**, or after the period of time involved. Although loan contracts will specify a total amount of interest that will be paid, the interest is not earned until the borrower has held the funds for the time period described.

At any point in time, the **payoff amount** of a loan is the amount of the payment needed to reduce the balance to zero. Since interest is paid in arrears, the payoff amount is generally not the same as the current balance. A borrower must pay off the balance plus the interest earned since the previous payment. Some loan statements may show both a balance and a larger payoff amount, making this anomaly more obvious.

A commonly used method for applying payments to loan balances is the **Actuarial Method**. This method computes interest on a regular (usually monthly) basis, and applies payments to the account as they occur. Since payments are typically received at the end of each interest period, the interest is computed on the previous balance before the payment is applied. The interest is then added to the balance, and the payment is subtracted from the balance.

EXAMPLE 1

Harvey signs a $25,000, 3-month, 14% exact simple interest note on April 7. He makes an $8,000 payment on May 7, but makes no payment in June. The Actuarial Method will be used, with monthly interest computations. What is the payoff amount on the maturity date of the note?

Solution

On May 7, at the end of the first month, one month's interest will be earned. The computation is:

$$I = PRT = 25000 \times 0.14 \times \frac{1}{12} \approx 291.67$$

The interest will be added to the balance, and the payment subtracted from the balance.

$$25000 + 291.67 - 8000 = 17291.67$$

The transactions are best organized in a table.

Date	Charges	Payments	Balance
4/7	25000.00		25000.00
5/7	291.67	8000.00	17291.67

The interest computation on June 7 will be:

$$I = PRT = 17291.67 \times 0.14 \times \frac{1}{12} \approx 201.74$$

This interest amount is added to the balance, but since there was no payment, the balance will increase. Here is the updated table.

Date	Charges	Payments	Balance
4/7	25000.00		25000.00
5/7	291.67	8000.00	17291.67
6/7	201.74		17493.41

The maturity date of the loan is July 7. On that date, the interest computation will be:

$$I = PRT = 17493.41 \times 0.14 \times \frac{1}{12} \approx 204.09$$

The $204.09 interest is added to the $17,493.41 balance, giving a payoff amount of $17,697.50. Here is the completed table.

Date	Charges	Payments	Balance
4/7	25000.00		25000.00
5/7	291.67	8000.00	17291.67
6/7	201.74		17493.41
7/7	204.09	17697.50	0

After his partial payments, Harvey will need to pay $17,697.50 on July 7 to pay off the loan.

The Actuarial Method is quite easy to implement. Interest charges are added to the balance, and payments are subtracted. But a close inspection reveals that if a payment is skipped (as it was on June 7 in Example 1), the Actuarial Method will compute the next month's interest on a balance that includes previously unpaid interest. In other words, interest is being compounded, which is to say that interest was computed on interest (as well as on principal). This is not beneficial to the borrower. Generally, though, as long as a borrower makes regular payments on a loan using the Actuarial Method, interest will not compound, because it will instead be paid.

Today, most of us take for granted that a payment on a loan ought to decrease the loan balance. But this was not always the case. In 1822, Edward Livingston borrowed a sum of money from Benjamin Story, and agreed to pay interest on the loan. The two men agreed that the loan's principal and interest payments would be made from the rental income of one of Livingston's properties in Louisiana, of which Story took temporary possession. Story received the rents, but continued to compute interest on the *original* balance of the loan, rather than applying the excess rents against the balance of the loan. By doing so, most of Livingston's payments were considered interest payments, and the loan balance decreased very slowly. The case went to court, which ruled in favor of Livingston, but Story appealed. In 1839 the U.S. Supreme Court ruled in favor of Livingston's widow (Livingston had died before the case was settled), and they also outlined a method by which loan payments should be applied to balances. The method is often called the **United States Rule**, or **U.S. Rule**, and is different than the Actuarial Method in two ways.

- ▲ Interest is computed by counting days between transactions.
- ▲ Interest is computed only on the outstanding principal borrowed, not on previously unpaid interest.

In essence, the United States Rule specifies a method by which payments are applied to a balance. It does not specify whether regular payments are necessary, or when a loan should become due, or whether ordinary or exact interest should be used. Typical lenders, though, will specify each of these details as well.

When the United States Rule is put into practice, the counting of days between transactions is easily handled. Furthermore, if a lender requires a minimum payment and the borrower never skips payments, interest will never be compounded. The next example illustrates this case.

EXAMPLE 2

Charlene borrowed $14,800 on August 15 at 17% ordinary interest. She made partial payments of $300 on September 8, and $2,200 on October 9. According to the U.S. Rule, how much does she need to pay on December 2 in order to pay off the loan?

SOLUTION

Consulting the Table of Days, we find that there are 24 days between August 15 and September 8. We compute the interest on the $14,800 balance for 24 days at 17%.

$$I = PRT = 14800 \times 0.17 \times \frac{24}{360} \approx 167.73$$

The $167.73 interest is added to the balance, and the $300 payment is subtracted. This gives a new balance of $14,667.73. Since the payment was larger than the interest, there was no unpaid interest. Here is the table (and we are including the day numbers with each date).

Date	Charges	Payments	Principal Balance
8/15 (227)	14800.00		14800.00
9/8 (251)	167.73	300.00	14667.73

At the time of the next payment on October 9, the principal will be the balance of $14,667.73, on which interest is computed at 17% for 31 days.

$$I = PRT = 14667.73 \times 0.17 \times \frac{31}{360} \approx 214.72$$

Once again, we add the interest and subtract the payment from the balance. And once more, the payment was larger than the interest, so there was no unpaid interest. Here is the updated table.

Date	Charges	Payments	Principal Balance
8/15 (227)	14800.00		14800.00
9/8 (251)	167.73	300.00	14667.73
10/9 (282)	214.72	2200.00	12682.45

In order to pay off the loan on December 2, both the balance and the interest earned on the principal must be paid. Using the current principal, the interest computation is:

$$I = PRT = 12682.45 \times 0.17 \times \frac{54}{360} \approx 323.40$$

To obtain the payoff amount, we add the $323.40 interest to the $12,682.45 balance, which gives $13,005.85. At this point, we have solved the problem, and here is the completed table.

Date	Charges	Payments	Principal Balance
8/15 (227)	14800.00		14800.00
9/8 (251)	167.73	300.00	14667.73
10/9 (282)	214.72	2200.00	12682.45
12/2 (336)	323.40	13005.85	0

Charlene needs to pay $13,005.85 on December 2 to pay off the loan.

In the previous example, the payments were always sufficient to pay the earned interest and leave a remainder to reduce the principal balance. Normally, most accounts will have sufficiently large payments. However, if a payment is smaller than the earned interest, the previous approach would allow interest to compound, and the United States Rule specifically prohibits compounding of interest. In such cases, the unpaid interest is set aside in an escrow (or holding) account to be paid at the next opportunity, and before the balance is reduced further.

EXAMPLE 3

On February 12, Tracy borrowed $8,500 at 12% exact interest for 180 days. She made partial payments of $300 on March 1, $40 on April 1, $80 on May 1, and $200 on June 1. What is the payoff amount on the due date, according to the U.S. Rule?

SOLUTION

After consulting the Table of Days, we find that there are 17 days between February 12 and March 1. The first interest computation is:

$$I = PRT = 8500 \times 0.12 \times \frac{17}{365} \approx 47.51$$

Now we add the interest and subtract the payment.

$$8500 + 47.51 - 300.00 = 8247.51$$

Since the new balance of $8,247.51 is smaller than the previous balance of $8,500, it does not include any unpaid interest. Here is the table.

Date	Charges	Payments	Principal Balance
2/12 (43)	8500.00		8500.00
3/1 (60)	47.51	300.00	8247.51

The next interest computation is:

$$I = PRT = 8247.51 \times 0.12 \times \frac{31}{365} \approx 84.06$$

Then we add the interest and subtract the $40 payment.

$$8247.51 + 84.06 - 40.00 = 8291.57$$

This amount, however, is larger than the previous principal balance of $8,247.51, so it includes unpaid interest. Subtracting the previous principal balance of $8,247.51 from the new balance of $8,291.57, we find that there is $44.06 in unpaid interest. According to the U.S. Rule, the unpaid interest is not part of the principal, so we move it to an escrow account. The principal will remain $8,247.51. Here is the updated table.

Date	Charges	Payments	Principal Balance	Escrow (unpaid interest)
2/12 (43)	8500.00		8500.00	
3/1 (60)	47.51	300.00	8247.51	
4/1 (91)	84.06	40.00	8247.51	44.06

When reading this table, we need to remember that the total balance includes both the principal balance and the unpaid interest. But the interest is only computed on the principal balance.

The next interest computation is:

$$I = PRT = 8247.51 \times 0.12 \times \frac{30}{365} \approx 81.35$$

To compute the new balance, we add the previous principal balance, the previous unpaid interest, and the new interest, and subtract the payment.

$$8247.51 + 44.06 + 81.35 - 80.00 = 8292.92$$

Since the $8,292.92 balance is still larger than the previous principal balance of $8,247.51, we can subtract these two values to find that $45.41 interest still remains unpaid. (This $45.41 is also the sum of the $44.06 left unpaid on April 1, and $1.35 unpaid on May 1.) We update the table.

Date	Charges	Payments	Principal Balance	Escrow (unpaid interest)
2/12 (43)	8500.00		8500.00	
3/1 (60)	47.51	300.00	8247.51	
4/1 (91)	84.06	40.00	8247.51	44.06
5/1 (121)	81.35	80.00	8247.51	45.41

The interest computation for June 1 will be:

$$8247.51 \times 0.12 \times \frac{31}{365} \approx 84.06$$

Adding the interest and subtracting the $200 payment gives us the new balance.

$$8247.51 + 45.41 + 84.06 - 200.00 = 8176.98$$

Since the $8,176.98 balance is smaller than the previous principal balance of $8,247.51, all of the previous unpaid interest has been paid, and all of the new balance is principal. We update the table.

Date	Charges	Payments	Principal Balance	Escrow (unpaid interest)
2/12 (43)	8500.00		8500.00	
3/1 (60)	47.51	300.00	8247.51	
4/1 (91)	84.06	40.00	8247.51	44.06
5/1 (121)	81.35	80.00	8247.51	45.41
6/1 (152)	84.06	200.00	8176.98	0

Now we perform the last interest computation.

$$I = PRT = 8176.98 \times 0.12 \times \frac{71}{365} \approx 190.87$$

The payoff amount is the total of the principal balance and the new interest, namely $8,367.85. The completed table follows.

Date	Charges	Payments	Principal Balance	Escrow (unpaid interest)
2/12 (43)	8500.00		8500.00	
3/1 (60)	47.51	300.00	8247.51	
4/1 (91)	84.06	40.00	8247.51	44.06
5/1 (121)	81.35	80.00	8247.51	45.41
6/1 (152)	84.06	200.00	8176.98	0
8/11 (223)	190.87	8367.85	0	

To pay off the loan on June 12, Tracy will need $8,367.85.

If you reflect upon the previous example, you may realize that Tracy, the borrower in that example, actually gained no benefit by making partial payments on April 1 and May 1 which were smaller than the interest earned. Since the principal was not reduced, the amount of interest being earned by the loan was not reduced. Essentially, when the lender receives a payment which is smaller than the interest, they can set it aside until additional payments bring the total above the interest earned. The effect on the account would be the same.

We should note that the Actuarial Method kept track of the total balance, while the U.S. Rule tracked the principal balance. These will be the same unless interest should go unpaid, which happens whenever a payment is smaller than the computed interest. In such cases, the U.S. Rule introduces an escrow column for unpaid interest, while the Actuarial Method simply adds the unpaid interest into the balance.

Name: ______________________ Date: __________

Exercises 6.1

* Find the number of days.

1. From July 17, 2013 to December 13, 2013.

2. From March 31, 2014 to August 25, 2014.

3. From April 7, 2011 to May 13, 2012.

4. From October 16, 2011 to July 21, 2012.

5. From January 3, 2013 to September 16, 2016.

6. From July 11, 2012 to February 18, 2016.

Find the simple interest earned.

7. $295 principal, 4%, 2 years

8. $3,550 principal, 7%, 4 years

9. $75,470 principal, 11.75%, 25 years

10. $750,000 principal, 16.32%, 10 years

11. $14,252.70 principal, 9.8%, 8 months

12. $859.44 principal, 21.3%, 3 months

13. $1,650 principal, $7\frac{1}{3}$%, 9 months

14. \$21,000 principal, $5\frac{1}{6}\%$, 13 weeks

15. \$420 principal, 5% exact, 90 days

16. \$6,251 principal, 9% exact, 35 days

17. \$15,240 principal, 7.2% ordinary, 120 days

18. \$9,334 principal, 8.1% ordinary, 84 days

19. \$480 principal, 5.2% exact, March 18 to July 7

20. \$525 principal, 6.9% ordinary, May 25 to October 10

21. \$1,404 principal, 3% ordinary, November 7 to February 16 (of the following year)

22. \$285 principal, 18% exact, August 12 to January 8 (of the following year)

23. \$657 principal, 9% exact, March 13, 2014 to January 6, 2016

24. \$2,400 principal, 13% ordinary, January 7, 2014 to July 19, 2016

** 25. Carrie deposited $375 into a savings account earning 2.5% simple interest. How much interest was earned in 2 years?

26. Ken deposited $850 into a savings account earning 3.25% simple interest. How much interest was earned in 5 years?

27. Tina borrowed $3,500 at 15% simple interest for 3 years. How much interest was earned by the lender?

28. Peter borrowed $5,200 at 17.9% simple interest for 6 years. How much interest was earned by the lender?

29. Andrew deposits $250 into a savings account earning 2.65% simple interest. How much interest will be earned in 7 months?

30. Casey deposits $465 into a savings account earning 3.05% simple interest. How much interest will be earned in 5 months?

31. Diane deposited $1,200 into a savings account earning 1.9% exact simple interest. How much interest was earned in 75 days?

32. Frank deposited $885 into a savings account earning 2.8% exact simple interest. How much interest was earned in 165 days?

33. John borrowed $7,250 at 12% ordinary simple interest for 120 days. How much interest was earned by the lender?

34. Jean borrowed $8,100 at 13.5% ordinary simple interest for 27 days. How much interest was earned by the lender?

35. Roger deposited $172 at 3% exact simple interest from May 17 to August 25. How much interest was earned?

36. Sharon deposited $7,300 at 2.5% exact simple interest from April 11 to November 26. How much interest was earned?

37. Alicia borrowed $6,200 at 17% ordinary simple interest from October 30, 2014 to April 10, 2015. How much interest was earned?

38. Benjamin borrowed $1,795 at 14% ordinary simple interest from July 5, 2015 to March 10, 2016. How much interest was earned?

*** 39. Suppose a loan of $1,000 is made for 90 days at 15% simple interest. How much more interest will be earned by using ordinary interest, rather than exact interest?

40. Suppose a loan of $5,000 was made at 16.9% ordinary simple interest for 365 days. Why might the borrower want an explanation for the amount of interest charged?

Name: ______________________________ Date: __________

Exercises 6.2

* Complete the table.

	Principal	Rate	Time	Interest
1.	_____	4%	12 years	$1,300
2.	_____	17%	5 months	$2,552.33
3.	_____	9.3% ordinary	120 days	$524.25
4.	_____	12.5% exact	270 days	$300
5.	_____	$8\frac{1}{3}$% ordinary	270 days	$37.50
6.	_____	$6\frac{2}{3}$% exact	135 days	$554.79
7.	$575	_____	6 years	$241.50
8.	$12,355	_____	7 months	$590.98
9.	$6,930	_____ exact	135 days	$108.93
10.	$1,255	_____ ordinary	84 days	$40.87
11.	$380	5.25%	_____	$179.55
12.	$5,310	11%	_____	$243.38
13.	$4,148.25	6% ordinary	_____	$25.58
14.	$451	8% exact	_____	$20.86

** 15. Kelly received $175 interest over the last three years on a deposit earning 2.3% simple interest. Find the amount of the deposit.

16. Clarissa earned $250 interest over the last eight months on a deposit earning 3.1% simple interest. What was the size of the deposit?

17. Jack paid $42.50 interest on a 60-day loan earning 14% ordinary simple interest. How much did Jack borrow?

18. Over the last 28 days, Craig's deposit earned 2.75% exact simple interest, for a total of $12.72. How much was Craig's deposit?

19. Daniel paid $825 simple interest on a $1,400 loan for 5 years. What was the interest rate?

20. Esther earned $38.77 simple interest on a $2,500 deposit for 9 months. What was the interest rate?

21. Rosa deposited $9,000 for 42 days and received $33 simple exact interest. What was the interest rate?

22. Lynn's loan balance for the last 28 days was $950, and she was charged $13.97 ordinary simple interest. Find the interest rate.

23. Lara's $600 deposit earned $120 at 2.7% simple interest. How long was the money on deposit?

24. How long will it take for a $1,200 balance to earn $300, at 3.25% simple interest?

25. At an ordinary simple interest rate of 4%, how many days are needed for Trudy's $800 account to earn $23 interest?

26. Tom's $924.36 savings account balance earned $12.35 at 2.5% simple exact interest. How many days was it on deposit?

∗∗∗ 27. At a rate of 3.5% simple interest, how long will it take for an investment to double?

28. At a rate of 2.92% simple interest, how long will it take for an investment to triple?

Name: ______________________________ Date: __________

Exercises 6.3

∗ Complete the table.

	Principal	Rate	Time	Interest	Maturity Value
1.	$25,300	7.35%	4 years	_____	_____
2.	$1,635.52	14.22%	9 months	_____	_____
3.	_____	5.85% exact	23 days	$174.47	_____
4.	_____	10.9% ordinary	126 days	$375.44	_____
5.	$727.33	_____	2 years	$206.56	_____
6.	$13,520	_____ exact	69 days	$95.84	_____
7.	$495	8.25% ordinary	_____	$17.02	_____
8.	$6,824	2.35%	_____	$26.73	_____
9.	$18,500	_____	8 years	_____	$31,820
10.	$795.95	_____ ordinary	90 days	_____	$825.80
11.	$16,533	14%	_____	_____	$28,106.10
12.	$855	6.3% exact	_____	_____	$883.92
13.	_____	7.13% ordinary	_____	$680.24	$96,085.57
14.	_____	11%	_____	$2,844	$6,537.51
15.	_____	_____	8 years	$1,152	$3,552
16.	_____	_____ exact	45 days	$7.11	$1,929.11
17.	_____	12%	9 years	_____	$645
18.	_____	4% exact	72 days	_____	$183.36
19.	_____	17% ordinary	155 days	_____	$2,352.41
20.	_____	13.5%	9 months	_____	$9,351.77

∗∗ 21. Connie deposits $1,500 into a savings account earning 3.5% simple interest. What will the balance be in 4 years?

22. Richard has $3,500 in a savings account earning 2.95% simple interest. How much will the balance be in 6 months?

23. Rosalind borrowed $680 at 17% ordinary simple interest for 30 days. How much will she pay back?

24. Terry borrowed $1,300 at 14% ordinary simple interest for 90 days. How much will he pay back?

25. On July 16, Jane signed a 120-day, $2,500 simple interest note earning 12.5% ordinary interest. Find the due date, interest, proceeds, and maturity value.

26. On March 11, Tim signed a 90-day, $3,000 simple interest note earning 13% ordinary interest. Find the due date, interest, proceeds, and maturity value.

27. On October 19, Alan signed a 6-month, $45,000 simple interest note earning 8%. Find the due date, interest, proceeds, and maturity value.

28. On July 3, Sherri signed a 3-month, $12,000 simple interest note earning $6\frac{1}{3}\%$. Find the due date, interest, proceeds, and maturity value.

29. On August 30, Danielle signed a 6-month, $15,000 simple interest note earning $5\frac{1}{3}\%$. Find the due date, interest, proceeds, and maturity value.

30. On October 31, David signed a 4-month, $5,000 simple interest note earning 7%. Find the due date, interest, proceeds, and maturity value.

31. Jackie must find $3,492.50 to pay off her 150-day, 14% ordinary, simple interest note. What was the principal?

32. Zeke paid $1,455.30 on the due date of his 270-day, 13.5% ordinary, simple interest note. What was the principal of the note?

33. Adrian's savings account balance grew to $7,199.50 after 6 years of 3.5% simple interest. What was his original principal?

34. Betty's account balance grew to $1,320 after 7 months of 4.32% simple interest. Find her original principal.

Name: ______________________________ Date: __________

Exercises 6.4

* Complete the table, using discount interest.

	Principal	Rate	Time	Interest	Proceeds
1.	$19,400	7.35% ordinary	42 days	_____	_____
2.	$1,256.22	14.22%	9 months	_____	_____
3.	_____	5.85%	7 months	$274.45	_____
4.	_____	10.9% exact	23 days	$335.24	_____
5.	$833.51	_____	2 months	$26.56	_____
6.	$14,744	_____ exact	69 days	$95.84	_____
7.	$866	8.25% ordinary	_____	$17.02	_____
8.	$7,325	2.35% exact	_____	$26.73	_____
9.	$19,500	_____	8 months	_____	$17,180
10.	$495.89	_____ ordinary	90 days	_____	$476.05
11.	$9,254	14%	_____	_____	$8,282.33
12.	$905	6.3% exact	_____	_____	$893.60
13.	_____	7.13% ordinary	_____	$680.24	$65,042.21
14.	_____	11% exact	_____	$644	$6,437.53
15.	_____	_____	8 months	$152	$3,732
16.	_____	_____ exact	45 days	$7.11	$1,955.11
17.	_____	12%	3 months	_____	$641
18.	_____	4% exact	72 days	_____	$182.36
19.	_____	17% ordinary	155 days	_____	$2,372.31
20.	_____	13.5%	9 months	_____	$8445.47

** 21. Ben borrows $25,000 at 11% ordinary discount interest for 30 days. What are his proceeds?

22. Brenda borrows $16,250 at 13% exact discount interest for 90 days. What are her proceeds?

23. Millie receives $3,200 from a 60-day 14.25% ordinary discount interest loan. What is the principal?

24. Alex needs $1,560 from a 120-day 12% ordinary discount interest loan. What will his principal be?

25. A simple discount note dated October 16 for $8,525 is payable in 180 days with 16% ordinary interest. Find the due date, interest, proceeds, and maturity value.

26. A simple discount note dated April 29 for $4,500 is payable in 270 days with 14.5% exact interest. Find the due date, interest, proceeds, and maturity value.

27. A 13-week $10,000 T-bill is sold at a 3.65% discount rate. What was the sale price?

28. A 26-week $50,000 T-bill is sold at a 3.24% discount rate. What was the sale price?

29. A 2-year $5,000 Treasury note is sold at a 4.35% discount rate. What was the sale price?

30. A 20-year $100,000 Treasury bond is sold at a 2.54% discount rate. What was the sale price?

31. A simple interest note dated March 16 for $7,500 is payable in 90 days with 13% ordinary interest. The note is sold on April 11 at a 12% ordinary discount rate. Find the bank discount and the proceeds from the sale of the note.

32. A $24,000 simple interest note dated May 15 is payable in 180 days with 12.9% exact interest. The note is sold on May 28 at a 12.4% exact discount rate. Find the bank discount and the proceeds from the sale of the note.

33. A $16,500 simple discount note dated August 10 is payable in 120 days with 14% ordinary interest. The note is sold on September 8 at a 13% ordinary discount rate. Find the bank discount and the proceeds from the sale of the note.

34. A $9,525 simple discount note dated November 16 is payable in 75 days with 9.25% ordinary interest. The note is sold on December 4 at a 9% exact discount rate. Find the bank discount and the proceeds from the sale of the note.

***35. A $15,000 simple interest note dated July 11 is payable in 180 days with 9% ordinary interest. The note is discounted at a bank on August 30 at a 10% ordinary discount rate.

a. Find the bank discount and the proceeds from the sale of the note.

b. Discuss the amount of profit (loss) to the firm holding the note.

c. Discuss the amount of profit (loss) to the bank purchasing the note.

36. A $75,000 simple interest note dated April 8 is payable in 270 days with 8% ordinary interest. The note is discounted May 3 at a bank which charges a 12% exact discount rate.

a. Find the bank discount and the proceeds from the sale of the note.

b. Discuss the amount of profit (loss) to the firm holding the note.

c. Discuss the amount of profit (loss) to the bank purchasing the note.

37. Tom signs a $14,000 simple interest note dated June 5, payable in 90 days with 16% ordinary interest. The lender sells the note to the Porter County Bank on June 7, at a 15% ordinary discount rate. The Porter County Bank sells the note to the Harrisville State Bank on June 11, at a 14.5% exact discount rate.

a. Find the proceeds of each transaction.

b. What exact rate of interest would a savings account need to produce the same growth in the same time as the original lender obtained?

c. What exact rate of interest would a savings account need to produce the same growth in the same time as Porter County Bank obtained?

Name: ______________________________ Date: __________

Exercises 6.5

* Find each effective rate.

	Proceeds	Maturity Value	Time
1.	$2,500	$3,750	4 years
2.	$186.44	$221.53	3 years
3.	$42,500	$43,500	3 months
4.	$695	$710	5 months
5.	$17,400	$17,600	45 days
6.	$185	$190	12 days

** Find the effective rate of each note.

7. A $25,000, 90-day ordinary simple interest note earning 13% interest.

8. A $16,400, 60-day exact simple interest note earning 15% interest.

9. An $8,950, 120-day exact simple discount note earning 14.5% interest.

10. A $9,300, 180-day ordinary simple discount note earning 11% interest.

11. A 60-day exact simple interest note earning 9% interest.

12. A 135-day ordinary simple interest note earning 12% interest.

13. A 270-day ordinary simple discount note earning 16% interest.

14. A 150-day exact simple discount note earning 18.9% interest.

15. Sheila borrows $4,000 for 120 days at 15% exact simple interest, and pays an application fee of $25. Find the effective rate of her loan.

16. Patrick borrows $3,500 for 60 days at 14% ordinary simple interest, and pays an application fee of $35. Find the effective rate of his loan.

17. Pearl pays an application fee of $65 to borrow $7,800 for 90 days at a 17% ordinary simple discount rate. What is the effective rate of her loan?

18. Edgar pays fees of $120 to borrow $36,000 for 120 days at a 14% exact simple discount rate. What is the effective rate of his loan?

Name: ____ Date: __________

Exercises 6.6

* Complete each table, applying payments according to the Actuarial Method, and using a 9% interest rate.

1.

Date	Charges	Payments	Balance
4/15	4900.00	______	______
5/15	______	600.00	______
6/15	______	______	0

2.

Date	Charges	Payments	Balance
7/29	9340.00	______	______
8/29	______	1800.00	______
9/29	______	______	0

3.

Date	Charges	Payments	Balance
2/7	6500.00	______	______
3/7	______	25.00	______
4/7	______	210.00	______
5/7	______	______	0

4.

Date	Charges	Payments	Balance
9/18	4400.00	______	______
10/18	______	2100.00	______
11/18	______	0	______
12/18	______	______	0

Complete each table, applying payments according to the U.S. Rule, and using an exact interest rate of 15%.

5.

Date	Charges	Payments	Balance
6/15	18000.00	______	______
7/23	______	4000.00	______
8/24	______	______	0

6.

Date	Charges	Payments	Balance
2/5	22310.00	______	______
3/16	______	5000.00	______
5/28	______	______	0

7.

Date	Charges	Payments	Balance
4/15	12350.00	______	______
5/23	______	3000.00	______
5/29	______	4500.00	______
7/15	______	______	0

8.

Date	Charges	Payments	Balance
2/15	48200.00	______	______
7/23	______	5000.00	______
9/29	______	3800.00	______
12/24	______	______	0

Complete each table, applying payments according to the U.S. Rule, and using an ordinary interest rate of 13%.

9.

Date	Charges	Payments	Balance
2/17	8200.00	______	______
3/17	______	80.00	______
4/17	______	120.00	______
5/17	______	______	0

10.

Date	Charges	Payments	Balance
3/19	10244.00	______	______
4/11	______	70.00	______
5/1	______	75.00	______
6/15	______	______	0

**11. Becky borrowed $3,955 on March 22 at 8.2% interest. She made payments of $600 on April 22, and $725 on May 22. Find her payoff amount for June 22, according to the Actuarial Method.

12. Chuck borrowed $43,250 on September 18 at 11.3% interest. He made payments of $2,500 on October 18, and $4,700 on November 18. Find his payoff amount for December 18, according to the Actuarial Method.

13. Donna signed a $5,385, three-month, 13% simple interest note on July 7. She made payments of $100 per month for the next two months. What was her payoff amount on the due date, according to the Actuarial Method?

14. George signed a $4,950, four-month, 15% simple interest note on April 3. He made payments of $250 per month for the next three months. What was his payoff amount on the due date, according to the Actuarial Method?

15. Kent borrowed $6,500 on January 11 at 12.5% exact interest. He made payments of $1,000 on February 16, and $1,500 on March 14. Find his payoff amount on April 10, according to the U.S. Rule.

16. Lavinia borrowed $8,200 on February 14 at 11% ordinary interest. She made payments of $350 on March 17, and $820 on June 2. Find her payoff amount on August 15, according to the U.S. Rule.

17. Barry signed a $5,000, 75-day, 15% ordinary simple interest note on March 14. He made a partial payment of $2,500 on April 12. Find his payoff amount on the maturity date of the note, according to the U.S. Rule.

18. Rebecca signed a $6,000, 120-day, 14% exact simple interest note on May 6. She made partial payments of $1,000 on June 4, and $2,000 on July 3. Find her payoff amount on the maturity date of the note, according to the U.S. Rule.

19. Oscar borrowed $9,500 on June 8 at 14% exact simple interest. He made payments of $100 each, on July 16, August 4, and August 28. Find his payoff amount on October 12, according to the U.S. Rule.

20. Catherine borrowed $12,520 on November 24 at 17% ordinary simple interest. She made payments of $180 each, on December 11, January 26, and February 5. Find her payoff amount on February 27, according to the U.S. Rule.

Name: ____________________ Date: ________

Chapter 6 Review

Summary of Important Concepts

- ▲ Principal, rate, time
- ▲ Exact and ordinary interest
- ▲ Proceeds and maturity value
- ▲ Discount interest
- ▲ Simple interest notes and simple discount notes
- ▲ Effective rate (APR), finance charge
- ▲ U.S. Rule, Actuarial Method

Exercises

1. Find the simple interest on $3,200 for five years at 7%.

2. Find the ordinary interest on $4,400 for 75 days at 11.5%.

3. Find the exact interest on $388 for 108 days at 13.1%.

4. Find the time needed for $2,800 to grow to $3,800 at 9%.

5. Find the number of days needed for $155 to earn $6 at 5% ordinary interest.

6. Find the rate needed for $455 to earn $68 in 4 years.

7. Find the principal needed to earn $3,500 in 3 years at 5.5%.

Find the due date, interest, proceeds, maturity value, and APR.

8. $2,400, 90-day, 6% ordinary simple interest note dated April 29.

9. $5,500, 150-day, 9% exact simple discount note dated October 16.

10. Find the proceeds on a 16% ordinary, 45-day, simple interest note which has a maturity value of $3,500.

11. Find the maturity value on a 15% ordinary, 125-day simple discount note which had proceeds of $1,755.

12. Find the effective rate of a 150-day, 12%, $17,500 ordinary simple discount note.

13. A $2,800, 45-day, 14% exact simple interest note dated March 25 is sold on April 1 at a 13% ordinary discount rate. Find the finance charge and the proceeds from the sale of the note.

14. Valerie borrowed $3,925 on March 13 at 11.4% interest. She made payments of $250 on April 13, and $450 on May 13. In order to pay off the debt, how much should Valerie pay on June 13, according to the Actuarial Method?

15. Tom borrowed $2,400 on June 26 at 15% simple exact interest. He made payments of $300 on August 14, and $500 on September 2. In order to pay off the debt, how much should Tom pay on October 15, according to the U.S. Rule?

7 Time Value of Money

7.1 TVM Variables

In the previous chapter, we studied simple interest. Each single use of the $I = PRT$ formula is a simple interest computation. However, most banks do not pay simple interest on the accounts of their customers, but use compound interest instead. **Compound interest** is the repeated application of simple interest, where the principal changes from one period to the next as interest is added. That is, interest will be added to the original principal, creating a new principal or balance. The **compounding period** is the period of time between interest computations. It may be any length of time, but typically interest is compounded annually, semiannually, quarterly, monthly, or daily.

A **time value of money problem**, or **TVM problem**, is a problem in which interest is being earned on a principal over some period of time. The interest may be compounded, or may not be compounded. Several varieties of time value of money problems exist. Among the most common varieties of TVM problems are

- Lump sum deposits (a one time deposit earning interest)
- Savings plans (regularly occurring deposits, with the balance earning interest)
- Savings withdrawals (regularly occurring withdrawals, with the balance earning interest)
- Loans (regularly occurring payments, with the loan balance earning interest)

Savings plans, savings withdrawals, and loans are all examples of a type of problem called an annuity. The mathematical definition of an **annuity** is a series of payments. Usually, it is assumed that the payments are equal, and are made at regular intervals. Annuities typically earn interest, and the interest may be compounded. Some insurance companies sell annuity policies, usually intended to provide the purchaser with a series of payments at some future date, often at retirement. Mathematically, however, an annuity is a much more general type of TVM problem.

There are several other approaches that can be used to solve TVM problems, including algebra, tables, spreadsheets, financial calculators, or repeated application of the simple interest formula. No matter which method is chosen, you will need to be able to identify all of the important variables in any given problem. This identification process is at the heart of every financial problem. There are six variables that are considered important variables. They are:

- N = Number of compounding (or payment) periods
- I/Y = Interest rate per Year
- P/Y = Periods per Year
- PV = Present Value
- PMT = Payment per period
- FV = Future Value

In this section, for each common variety of TVM problem, we shall identify the important variables and use repeated applications of the simple interest formula to exhibit the main features of the problem. In the remaining sections of this chapter, we shall concentrate only on the important variables, and assume that you will be using a financial calculator to solve these problems.

In a **lump sum deposit problem** a depositor makes exactly one deposit, and all other changes to the account are due to interest being earned. Typically the interest in a lump sum deposit problem is compounded.

EXAMPLE 1

Alexander deposits a lump sum of $8,000 into an account which earns 4% compounded semiannually. What will be the balance in the account after three years?

SOLUTION

The variable I/Y is 4%. Since interest is compounded semiannually, P/Y is 2 periods per year. With a total term of three years, at 2 periods per year, N consists of 6 semiannual periods. The variable PMT is zero, as it will always be in a lump sum deposit problem. The initial deposit of $8,000 is PV. The value of FV, the final balance, is unknown. This information is organized in the following chart.

N = 6	I/Y = 4	P/Y = 2
PV = 8000	PMT = 0	FV = ???

When using the simple interest formula, the computations must be done one period at a time. We shall arrange our work in a table.

Period	Principal	Interest: $I = PRT$	New Balance
1	8000.00	$8000.00 \times 0.04 \times 0.5 = 160.00$	$8000.00 + 160.00 = 8160.00$
2	8160.00	$8160.00 \times 0.04 \times 0.5 = 163.20$	$8160.00 + 163.20 = 8323.20$
3	8323.20	$8323.20 \times 0.04 \times 0.5 \approx 166.46$	$8323.20 + 166.46 = 8489.66$
4	8489.66	$8489.66 \times 0.04 \times 0.5 \approx 169.79$	$8489.66 + 169.79 = 8659.45$
5	8659.45	$8659.45 \times 0.04 \times 0.5 \approx 173.19$	$8659.45 + 173.19 = 8832.64$
6	8832.64	$8832.64 \times 0.04 \times 0.5 \approx 176.65$	$8832.64 + 176.65 = 9009.29$

Therefore, Alexander has $9,009.29 in his account after three years.

If Alexander's account had used simple interest, the interest computation would have been

$$I = PRT = 8000.00 \times 0.04 \times 3 = 960.00$$

That is, the principal would have remained $8,000 during each of the three years, and the balance in the account would have been $8,960 after three years. But with compound interest, each interest payment was used to increase the principal for the following year. Since the principal increases on a regular basis, the interest earned will be greater with compound interest than with simple interest, if all other things are equal. And when interest is compounded more frequently, the final balance will be greater.

In a **savings plan problem** the depositor makes deposits into an account at a regular interval. Once again, interest is typically compounded in a savings plan problem.

EXAMPLE 2

David deposits $80 at the end of each quarter into an account which earns 5% compounded quarterly. What will be the balance in the account after one year?

Solution

The variable I/Y is 5%. Since interest is compounded quarterly and the payments are made quarterly, P/Y is 4 periods per year. With quarterly periods and a total term of one year, N is 4. David's regular deposit is $80 per quarter, so PMT is 80. There is no initial deposit (the first regular deposit is part of the regular deposits, not an initial deposit), so PV is zero. The value of FV, the final balance, is unknown. This information is organized in the following table.

N = 4	I/Y = 5	P/Y = 4
PV = 0	PMT = 80	FV = ???

Now, we shall use the simple interest formula over the period of time. Again, we shall organize our work into a table. The deposit column has been placed after the interest column, since the deposit is being made at the end of each month and will not earn interest for that month.

Period (quarter)	Principal	Interest $I = PRT$	Deposit	New Balance
1	0	$0 \times 0.05 \times \frac{1}{4} = 0$	80.00	$0 + 0 + 80.00 = 80.00$
2	80.00	$80.00 \times 0.05 \times \frac{1}{4} = 1.00$	80.00	$80.00 + 1.00 + 80.00 = 161.00$
3	161.00	$161.00 \times 0.05 \times \frac{1}{4} \approx 2.01$	80.00	$161.00 + 2.01 + 80.00 = 243.01$
4	243.01	$243.01 \times 0.05 \times \frac{1}{4} \approx 3.04$	80.00	$243.01 + 3.04 + 80.00 = 326.05$

At the end of one year, David will have $326.05 in the account.

David's deposits were an example of an **ordinary annuity**, where payments were made at the end of each month. Another type of annuity is a **beginning annuity**, or **annuity due**, where payments are made at the beginning of each month. When a savings plan is a beginning annuity, each deposit will earn interest in the month it is deposited, and therefore the balances will be greater than in an ordinary annuity. Although this distinction is not represented by one of the important variables, it is nevertheless necessary to determine the timing of the payments in order to obtain correct solutions to annuity problems.

EXAMPLE 3

Cara, David's sister, deposits $80 at the beginning of each quarter into an account which earns 5% compounded quarterly. What will be the balance in the account after one year?

SOLUTION

The values of the important variables are the same as in the previous example, namely:

N = 4	I/Y = 5	P/Y = 4
PV = 0	PMT = 80	FV = ???

But there is a difference between the two plans, because Cara's first deposit will earn interest, and is therefore a beginning annuity. Once again, we shall organize our work into a table. The deposit column has been placed before the principal and interest columns, since the deposit is being made at the beginning of each month and will earn interest for that month.

Period (quarter)	Deposit	Principal	Interest $I = PRT$	New Balance
1	80.00	80.00	$80.00 \times 0.05 \times \frac{1}{4} = 1.00$	80.00 + 1.00 = 81.00
2	80.00	81.00 + 80.00 = 161.00	$161.00 \times 0.05 \times \frac{1}{4} \approx 2.01$	161.00 + 2.01 = 163.01
3	80.00	163.01 + 80.00 = 243.01	$243.01 \times 0.05 \times \frac{1}{4} \approx 3.04$	243.01 + 3.04 = 246.05
4	80.00	246.05 + 80.00 = 326.05	$326.05 \times 0.05 \times \frac{1}{4} \approx 4.08$	326.05 + 4.08 = 330.13

At the end of one year, Cara will have $330.13 in the account.

If you compare the two examples, you will see that David had $4.08 less than his sister after one year. This amount is exactly the amount of interest Cara earned during the fourth quarter. This result is a general one. That is, when payments are made to increase the balance of an account, an ordinary annuity always earns one month's less interest than a beginning annuity, if all other variables are identical. Over a short period of time, the difference may seem small, but for annuities which run several decades, the difference can be quite substantial.

Another distinction in an annuity problem is the type of payment being made. An **increasing annuity** is an annuity where the payments are made so as to increase the balance. The savings plan is an example of an increasing annuity. Also, payments can be made so as to decrease the balance of an annuity, and this is called a **decreasing annuity**. Both savings withdrawals and loan payments are types of decreasing annuities. The distinction between an increasing and a decreasing annuity is represented by the value of the variable PMT. For increasing annuities, PMT will be a positive number. For decreasing annuities, PMT will be a negative number.

In a **savings withdrawal problem** the account holder makes withdrawals from an account at a regular interval. However, since withdrawals are intended to decrease the balance in the account, the payments will be negative. As usual, interest is typically compounded. Withdrawals may be either ordinary or beginning annuities.

EXAMPLE 4

Fiona has a balance of $300 in her account, and it is earning 7% interest compounded monthly. She withdraws $20 at the beginning of each month. What will the balance be after six months?

SOLUTION

The variable I/Y is 7%. Since interest is compounded monthly, and the withdrawals occur each month, P/Y is 12 periods per year. With monthly periods and a total of six months, N is 6. The payment is $20, but since the payments are withdrawals, the payments will be negative. Therefore PMT is –20 per month. The value of PV is $300. The future value, FV, is unknown. The information is organized in the following table.

N = 6	I/Y = 7	P/Y = 12
PV = 300	PMT = –20	FV = ???

The payments are occurring at the beginning of each month, so this is a beginning annuity. Therefore, when using the simple interest formula, the withdrawal must be completed before computing the interest each month. We get the following table:

Period (month)	Withdrawal	Principal	Interest $I = PRT$	New Balance
1	20	$300.00 - 20.00 = 280.00$	$280.00 \times 0.07 \times \frac{1}{12} \approx 1.63$	$280.00 + 1.63 = 281.63$
2	20	$281.63 - 20.00 = 261.63$	$261.63 \times 0.07 \times \frac{1}{12} \approx 1.53$	$261.63 + 1.53 = 263.16$
3	20	$263.16 - 20.00 = 243.16$	$243.16 \times 0.07 \times \frac{1}{12} \approx 1.42$	$243.16 + 1.42 = 244.58$
4	20	$244.58 - 20.00 = 224.58$	$224.58 \times 0.07 \times \frac{1}{12} \approx 1.31$	$223.58 + 1.31 = 225.89$
5	20	$225.89 - 20.00 = 205.89$	$205.89 \times 0.07 \times \frac{1}{12} \approx 1.20$	$205.89 + 1.20 = 207.09$
6	20	$207.09 - 20.00 = 187.09$	$187.09 \times 0.07 \times \frac{1}{12} \approx 1.09$	$187.09 + 1.09 = 188.18$

Fiona's account will have $188.18 at the end of six months.

In a **loan problem** the borrower will make payments intended to bring his balance down, and interest will be computed on the balance. Typically, the loan payments will be large enough to cover all of the interest earned each period, so there will be no opportunity for interest to be compounded. If, however, a regular payment is too small or entirely skipped, then it is possible for interest to compound. Loan problems are typically ordinary annuities, since the first regular payment is not due the same day that the loan is made.

EXAMPLE 5

Kristi borrowed $6,500 at 12.9% interest. She makes payments of $919.75 at the end of each year. What will the balance be in three years?

SOLUTION

The interest rate, I/Y, is 12.9%. Since payments occur once every year, P/Y is 1 period per year. With annual periods and a total of three years, N is 3. The original balance on the account, $6,500, is the value of PV. Payments are made so as to decrease the balance in the account, so they will be negative. Therefore, the payment PMT is –919.75. The new balance in the account, FV, is unknown. We organize the results in the following table.

N = 3	I/Y = 12.9	P/Y = 1
PV = 6500	PMT = –919.75	FV = ???

Using simple interest, we can determine the loan balances one period at a time.

Period (year)	Principal	Interest $I = PRT$	Payment	New Balance
1	6500.00	$6500.00 \times 0.129 \times 1 = 838.50$	919.75	$6500.00 + 838.50 - 919.75 = 6418.75$
2	6418.75	$6418.75 \times 0.129 \times 1 \approx 828.02$	919.75	$6418.75 + 828.02 - 919.75 = 6327.02$
3	6327.02	$6327.02 \times 0.129 \times 1 \approx 816.19$	919.75	$6327.02 + 816.19 - 919.75 = 6223.46$

At the end of three years, Kristi's loan balance will be $6,223.46.

In all of the examples above, the future value was the unknown quantity. The arithmetical approach can always find the future value, but if the compounding period is small and the number of years involved is large, the number of computations can be overwhelming. Also, it is not easy to use the arithmetical approach to find some of the other important quantities, such as N, I/Y, PV, or PMT. Algebra, tables, spreadsheets, and financial calculators can all overcome this difficulty.

In the remaining sections of this chapter, we recommend the use of a financial calculator (rather than formulas or tables), because of their versatility and ease of use. Financial calculators are manufactured by several different companies. They all have certain features in common, as well as some differences. Here is some general information and some suggestions for using a financial calculator.

- ▲ Some calculators have a financial mode or financial application that must be accessed.
- ▲ Calculator variables are usually identified with the names N, I/Y, P/Y, PV, PMT, and FV, or something similar.
- ▲ Unless a menu is provided, data is generally entered by entering a value into the display, then pressing the appropriate variable key.
- ▲ If a "compute" key is provided, results are obtained by pressing the "compute" key, followed by the key of the variable desired.
- ▲ Financial data is rarely cleared by the CLEAR key. A special keystroke may be required, or zeros can be entered instead.
- ▲ A few older calculators may require the interest rate per period. In such a case, divide I/Y by P/Y to obtain this rate.
- ▲ To conform to standard accounting practice, future values will almost always have opposite signs from present values. In this book, we will almost always obtain negative numbers for future values, and almost always enter future values as negative numbers.
- ▲ For beginning annuities, there will be a BGN or BEG key that needs to be activated.

7.2 Lump Sum Deposits

The simplest financial problems involve **lump sum deposits,** or simple investments, where no regular payments are made. Since there are no regular payments, the variable PMT will always be zero in these problems, and the account balance will increase from PV to FV. We can solve for any of the variables in a lump sum deposit problem if the other three variables are known. In the last section, we described the use of the financial calculator, and discussed how to identify those important variables.

From this point on, you should work every example on *your* financial calculator, to make sure you understand how your calculator works.

EXAMPLE 1

Dawn inherits $5,000 from her Uncle Jim. She deposits it into a savings account earning 4.2% interest compounded monthly. What will be the account balance in 20 years?

SOLUTION

We identify the variables in the same manner as we did in the previous section.

N = 20 × 12 = 240	I/Y = 4.2	P/Y = 12
PV = 5000	PMT = 0	FV = ???

You should obtain 11,564.86 for the answer. Therefore, the account will have $11,564.86 at the end of 20 years.

Most likely, your calculator displayed the answer for Example 1 as a negative number. This is because your calculator is treating the future value as a withdrawal, which is a reduction in the balance of the account. From the point of view of the savings institution, this is an amount which they owe to their depositor. But for reporting the future value, we can ignore the negative sign when it appears in the displayed answer.

EXAMPLE 2

Eileen opens a savings account with a $4,000 deposit. The balance in the account earns 2.85% interest compounded daily. Find the balance after seven years, if no further transactions are made.

SOLUTION

We first identify our variables.

N = 7 × 365 = 2555	I/Y = 2.85	P/Y = 365
PV = 4000	PMT = 0	FV = ???

Computing the future value, we obtain $4,883.13 as the result, rounded to the nearest cent.

EXAMPLE 3

Frank wants to have one million dollars at the end of 30 years. How much does he need to deposit today in a savings account earning 4.15% interest compounded quarterly in order to meet his goal?

SOLUTION

We first identify our variables.

N = 30 × 4 = 120	I/Y = 4.15	P/Y = 4
PV = ???	PMT = 0	FV = –1000000

Computing the present value, we obtain $289,793.73.

Notice that in the previous example, we identified the future value as a negative number. This was in accordance with the standard sign convention which treats future balances as possible withdrawals. If, by chance, you forgot the sign and made the future value negative, you would have found that the present value was negative. Sometimes a sign error in the data entry will lead only to a sign error in the answer, and sometimes the error will be more serious. We strongly encourage you to always treat future values as possible withdrawals, and therefore enter them as negative numbers, so that you will avoid errors in other situations where they could arise.

Did the answer of Example 3 surprise you? Frank will deposit $289,793.73, and have $1,000,000 thirty years later. That is a lot of interest, and almost all of the interest is due to the power of compounding.

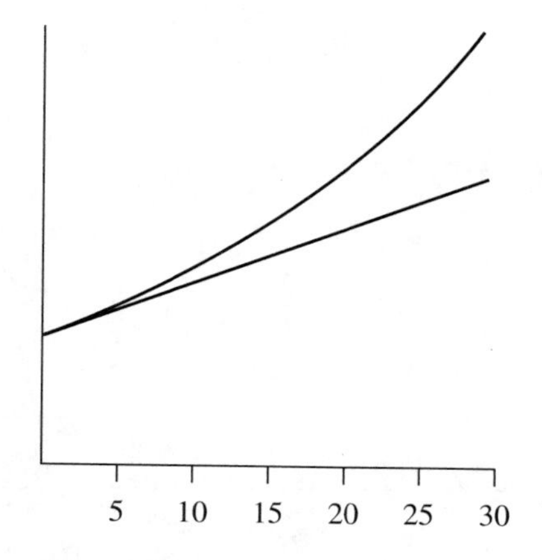

Figure 7.1 Comparison of Simple and Compound Interest.

What if simple interest had been used on Frank's deposit of $289,793.73? The simple interest computation would have been:

$$I = PRT = 289793.73 \times 0.0415 \times 30 \approx 360793.19$$

Adding the $360,793.19 interest to the $289,793.73 principal, we find that Frank's balance would have been $650,586.92, far short of one million dollars. Figure 7.1 provides a graphical view of the growth of Frank's balance over the 30 year period, both with and without compounding.

EXAMPLE 4

How long will it take for a $5,000 deposit to grow to $8,000, when interest is 3.9% compounded monthly?

SOLUTION

We first identify our variables.

N = ???	I/Y = 3.9	P/Y = 12
PV = 5000	PMT = 0	FV = – 8000

Computing the value of N, we obtain 144.85 periods. Since our periods are months, we divide this figure by 12 months per year to get approximately 12.07 years, or about 12 years and one month.

In this example, if you did not enter your future value as a negative number, you would likely have received an error message. Interest on a positive balance should cause that balance to grow, and thereby result in an amount that can be withdrawn. If you had not used a negative sign on the future value, you would have been telling the calculator that you want the future value to be an amount that the depositor should need to deposit to bring his balance to zero. In other words, the depositor would have owed the bank money in his savings account, not the other way around. The moral of this story is that you must pay close attention to the signs, especially when both present value and future value are given in the problem.

EXAMPLE 5

A deposit of $1,200 grew to $2,100 over 20 years, as interest was compounded semiannually. What was the annual interest rate (compounded semiannually) on this investment?

SOLUTION

We first identify the variables.

$N = 20 \times 2 = 40$	$I/Y = ???$	$P/Y = 2$
$PV = 1200$	$PMT = 0$	$FV = -2100$

Computing the value of I/Y, we find the rate was 2.82% per year, compounded semiannually.

Series EE U.S. Savings Bonds are issued by the U.S. government, and earn interest compounded semiannually. At the time of purchase, a guaranteed minimum interest rate is made, but the actual rate is tied to the securities market. The bonds are sold for half of their face value, and mature when the principal and interest equals the face value. They continue to earn interest after maturity, until a date called final maturity.

EXAMPLE 6

Isaac purchased a $50 Series EE U.S. Savings Bond. Five years later, he cashed it in and received $35. What average annual rate of interest did he earn?

SOLUTION

Since savings bonds are sold at half of their face value, Isaac paid $25 for his bond. The variables are:

$N = 5 \times 2 = 10$	$I/Y = ???$	$P/Y = 2$
$PV = 25$	$PMT = 0$	$FV = -35$

Solving for the interest rate, we get 6.84% per year. Although the actual rate paid by the U.S. government may have fluctuated every six months, the average rate was 6.84% per year.

An investor desiring a higher rate of return with minimal risk may choose a certificate of deposit account over a regular savings account. A **certificate of deposit**, or **CD**, (sometimes called a **time deposit account**), is a savings account for which the depositor agrees to leave the funds in the account for a fixed period of time. The CD reaches **maturity** when the fixed time period is completed. In return, the savings institution will pay a higher rate of interest on the funds in the account.

Penalties may be imposed if the funds in a CD account are withdrawn before maturity. Forfeiture of interest for a fixed time period is a frequently used penalty. Sometimes, the penalty will be greater than the interest earned, and some principal can also be lost. The next example will compare a CD that reaches maturity to a CD which is penalized.

EXAMPLE 7

Ken deposits $3,000 into a 5-year CD paying 4% interest compounded monthly. If withdrawn before the maturity date, six months interest will be forfeited. If Ken withdraws the money one month before the maturity date, how much will he receive, and how much would he forfeit?

SOLUTION

We first identify the variables. Five years of monthly periods is 60 periods, but Ken withdrew his money one month early. Furthermore, the early withdrawal penalty of the CD is the loss of six months interest. Therefore, the number of periods is 53, not 59.

N = 53	I/Y = 4	P/Y = 12
PV = 3000	PMT = 0	FV = ???

Computing the future value, we obtain $3,578.65. Ken receives $3,578.65 from his account.

To find the amount forfeited because of the early withdrawal penalty, we can simply compute the future value for 59 months of interest.

N = 59	I/Y = 4	P/Y = 12
PV = 3000	PMT = 0	FV = ???

With 59 months of interest, the future value is found to be $3,650.82. Subtracting the $3,578.65 that Ken actually received, we find that the early withdrawal penalty cost Ken $72.17.

7.3 Savings Plans

Savings plans are one of the common types of annuities. In fact, it is the standard example of an annuity problem having an increasing payment. In this type of problem, the balance increases from PV (which is sometimes zero) to FV. The value of PMT is the size of the payment each period. The values of N, I/Y, and P/Y are determined in the same fashion as in the lump sum deposit problem.

Once again, you should work every example on *your* financial calculator, to make sure you understand how your calculator works.

EXAMPLE 1

Larry is depositing $50 at the end of each month into an account earning 4% compounded monthly. How much will he have at the end of ten years?

SOLUTION

We first identify the variables.

N = 10 × 12 = 120	I/Y = 4	P/Y = 12
PV = 0	PMT = 50	FV = ???

Since payments were made at the end of each month, this is an ordinary annuity. We find that the future value is $7,362.49. This is the amount that Larry will have at the end of ten years.

EXAMPLE 2

Dawn inherits $5,000 from her Uncle Jim. She uses it to open an account for her future retirement. She then makes regular monthly deposits of $75 at the beginning of each month into that account. If 6% interest compounded monthly is earned, what will be the account balance in twenty years?

SOLUTION

We identify the variables first.

N = 20 × 12 = 240	I/Y = 6	P/Y = 12
PV = 5000	PMT = 75	FV = ???

Since payments were made at the beginning of each month, this problem is a beginning annuity, and you must set your calculator accordingly. You should find that the account will have $51,377.35 at the end of twenty years.

EXAMPLE 3

Frank wants to have one million dollars at the end of 30 years. In order to reach his goal, how much would he need to deposit at the beginning of each quarter in a savings account earning 5.25% interest compounded quarterly?

SOLUTION

We first identify the variables.

N = 30 × 4 = 120	I/Y = 5.25	P/Y = 4
PV = 0	PMT = ???	FV = – 1000000

This problem is a beginning annuity. We find that the payment needed is $3,425.88 per quarter.

EXAMPLE 4

Wanda wants to make regular payments of $200 at the beginning of each month, for three years, in order to save $9,000 for a down payment on a house. Is this a feasible plan? In other words, what interest rate would she need?

SOLUTION

We first identify the variables.

N = 3 × 12 = 36	I/Y = ???	P/Y = 12
PV = 0	PMT = 200	FV = – 9000

The savings plan is a beginning annuity. Computing the interest rate, we obtain 14.08% per year, compounded monthly. Typical savings rates are not usually this high. If Wanda is willing to risk the possibility of not making her goal, she might put her money in some higher yield investments. Otherwise, the plan is not feasible. If Wanda could increase the payment by a few dollars, she may find her goal much easier to obtain.

EXAMPLE 5

Manny wants to set aside $60 at the end of each month to save $3,000 for the down payment on a car. If interest rates are currently 3.5%, how long will it take?

SOLUTION

We first identify the variables.

N = ???	I/Y = 3.5	P/Y = 12
PV = 0	PMT = 60	FV = –3000

This savings plan is an ordinary annuity. When we compute the number of periods, we obtain 46.7 periods, which can be divided by 12 periods per year to get approximately four years.

EXAMPLE 6

Andy is making payments of $150 at the end of each month into a savings account earning 4.5% compounded monthly. After five years, his balance is $12,671.83. What was the original balance in the account?

SOLUTION

We first identify the variables.

$N = 5 \times 12 = 60$	$I/Y = 4.5$	$P/Y = 12$
PV = ???	PMT = 150	FV = – 12671.83

The payments form an ordinary annuity. We compute PV, the original balance, and find it to be $2,077.01.

Although we found PV in the previous example, the value we obtained is commonly referred to as the original balance, not the present value. The present value of an annuity can have a different meaning, and it will be discussed in the next chapter.

In the previous six examples of this section, we looked at every possible variation of a savings plan problem. If you look back at the six examples, you will find that we provided examples in which five of the six important variables, N, I/Y, PV, PMT, and FV, were found. Although you could set up a problem that asks to find P/Y, most calculators treat P/Y somewhat differently, and do not provide the option of finding the length of the compounding or payment period.

Businesses and governments often issue bonds to raise money. Basically, a **bond** is a loan from the buyer (investor) to the bond issuer. Most bonds come in $1,000 amounts. Interest-bearing bonds are sold to the investor for $1,000, and will earn interest over a certain time period. Bond issuers must raise money in order to eventually pay off the bonds. To do this, they can set up a sinking fund.

A **sinking fund** is an account which receives regular payments and whose purpose is to pay off the principal of a debt at maturity. By its very definition, a sinking fund is a savings plan. Sinking funds are typically assumed to be ordinary annuities.

EXAMPLE 7

Tuttle School District issued $7,500,000 in bonds earning 5.8% interest payable quarterly, and due in 10 years. For bond repayment, they set up a sinking fund earning 5.2% compounded quarterly. Find the quarterly payment necessary for bond interest and sinking fund combined.

SOLUTION

For the sinking fund, a future value of $7,500,000 will be needed. The variables are:

$N = 10 \times 4 = 40$	$I/Y = 5.2$	$P/Y = 4$
PV = 0	PMT = ???	FV = –7500000

We find that the quarterly payment for the sinking fund will be $144,145.34.

For the bond interest, we note that it is *payable* quarterly to the bondholders. By doing so, the interest is *not* compounded. This approach makes the bonds marketable, so that an investor may sell the bond at any time to another investor, and the interest will be paid to the appropriate investor. If an investor wants compound interest, he can put the interest payments into an account earning compound interest. Since the bond interest is not compounded, we will use the simple interest formula. And since the question asks for a quarterly payment, we shall compute the bond interest for one quarter.

$$I = PRT = 7500000 \times 0.058 \times \frac{1}{4} = 108750$$

Therefore, the school district's issuance of $7,500,000 in bonds will require payments of $252,895.34 each quarter for the next ten years. Of this quarterly payment, $144,145.34 is for the sinking fund and $108,750 will be mailed to the bondholders.

Compound interest can certainly provide large returns for those who understand its use. So which is more important in a savings plan, the amount set aside as a payment, the rate of interest paid, or the time over which the interest is earned? Consider the following example.

EXAMPLE 8

Ben and Jerry graduated from the same college class, went to work for the same company and made the same salary, but had very different feelings about the future. For his retirement, Ben began setting aside $1,500 at the end of each year, while Jerry preferred to spend rather than save. After ten years, Ben got tired of denying himself and stopped saving, while Jerry decided that he better get started on his retirement savings. So for the next thirty years, Jerry deposited $1,500 at the end of each year, while Ben let his retirement account sit unchanged, except for interest. If each account earned 7% compounded annually, whose retirement plan was better?

SOLUTION

Jerry's balance is actually easier to compute, since he did nothing for the first ten years. Here are the variables for the last thirty years of Jerry's savings plan.

$N = 30 \times 1 = 30$	$I/Y = 7$	$P/Y = 1$
$PV = 0$	$PMT = 1500$	$FV = ???$

Computing the future value, we find that Jerry's account will have $141,691.18 at the end of thirty years.

Ben's balance must be computed in two steps, starting with the first ten years.

$N = 10 \times 1 = 10$	$I/Y = 7$	$P/Y = 1$
$PV = 0$	$PMT = 1500$	$FV = ???$

Computing the future value, we find that Ben's account will have $20,724.67 after ten years. But this account will still earn interest for another thirty years. The variables for the second half of Ben's time period must now be identified.

N = 30 × 1 = 30	I/Y = 7	P/Y = 1
PV = 20724.67	PMT = 0	FV = ???

Again computing the future value, we find that Ben's account will now have $157,761.47. Ben has a larger retirement balance than Jerry.

Are the implications of this example clear? Ben made deposits for only ten years, while Jerry made deposits for thirty years. Yet Ben has more money. One major difference between the two strategies was the time when the deposits were made. By depositing early, Ben received much more benefit from the compounding of interest. This story has a moral. Don't wait to start your retirement savings, do it now. Time is extremely important where compounding is concerned.

Of course, it would have been better if either Ben or Jerry had decided to make deposits for all forty years. Can you determine what their retirement balance would have been then? When you find it, can you explain why the answer is exactly the same as the combined amount of Ben and Jerry's two accounts?

7.4 Savings Withdrawals

In the previous section, the balance in a savings plan was expected to grow. In this section, we consider how regular **savings withdrawals** interact with the balance in a savings plan. Retirees may be living off of their savings through such withdrawals. In this type of problem, the balance will generally be decreasing from PV to FV, although it is possible that the withdrawals are so small that the balance actually increases. In either case, the value of PMT will be the withdrawal payment, with a negative sign to indicate a decreasing payment situation.

EXAMPLE 1

Travis is withdrawing $3,000 at the end of each month from an account earning 3.8% compounded monthly. If his original balance was $525,000, what will the balance of the account be in ten years?

SOLUTION

We first identify our variables.

N = 10 × 12 = 120	I/Y = 3.8	P/Y = 12
PV = 525000	PMT = –3000	FV = ???

This is an ordinary annuity, and we find that the future value is $330,116.30. Travis will still have $330,116.30 in the account after ten years.

Some retirement plans may consist of stocks, bonds, mutual funds, or other investment instruments whose growth is determined by current economic factors, rather than the standard pre-defined fixed interest rate account. In this case, we will have to estimate the annual growth of our investments, and therefore our results will also be estimates. Growth rates for such investments are typically higher than the fixed interest account, but the rates are also much more volatile. No guarantees are possible, since the economy is subject to change. In the next example, we shall assume a retirement plan based on these investments.

EXAMPLE 2

Rhonda has $820,000 in her retirement account, and it is earning an average of 7.5% per year. How much can she withdraw at the beginning of each year, if she wants the account to last thirty years?

Solution

If the account is to last exactly thirty years, then the final balance at the end of that time would be zero. This approach leads to the following variables.

$N = 30 \times 1 = 30$	$I/Y = 7.5$	$P/Y = 1$
$PV = 820000$	$PMT = ???$	$FV = 0$

This is a beginning annuity, and we find that Rhonda could withdraw $64,586.43 each year.

In the previous example, if Rhonda wants to make monthly withdrawals, the computation will need to be redone with new values for N and P/Y. Simply dividing Rhonda's annual withdrawal by 12 would be equivalent to moving each year's withdrawal into the cookie jar until needed later that year, and would forfeit over one thousand dollars of interest each year.

Although we have only done two examples, it is possible to have retirement questions that would have you solve for any of the five major variables, N, I/Y, PV, PMT, or FV. The process for each of those types of questions is similar to the two examples we have already done.

One specific type of savings plan is often sold in connection with a life insurance policy. In an **annuity policy**, the customer will be making regular payments to the company until a certain age, after which the company will make regular payments to the customer. Annuity policies are frequently used for retirement purposes.

Actually, a retirement account does not have to be set up as an annuity policy, since a basic savings account can serve the same purpose. On the other hand, an annuity policy is a forced savings account, and the rate earned may be higher than your local savings institution offers. Annuity policies can also spread the risk of outliving your retirement account among large numbers of people. The annuity could then pay you more in retirement benefits than your principal and interest, if you live long enough, by using money from the annuity accounts of other persons who died earlier.

EXAMPLE 3

At the beginning of each month, Oscar makes a $150 payment into a retirement account earning 9% compounded monthly. After 40 years, he retires. He then chooses to withdraw at the end of each month an amount that would allow the retirement account to last twenty years. How large is his monthly withdrawal?

SOLUTION

This problem comes in two parts, before retirement and during retirement. We first identify the variables before retirement, noting that this part is simply the savings plan of the previous section.

$N = 40 \times 12 = 480$	$I/Y = 9$	$P/Y = 12$
$PV = 0$	$PMT = 150$	$FV = ???$

This is a beginning annuity, and we find the future value to be $707,464.53. This is the balance in the account on the day of retirement. Now, Oscar begins receiving payments from the account. We need to enter the displayed figure for FV, with a change of sign, into the register for PV, and also enter any other figures which have changed. The variables are:

$N = 20 \times 12 = 240$	$I/Y = 9$	$P/Y = 12$
$PV = 707464.53$	$PMT = ???$	$FV = 0$

This half of the problem is an ordinary annuity, and we need to compute the value of PMT. We find it to be $6,365.24 per month.

You should stop and reflect on some of the values which appear in this problem. Oscar made 480 payments of $150 each, so he deposited $72,000 of his own money while preparing for retirement. Certainly that was a lot of cash, but look at the balance at retirement, over $700,000. Oscar earned over $600,000 interest. If you are saving for a retirement plan, the bulk of your retirement will not come from your own funds, but from interest earned by your funds.

During retirement, Oscar received 240 payments of $6,365.24 per month, for a total of over 1.5 million dollars. All of this came from an account which had a maximum balance of just over $700,000. Again, interest earned from the balance provides all of the additional money.

Oscar's retirement income does not appear to be skimpy either. He saved just $150 per month, but is receiving $6,365.24 per month. His monthly payment into the account before retirement is less than 3% of his monthly withdrawal from the account during retirement. In other words, if Oscar's deposits were just 3% of his earnings before retirement, then his retirement income would be more than his income before retirement.

Obviously, there is a moral to this story. Don't neglect your retirement account. Money earning compound interest can work for you far more than you can scrape together yourself.

A variation on the previous example is to ask how long an account will last, given a certain withdrawal amount. Consider the next example.

EXAMPLE 4

Oscar's retirement account (from Example 3) currently holds $707,464.53. He already knows that $6,365.24 monthly payments will last twenty years. However, Oscar doesn't believe that he will need over $6,000 per month, and he is also worried that he will live longer than the account will last. If he withdrew $6,000 per month, how long would the account last? Or if he withdrew only $5,000 per month, how long would it last?

SOLUTION

If Oscar withdrew $6,000 per month, the variables would be:

N = ???	I/Y = 9	P/Y = 12
PV = 707464.53	PMT = –6000	FV = 0

Solving for the variable N, we get 288.7 months. If Oscar withdrew $6,000 per month, the account would last just over 24 years.

If Oscar withdrew $5,000 per month, then the variables would be:

N = ???	I/Y = 9	P/Y = 12
PV = 707464.53	PMT = –5000	FV = 0

Now when we solve for N, something strange happens. If you have entered everything correctly, your calculator will probably return an error message. But we can easily determine why, if we look just a little farther at this problem.

Oscar has $707,464.53 in his account. The account is still earning 9% interest compounded monthly. Using the simple interest formula, we can compute the interest for the first month after Oscar retires.

$$I = PRT = 707464.53 \times 0.09 \times \frac{1}{12} \approx 5305.98$$

Oscar's account will earn $5,305.98 interest during the first month after retirement. If Oscar withdraws only $5,000, then the balance will not have decreased, but it will have grown instead. In each succeeding month, Oscar's account would have an even larger balance, and collect even more interest, while his withdrawals are remaining constant. In other words, if Oscar withdraws $5,000 per month (or even $5,305.98 per month) the account would last forever. Oscar could never outlive the account.

Some benefactors provide endowments as a donation for a worthy cause, such as scholarship funds. An **endowment** is a sum of money intended to be invested, and only the interest is used for the designated purpose. Endowments can last forever, as the previous example suggests.

On the other hand, some accounts may last fewer years than expected. Consider the next example.

EXAMPLE 5

Charlene has a $300,000 account. Over the next ten years, she makes withdrawals that bring the balance to zero. If she had withdrawn $2,800 at the end of each month, what interest rate did she earn? What would the interest rate have been if she had withdrawn only $2,200 at the end of each month?

SOLUTION

If Charlene withdraws $2,800 per month, the variables would be:

$N = 10 \times 12 = 120$	$I/Y = ???$	$P/Y = 12$
$PV = 300000$	$PMT = -2800$	$FV = 0$

Solving for the variable I/Y, we get 2.29%. The account would be earning 2.29% interest compounded monthly, if it allowed Charlene to withdraw $2,800 at the end of each month for ten years.

If Charlene withdraws $2,200 per month, the variables would be:

$N = 10 \times 12 = 120$	$I/Y = ???$	$P/Y = 12$
$PV = 300000$	$PMT = -2200$	$FV = 0$

Now when we solve for the variable I/Y, we get a negative result, namely –2.48%. To understand this strange situation, consider the payments. Charlene has made 120 withdrawals of $2,200 each. We can multiply to find the total amount withdrawn from the account.

$$120 \times 2200 = 264000$$

Therefore, Charlene withdrew $264,000 from her $300,000 account, and it is now empty. Where did the rest of the money go? The negative interest rate means that the bank was charging Charlene interest for allowing her to deposit her money in the account, rather than paying her interest. Or more likely, the bank was charging fees for the use of the account that overcame any interest she might have received.

Negative interest rates may seem quite strange, but they are not impossible. At a treasury bill auction on December 9, 2008, investors purchased short-term T-bills at a price that would bring them no yield whatsoever, 0%. In the secondary market, where investors sell T-bills to other investors, there were individuals who reacted to the news by buying T-bills for a price greater than their eventual yield. That meant a negative return on their investment, equivalent to a negative interest rate. In the panic over the economy, these investors thought a –0.01% return was a better opportunity, or at least a safer investment, than putting their money in any other location.

7.5 Loans

Payments on a **loan**, like withdrawals from savings, are made so as to decrease the balance. The value of PMT will be the size of the regular payment, and be negative. The original balance of the loan is PV. The variable FV represents the future balance of the loan. For those problems where the loans are to be fully paid off, the value of FV will be zero. The values of N, I/Y, and P/Y are determined in the same fashion as previous time value of money problems. The computations of this section conform to the Actuarial Method described in section 6.6.

Most loans are ordinary annuities, since the first loan payment is not generally due on the same day that the loan is extended. Leases, however, often require the first payment at lease inception, and are therefore beginning annuities.

The process by which a debt is paid off is called **amortization**. In the Actuarial Method, payments are made on a regular basis and applied to the interest first. These conditions allow the repeated computation of interest to be simplified by use of annuity formulas, or by the financial registers of a financial calculator. Typically, the required payments on a loan will be large enough to cover the interest earned each period, so loan interest is rarely compounded.

Loan interest rates can be stated in many different ways. The most important loan rate is the **Annual Percentage Rate**, or **APR**, which (you may recall from section 6.5) is a measure of the annual rate of interest based on the actual proceeds to the borrower as the principal, the actual finance charge as the interest, and a true value for the time. APRs do take the size and frequency of payments into account, and they are required by U.S. law to be disclosed on most consumer loan contracts. If there are no additional fees, the annual rate used by the calculator, I/Y, will be equivalent to the APR.

EXAMPLE 1

Find the monthly payment for a two-year loan of $5,000 earning 14.7% APR.

SOLUTION

We shall assume that when the two-year term is over, the loan is paid off. Therefore, the future balance, FV, will be zero. The variables are:

$N = 2 \times 12 = 24$	$I/Y = 14.7$	$P/Y = 12$
$PV = 5000$	$PMT = ???$	$FV = 0$

Computing the monthly payment, we obtain $241.72. Your calculator probably reported a negative value for the payment. That is an indication that the payment is being used to decrease the balance, as loan payments should do.

EXAMPLE 2

Jeff is making payments of $188.02 per month on a $6,000 loan earning 8% APR. After one year, he wants to pay off the loan. What is the balance at that time?

SOLUTION

We first identify the variables.

N = 1 × 12 = 12	I/Y = 8	P/Y = 12
PV = 6000	PMT = – 188.02	FV = ???

When we compute the future value, we find the balance at the end of one year will be $4,157.16.

Basically, once all of the important variables are known for the entire term of the loan, those values can be used to obtain the future value at any specified date. Some calculators may have shortcut keys for this computation. However, we have chosen not to concentrate on learning quick keystrokes, but instead on understanding how the various aspects of a financial problem fit together. Therefore, our solution used only the standard keys of a financial calculator.

EXAMPLE 3

Will is making payments of $278.89 per month on a three-year $8,900 loan. What is the APR?

SOLUTION

We first identify the variables.

N = 3 × 12 = 36	I/Y = ???	P/Y = 12
PV = 8900	PMT = – 278.89	FV = 0

Computing the value for I/Y, we find that the loan has an APR of 8.00%.

A **mortgage** is a loan in which the property being purchased is used as security for the loan. Mortgages with fixed interest rates and equal payments are often called **conventional mortgages**. These problems are solved in the same fashion as typical loans.

EXAMPLE 4

Chelsea can afford payments of $750 per month toward the principal and interest on a home mortgage. If interest rates are currently 6.5% and she is willing to take out a thirty-year mortgage, how large a mortgage can she afford?

SOLUTION

We first identify the variables.

N = 30 × 12 = 360	I/Y = 6.5	P/Y = 12
PV = ???	PMT = −750	FV = 0

Computing the value for PV, we obtain $118,658.11. Chelsea can afford a thirty-year mortgage of $118,658.11 toward the purchase of a home.

Balances on loans can decrease rather slowly in the first half of a term. Consider the following example.

EXAMPLE 5

Melody has a thirty-year $134,000 mortgage that earns 6.8% APR interest. When will the balance be $67,000?

SOLUTION

Although the problem is asking for a time, we already know the length of the mortgage, and the size of the mortgage payment is not given. This is a situation which requires that the problem be done in two parts. We must first know all of the important values for the original mortgage transaction before we can find other related values. The original mortgage values are:

N = 30 × 12 = 360	I/Y = 6.8	P/Y = 12
PV = 134000	PMT = ???	FV = 0

Solving for PMT, we find that Melody's payment (for principal and interest) is $873.58 per month. Now we can identify variables to find the time that the balance reaches $67,000. Our selection of variables will examine the time period from the original transaction to the new balance.

N = ???	I/Y = 6.8	P/Y = 12
PV = 134000	PMT = −873.58	FV = −67000

Computing the value of N, we find that 259.1 periods were needed. This value can be divided by 12 periods per year to get approximately 21.6 years.

Since the new balance of $67,000 was exactly half of the original mortgage balance of $134,000, why did the half-way point of the balance not occur in fifteen years? At the beginning of a loan term, the balance is high, so a lot of interest is earned. Toward the end of a term, when the balance is low, very little interest is earned. If equal payments are made throughout the term, then the earlier payments are primarily interest, while the later payments are primarily principal. Therefore, the balance drops slowly at first, and does not drop quickly until the end of the loan. Figure 7.2 depicts a graph of Melody's loan balances over the 30-year period.

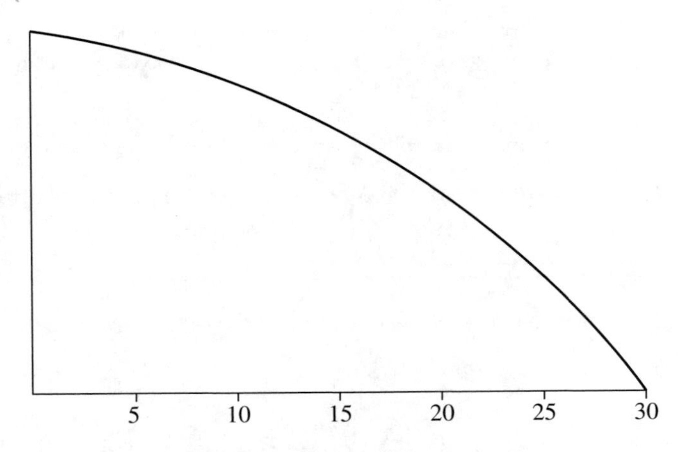

Figure 7.2 Decreasing balance of a 30-year mortgage.

EXAMPLE 6

Vincent bought a $190,000 home, paying 20% down and financing the rest for fifteen years at 8.25%, plus two points and a $300 origination fee. What was the Annual Percentage Rate?

Solution

This problem does have additional fees, so the APR will not be the originally stated 8.25% interest rate. We cannot answer this question until we have full information about the original mortgage, so we first identify the variables to determine the monthly payment. Note that since a 20% down payment was made, Vincent's mortgage was for 80% of the original price of the home.

$N = 15 \times 12 = 180$	$I/Y = 8.25$	$P/Y = 12$
$PV = 0.80 \times 190000 = 152000$	PMT = ???	$FV = 0$

We find the monthly payment to be $1,474.61. Vincent also paid two percentage points of the original mortgage when he obtained this loan. We multiply to find the value of the two points.

$$152000 \times 0.02 = 3040$$

Together with the $300 origination fee, the lender is charging a total of $3,340 in up-front fees. These fees effectively reduce the proceeds of the loan, so we deduct them from the principal to find the APR. The variables for the APR computation are:

$N = 15 \times 12 = 180$	I/Y = ???	$P/Y = 12$
$PV = 152000 - 3340 = 148660$	$PMT = -1474.61$	$FV = 0$

Computing the interest rate, we find an APR of 8.62%.

Any fee which is required for a credit purchase but not for a cash purchase should be reflected in the cost of borrowing. However, since the law does allow a few exceptions for the APR, the APR is not always the same as the cost of borrowing. Origination fees, points, and mortgage insurance are used in computing the APR, but other loan costs (such as credit report fees and title insurance fees) are not.

Name: ______________________________ Date: __________

Exercises 7.1

∗ Find each future value of each lump sum deposit by arithmetically computing a new balance for each period.

	Lump Sum Deposit	Interest Rate	Compounding Frequency	Time
1.	$500	4%	annually	3 years
2.	$6,500	2.25%	quarterly	1 year
3.	$375	3.9%	monthly	3 months
4.	$18,000	2.15%	daily	1 week

Find the future value of each savings account by arithmetically computing a new balance for each period.

	Lump Sum Deposit	Periodic Deposit	Periodic Deposit Timing	Period	Compound Interest Rate	Time
5.	$0	$2,000	end	annually	6%	3 years
6.	$0	$400	beginning	semiannually	8.2%	2 years
7.	$650	$75	beginning	monthly	15.3%	3 months
8.	$3,000	$100	end	quarterly	5.83%	1 year

Find the future balance of each savings account by arithmetically computing a new balance for each period. (Although phrased as a savings account withdrawal, the approach and answers are identical when dealing with loans. Simply change the words Periodic Withdrawal to Loan Payment each time they occur.)

	Original Balance	Periodic Withdrawal	Periodic Withdrawal Timing	Period	Compound Interest Rate	Time
9.	$8,000	$1,500	end	annually	7%	3 years
10.	$950	$300	beginning	semiannually	5.2%	2 years
11.	$650	$75	beginning	monthly	14.3%	3 months
12.	$3,000	$100	end	quarterly	5.94%	1 year

Identify the important variables being described.

13. Original principal of a savings account is $1,200.

14. Future balance of a savings account is $800.

15. The term consists of six years of annual periods.

16. The term consists of ten years of monthly periods.

17. The interest rate is 2.4% compounded monthly.

18. The interest rate is 2.9% compounded semiannually.

19. Original balance on a loan is $2,000.

20. The final balance on a loan is $5,750.

21. At the future date, the loan will be paid off.

22. Periodic deposits of $60 each are made into a savings account.

23. Periodic withdrawals of $80 each are made from a savings account.

24. Periodic payments of $120 each are made on a loan.

** Identify all of the important variables.

25. Alvin places $400 in an account earning 3% interest compounded annually for four years.

26. Cathy deposits a lump sum into an account earning 2.5% compounded monthly. After five years, the account contains $3,057.46.

27. Karen purchases a savings bond which will pay $100 in 18 years. It earns 4% interest compounded semiannually.

28. Timothy invests $5,000 at 17% interest compounded daily for three years.

29. Kelly's account grew from $1,592 to $1,844 in five years, with interest compounded quarterly.

30. Priscilla deposits $200 at the end of each month for seven years into a savings account earning 5% compounded monthly.

31. John deposits $10 at the beginning of each week for 45 weeks into a Christmas Club account earning 2.5% interest compounded weekly.

32. Carl borrows $3,700 at 17% interest, with six years of monthly payments.

33. Terry has made $1,180.89 monthly payments on her $124,000, 11% house mortgage for eight years.

34. Joan's quarterly payments have raised the balance in her account from $1,600 to $2,900 in three years. The account earns 4.35% compounded quarterly.

∗∗∗ 35. Write a paragraph explaining the similarities and differences between simple interest and compound interest.

36. Redo problem #2 using a formula from the appendix. Notice that the answers are different by one cent. Explain the discrepancy. Is one of the answers more correct than the other? If you think so, which is it, and why?

37. If interest is compounded daily during a leap year, should we use 360, 365, or 366 periods per year? Explain your answer.

38. Suppose $1,000 is to be deposited each year for five years into an account paying 9% compounded annually. How much more interest is earned by making the deposits at the beginning of each year, rather than at the end?

Name: ______________________________ Date: __________

Exercises 7.2

✳ Use your financial calculator to find each missing value.

	Lump Sum Deposit	Rate	Compounding Period	Time	Future Balance
1.	$1,200	4%	quarterly	3 yrs.	_____
2.	$80	2%	monthly	18 mos.	_____
3.	_____	3.35%	semiannually	10 yrs.	$30,000
4.	_____	1.75%	daily	20 yrs.	$1,000,000
5.	$100	3%	quarterly	_____	$200
6.	$3,500	3.6%	monthly	_____	$4,500
7.	$1,000	_____	annually	5 yrs.	$1,200
8.	$80,000	_____	daily	270 days	$90,000

✳✳ 9. John opens a passbook savings account with $100. It pays 3.5% interest compounded quarterly. What will be the balance after one year?

10. Springfield Florist plans to replace its delivery vehicle in three years. If they set aside $16,000 today, how much will they have in three years, if interest is 2.5% compounded monthly?

11. Tom wants to have $6,000 in three years. At 4.75% interest compounded monthly, how much does he need to deposit today, in order to obtain his goal?

12. Blue Spruce Motel will need to replace all of its bedding in six years, at a cost of $20,000. How much should they set aside today, at 3.5% compounded daily, in order to meet that expense?

13. Karen deposits a $9,100 inheritance in an account paying 4.2% compounded daily. How long will it take for the balance to grow to the $12,000 down payment she wants to have for her next home?

14. Bob's Grocery wants to offer a $5,000 cash giveaway in order to stimulate sales, so it sets aside $4,257 out of their current profits. If the money is earning 6% compounded quarterly, when would they have the $5,000?

15. Martha wants to have $3,000 six months from now. If she has $2,000 currently, what interest rate would she need, compounded monthly, to obtain her goal?

16. Tracy dreams of investing $1,000 in a high risk scheme, and having $100,000 one year later. What interest rate, compounded monthly, is her dream providing?

Suppose a 24-month CD worth $1,000 earns 5% compounded monthly. If the account is closed early, six months interest is forfeited. Find the amount received in each situation.

17. The account is closed after twelve months.

18. The account is closed after three months.

19. The account is closed after 23 months and 27 days.

20. The CD reaches maturity.

21. Suppose a 36-month $2,000 CD earns 6.2% compounded monthly. If withdrawn early, six months interest is forfeited. How much is received, if the money in the CD is withdrawn after 18 months? What is the size of the penalty?

22. What is the size of the penalty, if the money in a 60-month $2,500 CD earning 4.75% compounded monthly is withdrawn after 59 months? Assume the penalty is the forfeiture of six months interest.

*** 23. How long will it take for a lump sum deposit to double, if 5% interest is compounded quarterly?

24. Which will pay more, 5.25% compounded annually, or 5% compounded daily? Explain your answer.

25. Suppose $60,000 is deposited at 4% interest for seven years. Compare the future balances in the following situations:

    a. simple interest

    b. annual compounding

    c. quarterly compounding

    d. monthly compounding

    e. daily compounding

26. Suppose a savings account pays 4.5% exact interest, compounded daily, from the day of deposit to the day of withdrawal without penalty. A $600 deposit is made on June 2, another $350 is deposited on July 18, and $200 is withdrawn on August 15. What will be the balance on September 1?

27. You have $1,000 to invest today, but you will need it one year from now. Should you put the money in a 36-month CD earning 5% compounded daily, or a regular savings account earning 2% compounded quarterly? The early withdrawal penalty for the CD is forfeiture of six months interest. Explain your choice.

28. You invest $2,000 in a 24-month CD earning 5% compounded daily. If withdrawn early, six months interest will be forfeited. Twenty-two months later, you need the $2,000. Should you withdraw the money from the CD, or sign a $2,000, 60-day simple interest note with 18% interest? Explain.

29. Suppose a person wants to be a millionaire at age 65. If the interest rate is 5% compounded monthly, at what age would a lump sum deposit still be an affordable method for reaching this goal? Find present values for several different ages, and discuss the merits of your choice.

30. Draw a graph showing how a $1,000 investment at 6% interest compounded annually will grow over the next 40 years. What implications does your graph have for people who save?

31. If $400 grew to $488.24 at 4% compound interest in five years, how long is one compounding period?

Name: ______________________ Date: __________

Exercises 7.3

* For each savings plan, use your financial calculator to find the missing values.

	Time	Rate	Original Balance	Future Balance	Deposit	Type
1.	3 years	5%	$0	_____	$600 monthly	ordinary
2.	5 years	3%	$0	_____	$8,000 annually	due
3.	6 years	6.3%	$16,325	_____	$400 quarterly	due
4.	4 years	4.7%	$5,000	_____	$100 monthly	ordinary
5.	6 years	4%	_____	$9,000	$500 semiannually	ordinary
6.	2 years	6%	_____	$11,300	$25 weekly	due
7.	26 weeks	6%	$0	$5,000	_____ weekly	ordinary
8.	3 years	4%	$2,000	$12,000	_____ monthly	due
9.	_____	5.2%	$0	$90,000	$700 per quarter	due
10.	_____	3.6%	$1,750	$18,000	$2,000 per year	ordinary
11.	10 years	_____	$0	$10,000	$50 per month	ordinary
12.	5 years	_____	$3,000	$14,000	$175 per quarter	due

Find the sinking fund payment needed to raise each given amount.

	Amount Needed	Interest Rate	Period	Time
13.	$60,000	7%	quarterly	5 years
14.	$25,000	4%	monthly	3 years
15.	$850,000	4.5%	semiannually	20 years
16.	$350,000	6.7%	annually	25 years

**17. Alvin deposits $100 at the beginning of every month. It earns 6% interest, compounded monthly. How much will the account hold at the end of ten years?

18. Beatrice deposits $75 at the end of each month into an account earning 4.75% compounded monthly. How much will the account hold after eight years?

19. Connie deposits $2,000 at the end of each year into her Individual Retirement Account (IRA). It earns 8% compounded annually. How much will Connie have after twenty years?

20. David wants to retire in forty years. If he puts away $300 per quarter, at the end of each quarter, into an account earning 5.5% compounded quarterly, how much will he have when he retires?

21. Edgar wants to have $600,000 in his retirement account in thirty years. If he begins with a lump sum of $5,000, how much would he need to deposit at the end of each quarter in an account earning 9% compounded quarterly, in order to meet his goal?

22. Frances wants to have a $12,000 down payment for a house in three years. How much would she need to deposit at the beginning of each month in an account earning 4% compounded monthly, in order to meet her goal?

23. Gina wants to have $100,000 in ten years, and she can afford monthly payments of $450. If these are deposited at the beginning of each month, what interest rate would she need in order to meet her goal?

24. Jeanne plans to save $200 per month, depositing it at the end of each month. If she wants to have $25,000 in eight years, what interest rate would she need?

25. Harold is making $300 payments at the end of each month into an account earning 5.34% compounded monthly. In how many years will this account contain $60,000?

26. Chris makes payments of $140 at the beginning of each month into an account earning 3.75% compounded monthly. When will the account balance reach $20,000?

27. Tom wants to put aside $120 at the end of each month into an account earning 6% compounded monthly, and have $30,000 at the end of ten years. How much would Tom's initial balance have to be?

28. Sarah deposits $250 at the end of each quarter into an account earning 5% compounded quarterly. If the account has $30,000 after fifteen years, what was the initial balance?

29. Carroway Construction Company sets up a sinking fund to raise $150,000 in three years to replace equipment. How much do they need to set aside each quarter, if the interest rate is 2.3% compounded quarterly?

30. Dobson Door Manufacturers sets up a sinking fund to raise $75,000 to pay off the maturity value of a three-year note. If the sinking fund earns 3.8% compounded monthly, how much should they set aside each month?

31. The City of Springfield issues $30,000,000 in bonds due in twenty years, and earning 6% interest payable semiannually. The city sets up a sinking fund to save for the repayment of the principal. The balance in the sinking fund will earn 5.2% compounded semiannually. What should be the size of the city's semiannual payments for interest and sinking fund combined?

32. Clay County School District issues $8,000,000 in bonds due in ten years, and earning 5% interest payable quarterly. The district sets up a sinking fund earning 4.5% compounded quarterly to save for the repayment of the principal. What should be the size of the school district's quarterly payments for interest and sinking fund combined?

***33. Yolanda is making quarterly payments into an annuity due earning 3.5% compounded quarterly. The payments are just sufficient to raise $50,000 after ten years. When will her balance reach $25,000?

Name: ______________________________ Date: __________

Exercises 7.4

∗ For each savings plan, use your financial calculator to find the missing values.

	Time	Rate	Original Balance	Future Balance	Withdrawal	Type
1.	5 years	8%	$75,000	_____	$1,200 monthly	ordinary
2.	20 years	9%	$480,000	_____	$45,000 annually	due
3.	15 years	6.2%	$600,000	$0	_____ monthly	ordinary
4.	10 years	4.8%	$80,000	$0	_____ annually	due
5.	12 years	5%	_____	$0	$4,000 monthly	due
6.	9 years	8.5%	_____	$20,000	$3,000 monthly	ordinary
7.	_____	7%	$200,000	$0	$2,000 monthly	ordinary
8.	_____	6.5%	$140,000	$70,000	$1,300 monthly	due
9.	10 years	_____	$250,000	$0	$38,000 annually	ordinary
10.	20 years	_____	$500,000	$100,000	$2,000 monthly	due

For each retirement annuity, use your financial calculator to find the missing value. Assume payments occur at the end of each period.

	Before Retirement			After Retirement	
	Monthly Payment	Time	Interest Rate	Monthly Payment	Time
11.	$100	40 years	8%	_____	20 years
12.	$75	30 years	9%	_____	15 years
13.	$150	20 years	10%	$1,000	_____
14.	$120	25 years	12%	$2,400	_____

**15. Pat retires with $625,000 in her account, growing at a rate equivalent to 8.3% compounded monthly. If she wants her withdrawals to last thirty years, how much can she withdraw at the beginning of each month?

16. Roger's $495,000 retirement account is earning the equivalent of 9.2% compounded monthly. If the account is to last twenty years and he makes withdrawals at the end of each month, how large can each withdrawal be?

17. Nathan is making withdrawals of $3,500 at the end of each month from an account earning 4.7% interest compounded monthly. If the original balance in the account was $250,000, what will the balance be in five years?

18. Leticia withdraws $250 at the beginning of each month from an account earning 6.3% compounded monthly. The original balance in the account was $45,000. What is the balance after ten years?

***19. George invested $50 at the end of each month for forty years into an account earning 6% compounded monthly. If he withdraws $600 at the end of each month after retiring, how long will the withdrawal payments last?

20. Carolyn invested $80 at the beginning of each month for thirty years into an account earning 7% compounded monthly. After retirement, if she wants the withdrawal payments to last twenty years, how much can she withdraw at the beginning of each month?

21. Duncan invested $120 at the end of each month for 35 years into an account earning 7.5% compounded monthly. After retirement, he begins withdrawing $1500 at the end of each month. How long can these withdrawals last? Explain your answer.

22. In exercise #11, you explained how payments can be made so as to decrease the balance, but the balance actually increases. Is it possible for payments to be made so as to increase the balance, but the balance actually decreases? Explain.

23. Alicia earns $25,000 per year. She takes 7.65% of her gross monthly salary and invests it at the end of each month into an account earning 5.25% compounded monthly. After 45 years, she retires, and makes monthly withdrawals at the rate of $25,000 per year. How long can her withdrawals last?

24. Ken has $12,000 in an account earning 8% compounded monthly. He withdraws $50 at the end of each month. Find the balance after six years, and explain why the balance increases.

25. Sally and Sammy were twins. At age 20, they each got identical jobs, with identical year-end bonuses of $2,000. For the first ten years, Sally invested her bonuses at 8% compounded annually, while Sammy took vacations around the world. After ten years, they each had a change in heart. Then, for the next thirty five years, Sammy invested while Sally vacationed (leaving her original investment untouched). Who had the larger retirement fund at age 65? Give the details of the growth of the funds to support your answer.

26. Upon retirement, Tom must choose an option for receiving his retirement benefits. If the choices are $300 per month for life, or $30,000 in a lump sum now, which choice has the most value? Assume Tom's life expectancy is twenty years, and the interest rate is 8% compounded monthly.

Name: ______________________________ Date: __________

Exercises 7.5

∗ For each loan, use your financial calculator to find the missing value.

	Time	Rate	Original Balance	Future Balance	Payment	Type
1.	30 years	8.25%	$135,000	$0	___monthly	ordinary
2.	6 years	9.75%	$14,000	$0	___monthly	ordinary
3.	15 years	9%	$95,600	$0	___monthly	ordinary
4.	4 years	5%	$8,000	$4,000	___ quarterly	due
5.	5 years	11%	_____	$0	$600/month	ordinary
6.	4 years	15%	_____	$1,800	$500/quarter	due
7.	30 years	6%	$70,000	_____	$400/month	ordinary
8.	6 years	8%	$12,000	_____	$250/quarter	ordinary
9.	2 years	18%	$15,000	_____	$3,500/year	due
10.	3 years	21.9%	$4,500	_____	$120/month	due
11.	_____	12%	$6,800	$0	$80/month	ordinary
12.	_____	8.25%	$17,500	$10,000	$180/month	due
13.	30 years	____	$85,000	$0	$600/month	ordinary
14.	5 years	____	$6,500	$3,000	$250/quarter	due

∗∗ Find the intermediate balance on each loan, given that the term is sufficient to pay off the loan.

	Principal	Interest Rate	Term	Payment Period	Balance After . . .
15.	$1,500	18%	3 years	monthly	1 year
16.	$18,500	11.5%	5 years	monthly	6 months
17.	$72,900	7.75%	30 years	monthly	15 years
18.	$750,000	7.25%	10 years	annually	5 years

19. Jerry signs a $16,000 loan for the purchase of a new car. The term is for 48 months, at an interest rate of 4.8%. What is Jerry's monthly payment?

20. Karl and Karen take out a $108,000 mortgage to purchase their new home. The interest rate is 7.12%, and the term is thirty years. What is the monthly payment for principal and interest?

21. Alice is paying $75 at the end of each month on an outstanding debt of $2,500. If 7% interest is earned on the debt, what is her balance after one year?

22. Chad has been paying $900 per month on a $97,500 home mortgage earning 8.15%. Seven years later, he sells his home. What is the mortgage balance?

23. Quincy can afford $950 per month for principal and interest for a house payment. If interest rates are 7.5% for thirty years, how large a mortgage can Quincy afford?

24. Pete is willing to spend $340 per month on a car loan. If four-year rates are 9% and no down payment is needed, what is the maximum price Pete can spend on a car?

25. Ingrid's car loan stipulates payments of $299 per month for 60 months. The car was originally priced at $13,500. What is the Annual Percentage Rate?

26. Loren agreed to make $750 per quarter payments for 6 years, to pay off a debt of $11,000. What annual percentage rate is Loren paying?

27. Victoria borrowed $4,000 at 8.5% interest, and is paying back $40 each month. How long will it take Victoria to pay off the balance?

28. Tim has a $2,500 balance on his credit card which earns 18.9% interest. If he makes the minimum payment of $50 per month, how long will it take to pay off the balance?

∗∗∗ 29. Kenneth signed a fifteen-year 6.5% conventional mortgage for $80,000. If he makes monthly payments, what will be the balance after five years?

30. Larry signed a thirty-year 7.75% conventional mortgage for $95,000. If he makes monthly payments, what will be the balance after five years?

31. Mary signed a sixty-month $16,000 loan at 8.5% for the purchase of a car. What will be the balance after one year?

32. Nancy's monthly payments on an ordinary annuity earning 6% compounded monthly are just sufficient to obtain a $100,000 balance in fifteen years. What will be the balance after five years?

33. Bill can afford payments of $1150 per month for a house. He estimates taxes and insurance to be $120 of his monthly payment, and he has enough for a 20% down payment. If the interest rate is 8.75% for a thirty-year mortgage, what is the highest price he could pay for a house?

34. Draw a graph showing how the balance for a $100,000 thirty-year mortgage at 9% APR will decrease over its lifetime.

35. Describe the benefits and disadvantages of an 11% thirty-year mortgage versus a 10% 15-year mortgage.

Name: ______________________________ Date: __________

Chapter 7 Review

Summary of Important Concepts

- ▲ Compound Interest
- ▲ Annuity, Ordinary Annuity, Beginning Annuity
- ▲ Increasing or Decreasing Payments
- ▲ Lump Sum Deposits
- ▲ Savings Plans, Savings Withdrawals
- ▲ Bonds and Sinking Funds
- ▲ Loans

Exercises

1. Find the balance after four years when $400 is deposited into a savings account paying 3.35% interest compounded quarterly.

2. Find the lump sum deposit which will give $6,000 in 5 years in an account paying 4.7% compounded annually.

3. Find the number of years needed for a $900 deposit to grow to $1,650 when interest is 4.25% compounded daily.

4. Find the rate, compounded semiannually, which causes $4,000 to grow to $5,000 in 3 years.

5. Find the future value of a saving plan where $50 is deposited at the end of each month for seven years, if interest is 4.1% compounded monthly.

6. Find the future value of a saving plan where $7,200 is deposited at the beginning of each quarter for ten years, if interest is 5% compounded quarterly.

7. Find the time needed to raise $50,000 with $650 per quarter payments earning 6% interest compounded quarterly.

8. Seven years of $130 payments at the end of each month into an account earning 6% compounded monthly brought Dave's balance to $19,000. What was the original balance?

9. Find the payment needed at the end of each quarter into a sinking fund account paying 5.5% compounded quarterly, in order to raise $3,200,000 in twelve years.

10. A business issues $800,000 in bonds which mature in nine years and earn 7% interest payable quarterly. They also set up a sinking fund earning 5.2% compounded quarterly in order to pay off the bonds when they mature. If payments are made at the end of each quarter, what is the size of the total quarterly payment for interest and sinking fund combined?

11. Find the payment that can be withdrawn at the end of each month for the next 10 years from a $25,000 savings account earning 4.7% interest compounded monthly.

12. How long will a $300,000 account earning 5.6% interest compounded monthly last if $2,400 is withdrawn at the beginning of each month?

13. Find the monthly payment on a $133,500 loan for fifteen years with 9.5% APR interest.

14. Find the interest rate which produces $427 per month payments on a $12,000 three-year loan.

8 Financial Issues

8.1 Total Interest

In most time value of money problems, the interest earned will be different for each period. The **total interest** will be the sum of all of the different interest payments, but doing this computation by addition is much more difficult than necessary. At most three computations are all that are necessary.

For every TVM problem, the total interest will be the difference between the total payments and the balance change, ignoring signs at each step. The **total payments** can be obtained by a simple multiplication, but expressing the answer as a positive number.

$$\text{Total Payment} = N \times PMT$$

The **balance change** is a difference between the original and final balances, but expressing the answer as a positive number.

$$\text{Balance Change} = FV - PV$$

The total interest is the difference between these two quantities, but expressing the answer as a positive number.

$$\text{Total Interest} = \text{Balance Change} - \text{Total Payment}$$

Once again, when using this approach, use only positive numbers for every value. The following examples will make this clear.

EXAMPLE 1

Gina deposited $400 into an account earning 1.75% compounded quarterly. How much interest will the account earn during the first three years?

SOLUTION

We first identify the variables.

$N = 3 \times 4 = 12$	$I/Y = 1.75$	$P/Y = 4$
$PV = 400$	$PMT = 0$	$FV = ???$

Although the question does not ask for the final balance, in order to find the total interest, we first need to find the final balance. Therefore, we compute FV, and obtain $421.51. Then we find the balance change.

$$\text{Balance Change} = 421.51 - 400.00 = 21.51$$

Since a lump sum deposit has no payments, the total interest is equal to the balance change. Therefore, Gina's account earned $21.51 interest during the first three years.

EXAMPLE 2

For forty years, Joan set aside \$120 at the beginning of each month into an account earning 3.2% compounded monthly. Her original balance was \$12,000. Find the total interest earned by the account.

SOLUTION

We first identify the variables.

N = 40 × 12 = 480	I/Y = 3.2	P/Y = 12
PV = 12000	PMT = 120	FV = ???

This is a beginning annuity, and we find the future value is \$159,970.36. Using this result, we can subtract to find the balance change.

$$\text{Balance Change} = 159970.36 - 12000.00 = 147970.36$$

The total payments can be found by multiplying.

$$\text{Total Payment} = 480 \times 120.00 = 57600.00$$

We then subtract these two results to get the interest earned.

$$\text{Total Interest} = 147970.36 - 57600.00 = 90370.36$$

Therefore, Joan's account earned \$90,370.36 interest during the forty years.

In the previous example, you should observe just how much of the final balance in Joan's account was due to interest, and how much was due to her own efforts. The power of compounding is very evident in this example, and it is how retirement accounts are typically funded.

EXAMPLE 3

Gary's retirement account has a balance of \$850,000, and is earning 6.2% interest, compounded monthly. Over the next twenty years, he plans to withdraw \$4,500 at the end of each month. How much interest will be earned during those twenty years?

SOLUTION

We first identify the variables.

N = 20 × 12 = 240	I/Y = 6.2	P/Y = 12
PV = 850000	PMT = –4500	FV = ???

This is an ordinary annuity, and we find the future value is \$798,742.27. Using this result, we can subtract to find the balance change, although in the other order so as to obtain a positive number.

$$\text{Balance Change} = 850000.00 - 798742.27 = 51257.73$$

The total payments can be found by multiplying, but using a positive value for PMT.

$$\text{Total Payment} = 240 \times 4500.00 = 1080000.00$$

We then subtract these two results, in the order that would produce a positive answer.

$$\text{Total Interest} = 1080000.00 - 51257.73 = 1028742.27$$

Gary's retirement account earned $1,028,742.27 interest during those twenty years.

EXAMPLE 4

John purchased a new car with a five-year loan of $16,000 earning 7% APR, and requiring monthly payments. Find the total finance charge, and the amount of the interest paid during the first year.

SOLUTION

We first identify the variables associated with the original loan.

$N = 5 \times 12 = 60$	$I/Y = 7$	$P/Y = 12$
$PV = 16000$	$PMT = ???$	$FV = 0$

We then compute the monthly payment to be $316.82. Sixty payments were made over the five-year period, so the total payments was:

$$\text{Total Payment} = 60 \times 316.82 = 19009.20$$

Since FV was zero, the balance change is equal to the original loan balance, $16,000. We can subtract this value from the $19,009.20 total payments to find the finance charge.

$$\text{Total Interest} = 19009.20 - 16000.00 = 3009.20$$

The total finance charge on John's car loan was $3009.20. To determine the interest during the first year, we need to find the balance after one year.

$N = 1 \times 12 = 12$	$I/Y = 7$	$P/Y = 12$
$PV = 16000$	$PMT = -316.82$	$FV = ???$

Computing the future value, we find the balance after one year is $13,230.42. Since the original balance was $16,000, we can subtract to find the balance change.

$$\text{Balance Change} = 16000.00 - 13230.42 = 2769.58$$

The total of the first 12 payments can be found by multiplying.

$$\text{Total Payment} = 12 \times 316.82 = 3801.84$$

By subtracting the balance change from the total payments, we can obtain the total interest.

$$\text{Total Interest} = 3801.84 - 2769.58 = 1032.26$$

Therefore, John paid $1,032.26 interest on his loan during the first year.

8.2 Effective Rates and the APR

In section 6.5, we learned how the Annual Percentage Rate (APR), defined by the federal government, is used to help standardize the reporting of loan interest rates. In particular, three specific loan practices often caused an APR to be different than a nominal rate. These three practices were the use of ordinary interest, the use of discount interest, and the use of additional fees. One other practice can also significantly affect the reporting of an effective rate, namely a lack of clarity in the value of the original loan. As before, if none of these practices are present in the loan, then the nominal rate will be equal to the APR.

At the time we first introduced the APR, we were working only with simple interest. Now we shall revisit the issue in light of compound interest and annuities.

EXAMPLE 1

Pamela borrows $16,500 for 5 years at 6% interest. The loan has a $100 transaction fee, and requires monthly payments. What is the effective rate (APR) of the loan?

SOLUTION

Before we can answer the question about the APR, we need to know the monthly payment on the loan. Here are the variables.

N = 5 × 12 = 60	I/Y = 6	P/Y = 12
PV = 16500	PMT = ???	FV = 0

Computing PMT, we find Pamela will be making payments of $318.99 per month. But the $100 transaction fee affects the actual proceeds Pamela received from this transaction. In other words, she did not have full use of the original $16,500, since she had to pay $100 to receive the loan. So we recompute the interest rate based on her actual proceeds.

N = 5 × 12 = 60	I/Y = ???	P/Y = 12
PV = 16500 – 100 = 16400	PMT = –318.99	FV = 0

Computing I/Y, we obtain a rate of approximately 6.25%. Therefore, the effective rate (APR) of this loan is 6.25%.

Up-front transaction fees are quite common in some loan transactions. For example, when a home mortgage is obtained, a customer may decide to pay points in order to reduce the interest rate on the loan. One point is one percent of the original loan balance. These points reduce the actual proceeds that the loan provides, in the same fashion that the transaction fee reduced the proceeds of the loan in the previous example.

When discount interest is combined with periodic payments, **precomputed interest** results. Consider the following example.

EXAMPLE 2

Tyler borrows $9,000 for six months at 8% discount interest. Equal monthly payments are required. What is the effective rate (APR) of this loan?

SOLUTION

When discount interest is used, the interest is precomputed, and then subtracted from the principal to obtain the proceeds.

$$I = PRT = 9000 \times 0.08 \times \frac{6}{12} = 360$$

$$\text{Proceeds} = 9000 \times 360 = 8460$$

Therefore, Tyler receives $8,640 when the transaction is made, and has promised to pay back $9,000. The amount to be paid back will be divided into six equal monthly payments.

$$\text{Monthly payment} = \frac{9000}{6} = 1500$$

Now, we can compute the APR. The financial calculator is required because of the presence of the series of payments.

N = 6	I/Y = ???	P/Y = 12
PV = 8640	PMT = −1500	FV = 0

Computing I/Y, we obtain 14.15%. Tyler's 8% discount interest loan has an effective rate of 14.15%.

As can be seen in the previous example, discount interest has a serious effect on the actual interest rate a borrower pays.

The last two examples demonstrate how the effective rate really depends upon the value of the transaction, and if that value is up for negotiation, the APR may not accurately portray the effective rate.

EXAMPLE 3

Keith decides to purchase a car advertised at $16,000. The dealer offers him the choice of $1,000 cash back or 2.9% interest. He makes a down payment of $2,000, and agrees to make 48 monthly payments. If Keith takes the 2.9% interest rate, what is his effective rate?

SOLUTION

If Keith had made a cash purchase, he would undoubtedly have taken the $1,000 cash back. Therefore, the true value of the car is not $16,000, but $15,000. However, by opting for the 2.9% interest rate, Keith will not receive the $1,000 discount, and the computations for his loan will be based on a $16,000 principal, less his $2,000 down payment. To find Keith's monthly payment, we use the following variables.

N = 4 × 12 = 48	I/Y = 2.9	P/Y = 12
PV = 16000 − 2000 = 14000	PMT = ???	FV = 0

Keith's monthly payment will be $309.26. Now, to find the true cost of borrowing, we refigure the interest rate based on a $15,000 car (the cash price), less the $2,000 down payment.

N = 4 × 12 = 48	I/Y = ???	P/Y = 12
PV = 15000 – 2000 = 13000	PMT = –309.26	FV = 0

We obtain a rate of 6.66% per year. If Keith takes the 2.9% APR, his effective rate of borrowing is actually 6.66% per year.

The two options available to Keith actually value the car in different ways, and when interest is required, it is computed on the agreed-upon value. Legally, the APR of the proposed credit transaction is 2.9%. But if Keith can obtain a loan from another source with an APR of less than 6.66%, he would be better off to take the $1,000 cash back from the dealer and borrow the money from the other institution. Otherwise, the dealer's offer of a 2.9% APR is better. When the cash back option is taken into account, the 2.9% APR is really equivalent to a cost of borrowing of 6.66% APR from any other institution.

In the previous example, we see how the bargaining process for the car can affect the actual value borrowed. And once the value is uncertain, the effective rate to the borrower may not be the same as the effective rate for the lender.

Music stores often offer rent-to-own plans for musical instruments, especially each September when another group of students takes beginning band. Parents are reluctant to purchase an instrument in case their child decides to quit after a few months. But with a rent-to-own plan, the payments are not being wasted. If the student quits and the instrument is returned, the payments were the rental fee. If the student continues, the payments will eventually be sufficient to own the instrument. The rent-to-own contract will specify these two options. The following example, however, includes a third option, and is another instance of a choice affecting the value borrowed, and thus the cost of borrowing for the consumer. This example contains the details of an actual transaction, which we have left intact in order that you might learn how to deal with some of the other wrinkles which can occur in loan contracts.

EXAMPLE 4

Steve purchased a $585 trumpet, plus 6.5% sales tax, with $25 down, payments of $25 per month at 15% APR, and a smaller final payment. The third option in the rent-to-own contract was a 25% discount on the unpaid balance, if the instrument was paid in full within ninety days of the date of the contract. What is the borrower's effective rate in the payment plan that is being offered?

Solution

The effective rate will depend on the true value placed on the instrument, and the details of the loan contract. We begin with the loan contract, for which neither the term nor the size of the final payment are given. The amount financed will be the cost of the trumpet plus sales tax, less the down payment. Here is the computation.

$$585 \times 1.065 - 25.00 = 623.03 - 25.00 = 598.03$$

Therefore, we use the following variables to solve for the number of payments.

N = ???	I/Y = 15	P/Y = 12
PV = 598.03	PMT = –25.00	FV = 0

Computing the value of N, we obtain 28.60 monthly periods. Therefore, the music store established a 29-month term for the contract. Of course, the extra part of a month would have caused Steve to overpay, but that is rectified by a smaller last payment. One way to compute that last payment is to assume all 29 payments are $25 each, and find the size of the overpayment. (If you choose to compute the balance after 28 payments, don't forget to add another month's worth of interest.)

N = 29	I/Y = 15	P/Y = 12
PV = 598.03	PMT = –25.00	FV = ???

We compute the value of FV to be 9.99, but note that the sign is positive, opposite what you usually obtain when computing FV. In other words, 29 monthly payments will cause an overpayment (not a balance) of $9.99. Subtracting this from the last $25 payment, we find that the loan contract should contain 28 monthly payments of $25 and a final payment of $15.01.

Now let us consider the actual value of the trumpet. Since a 25% discount on the unpaid balance was available, the true value of the loan contract was not $598.03, but 75% of that number, or $448.52. (The true value for the trumpet, with tax, would be $25 larger, or $473.52, but our concerns are actually with the loan contract and its interest rate.) In other words, if Steve paid off the loan contract immediately, he could do so with $448.52 cash, not $598.03.

So what is the effective rate extended by this payment plan, if the loan contract is really valued at $448.52? Here are the variables.

N = 29	I/Y = ???	P/Y = 12
PV = 448.52	PMT = –25.00	FV = + 9.99

Computing the interest rate, we obtain a whopping 41.71%. The 25% discount option changed the situation substantially. If Steve is certain that his child will continue in band, it is certainly worthwhile for him to take advantage of the 25% discount offer. In fact, he should pay off this contract even if he has to borrow on a 24.9% APR credit card.

We have given two examples where the APR quoted by the lender is not the same as the effective rate experienced by the borrower. In other words, it is possible for conditions in the loan to exist that are not required to be included in the APR, because of the government definition of that rate. In general, the APR does a very effective job of allowing consumers to know what the true cost of credit is, but there are some loopholes in the law. When the value of the item being purchased is not clear, there is a strong possibility that the cost of credit to the consumer may be understated.

8.3 Rates of Return and APY

In the previous chapter, we learned how to use the financial calculator to find any of the basic numerical values associated with the growth in value of both lump sum deposits and of savings plans. Another quantity that is important in the study of investments is the rate of return.

A **rate of return** on an investment is a ratio of the interest earned to the amount invested. This rate is a measure of growth of an investment, and is usually expressed as a percentage. Rates of returns are sometimes given as annual rates, and sometimes as overall rates. That is, numerical values used for the interest earned and the investment made are either for one year's worth of time, or for the length of time of the entire investment.

An **overall rate of return** is the rate of return for the investment over its entire lifetime. Consider the following example.

EXAMPLE 1

Terry's investment grew from $9,000 to $32,500 after fifteen years. What was his overall rate of return?

SOLUTION

First, we subtract to find the growth in Terry's investment.

$$32500 - 9000 = 23500$$

The overall rate of return is the ratio of the growth to the original investment. Therefore,

$$\frac{23500}{9000} \approx 2.6111 = 261.11\%$$

The overall rate of return was about 261%. But remember, it took fifteen years to get it. This is not an annual rate.

EXAMPLE 2

Harvey deposits $3,560 into an account earning 3.4% compounded monthly. What will be the overall rate of return after five years?

SOLUTION

We first identify the variables.

$N = 5 \times 12 = 60$	$I/Y = 3.4$	$P/Y = 12$
$PV = 3560$	$PMT = 0$	$FV = ???$

We need to compute the future value first, and we find its value to be $4,218.67. Since there were no payments, the total interest is the balance change.

$$4218.67 - 3560.00 = 658.67$$

The overall rate of return is the ratio of the total interest to the total deposit. Therefore,

$$\frac{658.67}{3560.00} \approx 0.1850 = 18.50\%$$

Harvey's account provided an overall rate of return of 18.50% over five years. (Once again, this is not a rate per year, but an overall rate.)

Actually, the overall rate of return for a lump sum deposit does not depend on the amount invested, but only on the interest rate being offered. Therefore, we did not need to know the size of Harvey's deposit in the previous example. Any size deposit would give the same result. With this in mind, we can choose deposit amounts which make our computations easier. Using $100 instead of Harvey's original amount, we would have obtained different variables.

N = 5 × 12 = 60	I/Y = 3.4	P/Y = 12
PV = 100	PMT = 0	FV = ???

Computing the future value, we obtain \$118.50, rounded to the nearest cent. Of that amount, \$100 was principal, so \$18.50 was interest. Since our investment (the base of the percent we are seeking) was \$100, the overall rate of return is the same as the dollar amount of the interest, namely 18.50%.

We can also compute an overall rate of return for a savings plan or annuity.

EXAMPLE 3

Nina is depositing \$125 at the end of each month into an account paying 4.8% compounded monthly. After ten years, what will be the overall rate of return?

SOLUTION

We first identify the variables.

N = 10 × 12 = 120	I/Y = 4.8	P/Y = 12
PV = 0	PMT = 125	FV = ???

Computing the future value, we find that the account will contain \$19,203.99 at the end of ten years. Since 120 payments of \$125 each were made, we can subtract the total payments from the balance change to obtain the total interest earned.

$$120 \times 125 = 15000$$

$$19203.99 - 15000.00 = 4203.99$$

We then divide the interest by the principal (total payments) to obtain the overall rate of return.

$$\frac{4203.99}{15000} \approx 0.2803 = 28.03\%$$

The overall rate of return will be 28.03%.

Unlike rates of return for lump sum deposits, we cannot easily change the amount invested when computing the overall rate of return of an annuity or savings plan. The payments complicate the situation too much. It is easier to find rates of return of annuities by using the given numbers, rather than by changing numbers.

An **annual rate of return** is the rate of return for a one-year investment. It is also the interest rate, compounded annually, which would be necessary to achieve the same total rate of return. This value is also known as the **effective yield**. Furthermore, in 1991, with passage of the Truth in Savings Act, Congress introduced the term **Annual Percentage Yield**, or **APY**, for this quantity in connection with savings accounts. Just as it was with the overall rate of return, the annual rate of return of a lump sum deposit does not depend on the actual amount invested. Annual rates for lump sum deposits are much easier to compute using an arbitrary investment amount of \$100. The following example illustrates the computation.

EXAMPLE 4

Clay County Bank has a savings account plan which pays 3.25% compounded daily. What is the Annual Percentage Yield for such an account?

SOLUTION

We first identify some variables, arbitrarily choosing $100 for our investment because of the simplicity which will result, and one year because we desire an annual yield.

$N = 1 \times 365 = 365$	I/Y = 3.25	P/Y = 365
PV = 100	PMT = 0	FV = ???

Computing the future value, we find $103.30. Subtracting the original balance of $100, we find the interest earned is $3.30, and the APY is 3.30%.

The previous example shows that 3.25% interest compounded daily is the same as 3.30% compounded annually. We referred to the 3.30% as the effective yield or APY. The original 3.25% rate is called the **nominal rate**, or stated rate of the account.

Some financial calculators have shortcut keys to change nominal rates to Annual Percentage Yields. We have not discussed Annual Percentage Yields in this fashion for two reasons. First, we feel that our method will allow you to get a better conceptual handle on just what the Annual Percentage Yield is measuring. Second, our method is not that long, so we feel that the shortcut keys do not save as much time as the extra instruction needed to use them. If you have need of this computation repeatedly in your business, you may find that the shortcut keys will improve your efficiency. If so, you should read your calculator's manual.

Sometimes, we wish to do the above question in reverse. That is, if we are given a desired annual percentage yield, we want to find the nominal rate. The next example considers such a situation.

EXAMPLE 5

Big City Bank wants to set up an account which it can advertise as having an Annual Percentage Yield of 3.75%. If interest is compounded quarterly, what would the nominal interest rate have to be?

SOLUTION

Since we want a 3.75% APY, a $100 account would need to earn $3.75 interest over the course of one year, for a future value of $103.75. We identify the following variables.

$N = 1 \times 4 = 4$	I/Y = ???	P/Y = 4
PV = 100	PMT = 0	FV = −103.75

Computing I/Y, we find the nominal rate needs to be about 3.70% per year, compounded quarterly.

We can also find the Annual Percentage Yield of investments when the rate of interest is not given. Let us reconsider the first example from this section.

EXAMPLE 6

Terry's investment grew from $9,000 to $32,500 after fifteen years. What was his annual rate of return?

SOLUTION

We use the following values for our variables.

$N = 15 \times 1 = 15$	$I/Y = ???$	$P/Y = 1$
$PV = 9000$	$PMT = 0$	$FV = -32500$

Computing the interest rate, we obtain 8.94% per year. This is the average annual rate which Terry received over the fifteen-year period of his investment.

An annual rate of return can also be computed for annuities, by computing an overall rate of return for a one-year period. However, the annual rate of return would be different for each year, because of the way the amount previously invested changes over time. So this quantity is not typically used for annuities.

An **internal rate of return**, or **IRR**, is used for the true annual rate of earnings of an investment, where the time each payment was made is considered. For an annuity with a fixed interest rate, the IRR is the effective annual yield for the nominal rate of the account. If the rate is variable, the problem of finding the IRR is much more complex. Advanced financial calculators can handle the IRR computation, but it is beyond the scope of this course.

8.4 Present Worth

Often, we think of the value of an investment as the amount of the proceeds that would be obtained if that investment were cashed in. Interestingly, it turns out that some investments are worth more than their cash value, and others less. A prime reason for this situation is the variety of interest rates in the marketplace. Investments providing high interest rates are more valuable than investments with low rates of return. The present worth of an investment takes this future earning power of the investment into account.

The **present worth** of an investment is the lump sum that would need to be placed into an alternative investment today at the prevailing rate of interest in order to obtain the same future result as the investment under consideration. When considering the present worth of a lump sum deposit, the future result is the future value of the investment under consideration. When considering the present worth of an annuity, the future result is the same stream of payments as the investment under consideration. The present worth of an investment is often called the **present value of an investment**, but that may or may not be the same value as the variable PV.

When comparing an investment with a hypothetical alternative investment, both will have rates and times, but the rates and times may not be equal. However, by definition the future results will be equal.

In present worth problems, the simplest examples will already provide the information about the future result. In such cases, a comparison is not needed, and a single computation that finds PV will be sufficient.

EXAMPLE 1

Sally signed a contract for a car loan, promising to pay $325.53 per month for 36 months. She is paying 8.5% APR. What is the present value of her loan contract?

SOLUTION

Since only one rate is provided, we assume that the loan rate is the same as the prevailing rate. The future outcome is the series of payments, which are known. So we want to find the present value of an account that would produce those payments. The variables are:

N = 36	I/Y = 8.5	P/Y = 12
PV = ???	PMT = –325.53	FV = 0

Loans are typically ordinary annuities. We find the present value to be $10,312.18. If Sally's lender sells the loan contract to another lender, $10,312.18 is the value of that sale. (Since the prevailing rate matched her loan rate, $10,312.18 would also have been the original balance on her car loan.)

The present value of a loan contract actually depends on the prevailing rate, not the rate being paid by the borrower. When both are provided, the loan contract rate is irrelevant (unless it is needed to determine the details of the loan).

EXAMPLE 2

Tom took out a $14,300 car loan at 2.9% APR with 48 monthly payments. Find the present value of the loan contract if the prevailing rate is 6.75%.

SOLUTION

Before we find the present value of the loan contract, we need to know the amount of the monthly payment. The variables are:

N = 48	I/Y = 2.9	P/Y = 12
PV = 14300	PMT = ???	FV = 0

The monthly payment on the loan is $315.89. Using this value and the 6.75% prevailing rate, we can determine the present value of the loan contract.

N = 48	I/Y = 6.75	P/Y = 12
PV = ???	PMT = –315.89	FV = 0

The present value is found to be $13,255.74. Even though Tom borrowed $14,300 for his car, the loan contract will bring only $13,255.74 if sold by the dealer to another party. (And quite likely, the dealer would have been willing to accept $13,255.74 cash for the car as well.)

EXAMPLE 3

Margaret's tenant has signed a one-year rental contract for an apartment. The rent is $595 per month, due at the beginning of each month. The prevailing rate of interest (available in the marketplace, not part of the contract) is 4% compounded monthly. What is the present value of the rental contract?

SOLUTION

In this case, Margaret's investment is in the rental property, and the rental contract is producing a known series of payments. Since the future outcome is known, we need only consider the alternative investment that would produce this series of payments. In other words, Margaret could withdraw these payments from the alternative investment account. The variables will be:

$N = 1 \times 12 = 12$	$I/Y = 4$	$P/Y = 12$
$PV = ???$	$PMT = -595$	$FV = 0$

Since the payments were made at the beginning of each month, this is a beginning annuity. We compute the present value, and find it to be $7,010.97. This is the present value of the one-year rental contract.

The present value of the rental contract is the value of the contract if it were to be sold in the marketplace. If Margaret's tenants wanted to prepay their rent for the year, the present value of $7,010.97 would also be the fair price. Of course, this is less than the $7,140 that twelve $595 monthly payments would produce, but the present value could be invested at 4% per year to produce that same $7,140. In other words, Margaret would be earning the same future value from her investment, and the tenants would receive a discount for early payment of their rent.

EXAMPLE 4

Gary won a million dollars in the lottery. He can choose to receive the million dollars spread out over 20 years, with one payment at the end of each year. Or he can take a lump sum payment now, equal to the present value of the $1,000,000 series of payments. If interest rates are currently 6% compounded annually, how much would he receive if he took the lump sum now?

SOLUTION

Since the question is seeking a present value, we should think of the account in a way that makes the present value unknown. To do this, think of the account that the lottery officials have set aside that makes the payments. We want to know how much is in that account now. (If you take Gary's point of view, his account has nothing now, until he receives some payments, so that is not the point of view we want.) The account will need to provide 20 payments that total $1,000,000, so each annual payment will be $50,000. The variables are:

$N = 20 \times 1 = 20$	$I/Y = 6$	$P/Y = 1$
$PV = ???$	$PMT = \dfrac{-1000000}{20} = -50000$	$FV = 0$

We find the present value of the account is $573,496.06. That amount is sufficient to produce payments of $50,000 per year for 20 years (for a total of one million dollars), if interest is 6% compounded annually. Gary can receive the payments from that account, or he can take over the entire account now.

EXAMPLE 5

Don signs a contract with Wrightwood Mortgage for a 30-year $86,000 mortgage earning 7% APR interest and requiring monthly payments. Two years later when interest rates are 10% compounded monthly, the mortgage is sold to the Baylor Bank. What was the present value of the mortgage contract at the time it was sold?

SOLUTION

The original contract is an investment by Wrightwood Mortgage for a series of payments over 30 years. Since we don't know the size of the payment, and the payments are the future result which must be used in the computation of present value, we first need to find the monthly payment of the mortgage. The variables are:

$N = 30 \times 12 = 360$	$I/Y = 7$	$P/Y = 12$
$PV = 86000$	$PMT = ???$	$FV = 0$

Computing the value of the payment, we find it to be $572.16 per month. Now we turn our attention to the alternative investment, a lump sum deposit that would produce the same series of payments for the remaining 28 years. The variables are:

$N = 28 \times 12 = 336$	$I/Y = 10$	$P/Y = 12$
$PV = ???$	$PMT = -572.16$	$FV = 0$

Computing the present value, we obtain $64,435.31. When Don's mortgage was sold by Wrightwood Mortgage to Baylor Bank, the value of the mortgage contract (and the fairest price for the sale) was $64,435.31.

We need to point out that the present value (and sale price) of the mortgage in the previous example, $64,435.31, was not the same as Don's balance on that mortgage. To find his balance after two years, we would have used his interest rate of 7%, not the prevailing rate of 10%. The variables are:

$N = 2 \times 12 = 24$	$I/Y = 7$	$P/Y = 12$
$PV = 86000$	$PMT = -572.16$	$FV = ???$

Computing the future value, we find Don's balance after two years was $84,189.66.

Fluctuations in interest rates are the prime reason for changes in the market value of bonds. Basically, a **bond** is a loan from the buyer (investor) to the bond issuer. Most bonds come in $1,000 amounts. Interest-bearing bonds are sold to the investor for $1,000, and will earn interest over a certain time period. **Zero coupon bonds** are sold to the investor at a discount (below $1,000), and will pay the investor $1,000 at maturity.

EXAMPLE 6

Terry purchases a $1,000 five-year zero coupon bond for $725. Before the end of the day, market jitters cause interest rates to jump half a percentage point. Find the present worth of Terry's bond at the end of the day.

SOLUTION

In this problem, we do know the future result of Terry's investment, but we don't know the prevailing rate, so we cannot simply work back from the future value to the present worth. We must first determine the original growth rate of Terry's investment in order to find the prevailing rate. Note that we are looking for an annual rate. The variables for Terry's bond are:

$N = 5 \times 1 = 5$	$I/Y = ???$	$P/Y = 1$
$PV = 725$	$PMT = 0$	$FV = -1000$

Computing the annual rate of return, we obtain 6.64%. The half-point increase in interest rates would give a prevailing rate of 7.14% at the end of the day. With this amount, we can compute a new present value.

$N = 5 \times 1 = 5$	$I/Y = 7.14$	$P/Y = 1$
$PV = ???$	$PMT = 0$	$FV = -1000$

The present value is now $708.24. Terry's bond has dropped in value from its original $725.

The previous example illustrates a general relationship between interest rates and bond values. When interest rates rise, bond values will drop. When rates drop, bond values will rise.

EXAMPLE 7

Tom owns a business currently appraised at $427,000, and it is growing at an annual rate of 24%. Tom wants to retire in five years and sell his business then, but he will accept an offer today if, by investing the offer at the prevailing rate of 5.5% compounded quarterly, he can obtain the same sized retirement account. What amount would Tom accept for his business?

SOLUTION

The amount Tom would accept is the present worth of the business. First, we need to find the future value of the business. Identifying variables, we find:

$N = 5 \times 1 = 5$	$I/Y = 24$	$P/Y = 1$
$PV = 427000$	$PMT = 0$	$FV = ???$

The future value of the business is $1,251,803.90. Now, we need to find the present value of the alternative investment at the prevailing rate which has this same future value. Here are the variables for the alternative investment.

N = 5 × 4 = 20	I/Y = 5.5	P/Y = 4
PV = ???	PMT = 0	FV = –1251803.90

The present value of the necessary investment would be $952,618.38. Therefore, if Tom receives an offer less than $952,618.38, he could not obtain the same retirement benefit at the prevailing rate.

The present worth of Tom's business, $952,618.38, was substantially more than its present appraised value of $427,000. The difference of $525,618.38 is the value of the high growth rate over the next five years. Will a buyer be willing to pay Tom the value of five years of growth? It would be a risk for the buyer, but an investor looking for long-term growth might be interested.

EXAMPLE 8

Jennifer has some land that she wants to sell. Bob, a prospective buyer, has made an offer of $75,000 down and $2,000 at the end of each month for the next three years. Sarah, another prospective buyer, proposes to pay cash. How much does Sarah need to offer in order to match Bob's offer, if Jennifer can invest the money at 5% compounded monthly?

SOLUTION

We might expect Sarah to match Bob's payments, which total $147,000. But this ignores the fact that Bob's offer does not give Jennifer the entire amount of money today, but Sarah's offer will. So we need to take interest into account over the next three years to see how Jennifer would do.

Bob's offer is a down payment today (whose present value is $75,000 today) plus a series of future payments. We would like to know the present value of the future series of payments. The variables are:

N = 3 × 12 = 36	I/Y = 5	P/Y = 12
PV = ???	PMT = –2000	FV = 0

Computing the present value, we find the future series of payments is worth $66,731.40. Adding this to the down payment of $75,000, we find that Bob's offer is worth $141,731.40 today. If Sarah's offer is more than this amount, her offer is capable of providing more principal and interest over the next three years than Bob's offer can provide.

In the previous example, the interest rate was actually a very important factor. With a change in interest rates, the value of Bob's offer will change. If, for example, Sarah offered $142,000 cash, we see that her offer would be better than Bob's when the interest rate is 5%. You might try to find out which offer would be better if the interest rate was 3%, or 10%.

In this section, we have analyzed only those situations which had a single series of payments. It is also possible to consider the present value of any investment proposal, which may have both an original outlay and a future value, as well as both increasing and decreasing payments of different sizes at various times. When numerous cash flows are involved, the present values of each are combined into a **net present value**, or **NPV**. Computations of NPV are possible with advanced financial calculators, but are beyond the scope of this course. They are important, though, for serious students of business analysis.

8.5 Effects of Inflation

All of us are aware that prices of goods and services are not the same from day to day. Gasoline prices fluctuate regularly, and prices of new cars always seem to increase. In the marketplace, supply and demand help determine prices of various goods and services. If the supply of an object is greater than the demand, prices will generally be low, in order to entice more purchasers to take up the excess supply. When the demand for an object is greater than the supply, prices will generally be high, as retailers can take advantage of the willingness of some customers to buy at higher prices, and not have excess quantities of merchandise on hand.

Consumers generally perceive inflation to be an increase in prices. Actually, **inflation** generally occurs when the increase in demand for goods and services is greater than the increase in the supply of goods and services. This may occur with an overly large increase in the money supply, or a sudden decrease in goods available for purchase. An increase in the money supply by itself may not cause inflation, if there is a corresponding increase in goods and services available for purchase.

In this course, we are concerned with the effect of inflation on the value of goods and services. Mathematically, the effect of inflation is the same as the effect of compound interest upon a lump sum deposit. Therefore, problems involving inflation can be treated as if they were lump sum deposits, using annual compounding. Consider the following example.

EXAMPLE 1

If a new sports car costs $49,995 today, what will a new sports car cost in ten years, if the price rise is completely attributable to 5% inflation?

SOLUTION

We first identify the variables.

$N = 10 \times 1 = 10$	$I/Y = 5$	$P/Y = 1$
$PV = 49995$	$PMT = 0$	$FV = ???$

Computing the future value, we obtain $81,436.59. Therefore, a new sports car will cost about $81,000 ten years from now.

We rounded the answer in the previous example, because the future value of an item after inflation should be considered an estimate at best. We certainly cannot predict the inflation rate for even next year, but the historical average rate of inflation is approximately 5% per year. If, however, inflation runs 4.9% one year and 5.1% the next, it turns out that prices have increased less (just slightly) than if inflation had been 5% each year. So inflation problems are not quite as precise as they might seem at first.

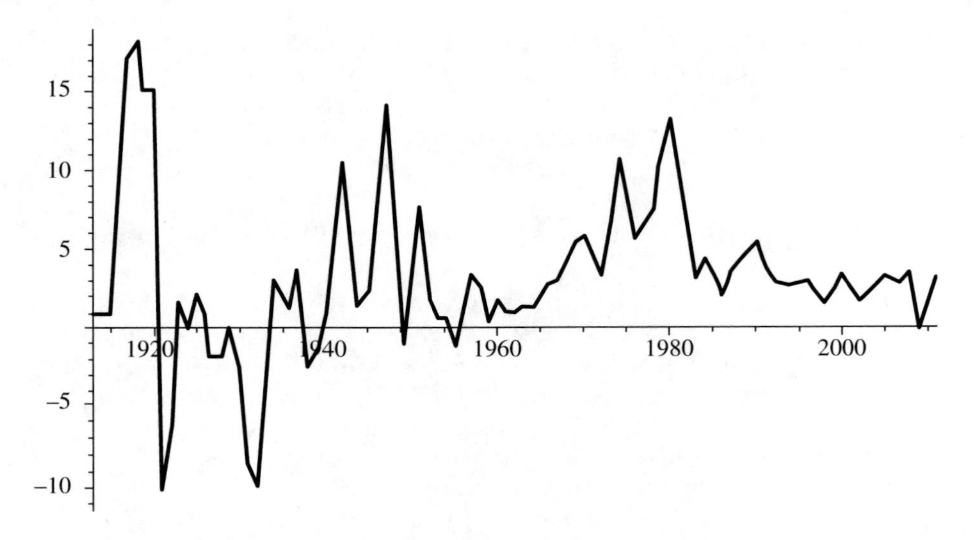

Figure 8.1 Inflation Rates (Changes in the Consumer Price Index)

We often think of inflation as having its primary effect on prices which consumers pay. Of course, inflation can also affect income (some retirement incomes excepted). In fact, regular increases in income (whether price inflation exists or not) can be handled in the same fashion. Consider the next example.

EXAMPLE 2

Cora is earning a salary of $36,500 this year. If she receives raises of 6% each year for the next twelve years, what will her salary be?

SOLUTION

We first identify the variables.

$N = 12 \times 1 = 12$	$I/Y = 6$	$P/Y = 1$
PV = 36500	PMT = 0	FV = ???

Solving for the future value, we obtain $73,445.17. In twelve years, Cora's salary will be about $73,400. In fact, if Cora's raises are exactly 6% each year, then theoretically her salary would be exactly $73,445.17. However, since her salary would be rounded to the nearest penny (or further) each year, the cumulative effects of rounding may cause her salary to be a few cents (or more) different.

Inflation problems can also occur where the newer value is known, and some other value is needed. The next two examples describe this situation.

EXAMPLE 3

Grandpa is always talking about prices in the good old days. If inflation has averaged 5% over the last 40 years, what was the price of a hamburger sandwich which sells for $3.59 today?

SOLUTION

We first identify the variables.

N = 40 × 1 = 40	I/Y = 5	P/Y = 1
PV = ???	PMT = 0	FV = –3.59

Solving for the present value, we find that forty years ago a hamburger sandwich would have cost about 51 cents.

EXAMPLE 4

Russia experienced some large increases in prices during the early 1990s. If a loaf of bread cost 5 rubles in 1992 and 270 rubles in 1995, what was the annual rate of inflation?

SOLUTION

We can treat rubles exactly as if they were dollars. The variables are:

N = 3 × 1 = 3	I/Y = ???	P/Y = 1
PV = 5	PMT = 0	FV = –270

Solving for the rate of interest, we obtain approximately 277.98%. That is, during that three-year period the price of a loaf of bread increased about 278% each year. The increase was about three times the original price each year, so that the new price was about four times the old price each year. In other words, the price almost quadrupled each year.

Excessively high inflation is known as **hyperinflation**, which may occur in conjunction with social or political upheavals. At these times, inflation rates may even be in the million or billion percent range.

For many years, Americans have lived in a society which has experienced some inflation each year. However, there have been times during our history where we have experienced **deflation** and prices have gone down, not up. In these situations, the variable I/Y will be a negative quantity.

EXAMPLE 5

Lonnie purchased his house for $185,000. Over the last six years, the housing market has become depressed, and the current market value of his house is $162,300. Find the rate of deflation experienced in this housing market.

SOLUTION

First, we identify the variables.

N = 6 × 1 = 6	I/Y = ???	P/Y = 1
PV = 185000	PMT = 0	FV = −162300

Computing I/Y, we obtain a value of approximately negative 2.16%. Housing prices have decreased about 2.16% per year in this market.

Inflation can have a serious effect on a retirement account. When prices increase, our savings will not go as far.

EXAMPLE 6

Pamela deposits $180 at the end of each month into an account earning 8% compounded monthly. What will the balance of the account be in thirty years, measured in today's dollars, if inflation is 3% per year?

SOLUTION

First, we must find the unadjusted future balance of the retirement account.

N = 30 × 12 = 360	I/Y = 8	P/Y = 12
PV = 0	PMT = 180	FV = ???

Computing the future value of this ordinary annuity, we find the balance will be $268,264.69. But these dollars are not available today. Essentially, the value in today's dollars is the same as the present value of the annuity, using a 3% per year prevailing rate. So we now compute the present worth of the $268,264.69 future balance.

N = 30 × 1 = 30	I/Y = 3	P/Y = 1
PV = ???	PMT = 0	FV = −268264.69

The present worth of the balance is $110,521.50. That is, the $268,264.69 which the account will hold in thirty years will buy only $110,521.50 of today's goods. Inflation eroded over half of the value of Pamela's account.

A common misconception is to assume that a 3% inflation rate will reduce the earning power of an 8% compounded monthly account to a 5% compounded monthly account. But this is not the case. Here are the values of the variables needed for Pamela to obtain a present worth of $110,521.50 in her account.

N = 30 × 12 = 360	I/Y = ???	P/Y = 12
PV = 0	PMT = 180	FV = −110521.50

Computing the value of I/Y, we find that Pamela's account earned an inflation adjusted 3.30% per year. This result is quite different than the simplistic 5% per year estimate found by subtracting. Once again, we see that inflation severely erodes the value of an investment.

Let us suppose, then, that we want to increase our payments according to the rate of inflation. That is, if inflation is 3% per year, then we want next year's payment to be 3% greater than this year's payment. Since the payments will be different each year, we will not be able to use the financial registers of a basic financial calculator. So we will set up our work in table form, in the same fashion that we did when we first discussed time value of money problems. In the following example, we will keep the number of periods small, so that our work is not too tedious.

EXAMPLE 7

Carla wants her savings plan to keep pace with the 3% annual inflation rate. She will deposit $2,000 into an account earning 8% compounded annually at the beginning of this year. Each future annual deposit will be 3% larger than the previous deposit. After four years, what is Carla's actual balance, and the present value of that balance? How does this plan compare to a no-inflation scenario?

SOLUTION

The 3% increases in the payment can be most easily found by multiplying by the augmented percent, 103%, in decimal form. The three future payments will be:

$$2000.00 \times 1.03 = 2060.00$$

$$2060.00 \times 1.03 = 2121.80$$

$$2121.80 \times 1.03 \approx 2185.45$$

We set up the computations in the following table. The deposits are the values given above. The new principal is the deposit plus the previous ending balance. Interest is computed on the principal with the simple interest formula. The new ending balance is the principal plus the interest.

Year	Deposit	Principal	Interest	Ending Balance
1	2000.00	2000.00	$2000.00 \times 0.08 \times 1 = 160.00$	2160.00
2	2060.00	4220.00	$4220.00 \times 0.08 \times 1 = 337.60$	4557.60
3	2121.80	6679.40	$6679.40 \times 0.08 \times 1 \approx 534.35$	7213.75
4	2185.45	9399.20	$9399.20 \times 0.08 \times 1 \approx 751.94$	10151.14

After four years, Carla's balance will be $10,151.14. To find the present value of Carla's account, we use the financial calculator to determine the amount needed to obtain the same future value, given a 3% interest rate compounded annually (to match the inflation rate).

$N = 4 \times 1 = 4$	$I/Y = 3$	$P/Y = 1$
$PV = ???$	$PMT = 0$	$FV = -10151.14$

The value of the account, in today's dollars, is $9,019.16.

So has Carla counteracted inflation by increasing her deposits with the rate of inflation? To know the answer to that question, we compute the value of her account having $2,000 deposits each year for four years, earning 8% compounded annually, but without inflation.

N = 4 × 1 = 4	I/Y = 8	P/Y = 1
PV = 0	PMT = 2000	FV = ???

This is a beginning annuity, and its future value is $9,733.20. Of course, when Carla increased her deposits, the final balance was higher. She had $10,151.14 instead of $9,733.20 after four years. But the 3% annual increase in the size of the deposit did not counteract the 3% inflation. Carla's purchasing power was reduced from $9,733.20 to $9,019.16, as measured in today's dollars.

Name: ______________________________ Date: __________

Exercises 8.1

∗ Find the total interest for each scenario.

	Type	Periods	Payment	Present Value	Future Value
1.	Lump Sum	60	$0	$8,000	$12,000
2.	Lump Sum	300	$0	$17,200.00	$24,733.55
3.	Savings Plan	240	$50	$0	$23,859.12
4.	Savings Plan	40	$200	$0	$9,553.31
5.	Savings Plan	72	$85	$3,000	$14,000
6.	Savings Plan	120	$130	$7,500	$32,000
7.	Withdrawals	96	$120	$8,000	$0
8.	Withdrawals	15	$2,000	$25,000	$0
9.	Withdrawals	36	$500	$85,000	$70,000
10.	Withdrawals	20	$4,000	$60,000	$14,000
11.	Loan	48	$239.95	$9,500	$0
12.	Loan	180	$957.44	$121,350	$0
13.	Loan	320	$894.55	$147,200	$13,500
14.	Loan	72	$349.12	$29,355	$9,247

∗∗ 15. Corinne invests $4,200 at 4.5% interest compounded daily. How much interest will she earn during the first five years?

16. Over the last 25 years, Tim's account earned 3.5% interest, compounded quarterly. Today, his account holds $25,000. How much of the balance was derived from interest?

17. Susan pays $60 at the end of each month into an annuity earning 4.7% interest compounded monthly. If she does this for forty years, how much interest will she earn?

18. Amanda deposits $80 at the beginning of each month into an account earning 3% compounded monthly. How much interest is earned during the first ten years?

19. Joshua's retirement account holds $800,000, and earns 7% compounded monthly. He makes withdrawals at the end of each month that will deplete the account in 20 years. How much interest will be earned during those 20 years?

20. Kimberly makes withdrawals of $350 at the beginning of each month from an account that earns 2.5% compounded monthly. If the account began with $15,000, how much interest is earned during the first two years?

21. Roxanne signed a $95,000 thirty-year mortgage at 8.75% interest If Roxanne makes the monthly payments according to the schedule, how much interest will she pay?

22. Terry took out a $12,000 loan for 36 months at 4.5% for the purchase of her new car. What was the finance charge?

***23. If $1,000 is deposited at 4.6% interest for five years, how much more interest will be earned if annual compounding is used, rather than simple interest?

24. Jean is purchasing a $120,000 house with a 20% down payment and a mortgage for the balance. How much interest would she save if she opts for a fifteen-year 8.5% mortgage instead of a thirty-year 9.5% mortgage?

Name: ______________________________ Date: ____________

Exercises 8.2

** 1. Carson borrows $8,750 for 4 years at 6% interest with monthly payments, but pays a $50 transaction fee. What is the effective rate of the loan?

2. Danae borrows $11,400 for 5 years at 7% interest with monthly payments, but pays a $100 transaction fee. What is the effective rate of the loan?

3. James borrows $5,300 for 6 months at 4% discount interest, and equal monthly payments are required. What is the effective rate of the loan?

4. Olivia borrows $7,200 for 4 months at 13% discount interest, and equal monthly payments are required. What is the effective rate of the loan?

5. Bethany wants to buy a $19,000 car. She will be making 48 monthly payments, and she has the choice of 0% interest or $4,000 cash back. If Bethany makes a down payment of $2,000, what is the effective rate of her loan?

6. Jason wants to buy a $27,300 truck. He will be making 72 monthly payments, and has the choice of 1.9% interest or $5,000 cash back. If Jason makes a down payment of $2,730, what is the effective rate of his loan?

7. Elias agrees to buy a car for payments of $79 per week for 234 weeks. If the car is valued at $8,520, what is the effective rate of his loan?

8. Vivian buys a $999 television for 91 weekly payments of $19.99. If the same television could have been purchased online for $749, what is the effective rate of her loan?

9. Amy borrows $769 at 14% interest to purchase a flute. She makes payments of $30 per month. How many payments will there be, and what will be the size of the final payment?

10. Sarah borrows $949 at 17% interest to purchase a cello. She makes payments of $35 per month. How many payments will there be, and what will be the size of the final payment?

11. Musial's Music has a $1,250 price on a bassoon. If the customer wants to use credit, the store is offering 15% interest for thirty months. Cash customers, however, get a 25% discount. What is the true annual percentage rate for the credit purchase?

12. Albertson's Auto Plaza has a $24,000 sticker price on a new automobile. They are offering 3.9% interest on sixty-month loans with 10% down, or $2,000 rebates for a cash purchase. What is the true annual percentage rate for the credit purchase?

Name: ______________________________ Date: __________

Exercises 8.3

* Find the overall rate of return for each situation.

1. A $2,000 deposit earns $400 interest.

2. A $400 deposit earns $2,000 interest.

3. A $500 deposit earns $37 interest.

4. A $600 deposit grows to $800.

Find the overall rate of return for each annuity.

	Periodic Payment	Interest Rate	Period	Time	Type
5.	$50	5%	monthly	8 years	ordinary
6.	$200	7%	quarterly	12 years	ordinary
7.	$1,200	6.5%	annually	20 years	due
8.	$800	9.75%	semiannually	9 years	due

Find the annual rate of return, or APY, for each situation.

9. 2.5% compounded quarterly.

10. 4% compounded monthly.

11. 5.3% compounded daily.

12. 4.82% compounded monthly.

13. A $1,500 investment grows to $2,750 in four years.

14. A $30,000 investment grows to $36,000 in eight years.

15. A $2,400 deposit earns $412.15 interest in three years.

16. A $918 deposit earns $236 interest in five years.

Find the nominal percentage rate for each APY.

17. APY is 3%, account is compounded monthly.

18. APY is 5%, account is compounded semiannually.

19. APY is 4.91%, account is compounded quarterly.

20. APY is 2.48%, account is compounded daily.

**21. John invests $4,000 at 6% compounded annually for seven years. What are his annual and overall rates of return?

22. Patricia's investment yielded $18,000 after ten years earning 5% compounded quarterly. What were her annual and overall rates of return?

23. Cory's investment grew from $1,500 to $2,255 in four years. What were his annual and overall rates of return?

24. Herman makes payments of $125 at the beginning of each month into an account earning 6% compounded monthly for 45 years. What is his overall rate of return?

25. Peter makes payments of $300 at the end of each quarter into an account earning 5.5% compounded quarterly for 25 years. What is his overall rate of return?

26. Kathleen's investment doubled in five years. Find her annual rate of return.

27. Eastside Bank's savings account pays 5.3% compounded quarterly. What is the Annual Percentage Yield of the account?

28. Commercial Bank pays 5.75% compounded daily. What APY can they advertise?

29. Dennis County Bank advertises a savings account having 5% APY. If interest is compounded daily, what is the nominal rate?

30. North Springs Bank wants to be able to advertise a 4% APY, but compound interest quarterly. What rate should they use?

31. The Carroll Street Bank is planning to change from quarterly compounding to daily compounding. If their current savings interest rate is 4.75%, what new rate would pay the same dollar amount of interest per year?

32. A competitor is paying 4.4% compounded daily. What rate, compounded quarterly, would provide the same APY?

***33. What will the overall rate of return be on a five year investment earning 6% APY?

34. What will the annual rate of return be on an investment whose overall rate of return is 48% over six years?

35. Is a 5% annual rate of return for five years the same as a 25% overall rate of return? Explain.

36. Suppose a $2,000, 12-month CD earns 4.6% interest compounded monthly. If withdrawn, six months interest is forfeited. If the account is closed after 8 months, what Annual Percentage Yield was received?

Name: ______________________________ Date: __________

Exercises 8.4

∗Find the present worth of each investment.

1. $16,000 at 14% compounded annually for five years, if the prevailing rate is 3% compounded monthly.

2. $5,200 at 18% compounded annually for three years, if the prevailing rate is 5% compounded quarterly.

3. $85,000 at 21% compounded annually for two years, if the prevailing rate is 4% compounded daily.

4. $4,800 at 9% compounded annually for four years, if the prevailing rate is 3.5% compounded semiannually.

Find the present value of each annuity.

	Periodic Payment	Interest Rate	Period	Time	Type
5.	$750	8%	quarterly	4 years	ordinary
6.	$85	11%	monthly	8 years	due
7.	$2,000	9.5%	annually	25 years	due
8.	$6,500	15%	semiannually	10 years	ordinary

** 9. An $8,000 four-year note is earning 9.5% interest compounded annually. Find the present worth of the note, if the prevailing rate is 4.25% interest compounded quarterly.

10. A $6,000 three-year note is earning 3.5% interest compounded annually. Find the present worth of the note, if the prevailing rate is 5.75% compounded quarterly.

11. What is the present worth of a 48-month CD worth $5,000 and earning 8% interest compounded daily, if the prevailing rate is 3.95% compounded quarterly?

12. George Beck's business is currently worth $157,290, and is growing at an annual rate of 9%. The prevailing rate of interest is only 3.2% compounded monthly. If George plans to sell the business within three years, what offer could he accept today without losing the future value of the business?

13. Landon is paying $220 per month for one year on a debt he owes. At 6% interest compounded monthly, what is the present value of the series of payments?

14. Michael's one-year rental agreement stipulates monthly payments of $650 per month, at the beginning of each month. If these payments are deposited in an account earning 5.25% interest compounded monthly, what is the present value of the series of payments?

15. Nora's pension will pay $450 at the end of each month for the next twenty years. What is the present value of the pension, if the interest rate is 6% compounded monthly?

16. Oscar wins the $1,000,000 prize in the state lottery. If the state pays out the prize money in twenty annual payments of $50,000 (at the beginning of each year) and the interest rate is 5% compounded annually, what is the present value of the prize?

17. Carl's three-year $22,500 car loan has monthly payments and earns 2.9% interest. What is the present value of the loan contract, if the prevailing rate is 7%?

18. Kendra's $86,500 15-year home mortgage earns 6.75% interest. What is the present value of the contract, if the prevailing rate is 9.5%?

19. Peter and Pamela are partners in a business. They wish to set up a retirement fund for their secretary. Peter agrees to set aside $100 at the end of each month for the next ten years. Pamela wishes to make a lump sum deposit. If each contribution can earn 4% interest compounded monthly, and the present values of the contributions of the two partners are to be equal, what amount should Pamela contribute today?

Name: ______________________________ Date: __________

Exercises 8.5

✳ Use your financial calculator to find each missing value.

	Current Price	Inflation Rate	Time	Future Price
1.	$600	5%	8 years	_____
2.	$950	2%	4 years	_____
3.	_____	2.5%	12 years	$30,000
4.	_____	6.75%	20 years	$1,000,000
5.	$100	3%	_____	$200
6.	$3,500	1.4%	_____	$4,500
7.	$1,000	_____	5 years	$2,000
8.	$800	_____	9 years	$940

✳✳ 9. If you can expect 4% cost-of-living adjustments to your annual salary each year for the next four years, what will your salary be then, if it is $31,000 per year now?

10. A certain sports car costs $24,000 today. If inflation averages 5% over the next ten years, how much will it cost in ten years?

11. If the price of tuition at a certain college rose from $21,000 per year to $28,500 per year over four years, what was the annual inflation rate?

12. Tom purchased his house for $185,800 three years ago, and just sold it for $225,800. What was the rate of increase in housing prices?

13. If inflation was 4% over the past eight years, how much did a $12 pizza cost eight years ago?

14. Suppose the average salary today is $30,000 per year, and inflation rates averaged 5% over the last forty years. What was the average salary during your grandfather's day, forty years ago?

15. If a loaf of bread costs $1.59 today, what would it cost in five years with 4% deflation?

16. Terry was earning $35,000 per year. After three years of 6% deflation, and cuts in salary to match, what will his salary be?

∗∗∗17. If inflation is 5%, then $50,000 ten years from now is worth how much in today's dollars?

18. During a trip to Germany in 1923 (a year of notorious hyperinflation), Hilda Wenk recorded in her diary that the price of a loaf of rye bread was 2,800 marks on June 15, and 85,000 marks on August 3. What was the inflation rate during that period?

19. If inflation is 6%, what interest rate compounded monthly do your investments need to earn to keep up with inflation?

20. Suppose inflation is 3%. Adjust the graph you made in problem 30 of section 7.2, so that the growth of the investment is given in constant dollars (i.e. all future values are in today's dollars). Then describe the effect inflation can have on a lump sum investment.

Name: ______________________________ Date: __________

Chapter 8 Review

Summary of Important Concepts

- ▲ Total Interest
- ▲ Effective Rates, APR
- ▲ Rates of Return, APY
- ▲ Present Worth
- ▲ Inflation

Exercises

1. How much interest (in dollars) will be earned on a $15,700 deposit at 4% interest compounded semiannually for nine years?

2. How much interest (in dollars) will be paid on a $12,000 car loan with 36 monthly payments, if the Annual Percentage Rate is 9.9%?

3. Matt borrows $18,300 for 8 years at 9% interest, and pays a $125 transaction fee. What is the effective rate of the loan?

4. Find the overall rate of return for a $725 deposit earning 3% interest compounded quarterly for five years.

5. Monthly payments of $160 are made at the end of each month into a pension fund earning 4.7% interest compounded monthly, for three years. Find the overall rate of return of this series of payments.

6. Find the Annual Percentage Yield of a savings account which pays 5% compounded monthly. Write your answer to the nearest hundredth of a percent.

7. Find the present value of an annuity which pays $900 per month for three years, if the interest rate is 6% compounded monthly.

8. Find the present worth of a $400,000 investment at 21% compounded annually for 5 years, if the prevailing rate is 4% compounded quarterly.

9. If the inflation rate is 6%, what will a $22,000 car cost twenty years from now?

Appendices

Besides the appendices included in the text, additional information can be found on the Business Math Corner website. Point your browser to http://www.milefoot.com/math/businessmath/. Here you will find

- Current Tax Information
- Historical FICA Information
- Historical FUTA Information
- FWT Information
- A Summary of Financial Calculators
- Specific Financial Calculator Information
- Identifying the Conventions Used by a Mystery Financial Calculator

Withholding Tax Tables

Federal Allowance Values - 2012	
Payroll Period	One Withholding Allowance
Weekly	$ 73.08
Biweekly	146.15
Semimonthly	158.33
Monthly	316.67
Annually	3,800.00

State Allowance Values - 2012	
Payroll Period	One Withholding Allowance
Weekly	$ 43.27
Biweekly	86.54
Semimonthly	93.75
Monthly	187.50
Annually	2,250.00

Tables for Percentage Method of Federal Withholding (For Wages Paid in 2012)

TABLE 1 – WEEKLY Payroll Period

(a) SINGLE person (including head of household)–
If the amount of wages (after subtracting withholding allowances) is: The amount of income tax to withhold is:

Not over $41 . . . $0

Over–	But not over		of excess over–
$41	–$209	10%	–$41
$209	–$721	$16.80 plus 15%	–$209
$721	–$1,688	$93.60 plus 25%	–$721
$1,688	–$3,477	$335.35 plus 28%	–$1,688
$3,477	–$7,510	$836.27 plus 33%	–$3,477
$7,510		$2,167.16 plus 35%	–$7,510

(b) MARRIED person (including head of household)–
If the amount of wages (after subtracting withholding allowances) is: The amount of income tax to withhold is:

Not over $156 . . . $0

Over–	But not over		of excess over–
$156	–$490	10%	–$156
$490	–$1,515	$33.40 plus 15%	–$490
$1,515	–$2,900	$187.15 plus 25%	–$1,515
$2,900	–$4,338	$533.40 plus 28%	–$2,900
$4,338	–$7,624	$936.04 plus 33%	–$4,338
$7,624		$2,020.42 plus 35%	–$7,624

TABLE 2 – BIWEEKLY Payroll Period

(a) SINGLE person (including head of household)–
If the amount of wages (after subtracting withholding allowances) is: The amount of income tax to withhold is:

Not over $83 . . . $0

Over–	But not over		of excess over–
$83	–$417	10%	–$83
$417	–$1,442	$33.40 plus 15%	–$417
$1,442	–$3,377	$187.15 plus 25%	–$1,442
$3,377	–$6,954	$670.90 plus 28%	–$3,377
$6,954	–$15,019	$1,672.46 plus 33%	–$6,954
$15,019		$4,333.91 plus 35%	–$15,019

(b) MARRIED person (including head of household)–
If the amount of wages (after subtracting withholding allowances) is: The amount of income tax to withhold is:

Not over $312 . . . $0

Over–	But not over		of excess over–
$312	–$981	10%	–$312
$981	–$3,031	$66.90 plus 15%	–$981
$3,031	–$5,800	$374.40 plus 25%	–$3,031
$5,800	–$8,675	$1,066.65 plus 28%	–$5,800
$8,675	–$15,248	$1,871.65 plus 33%	–$8,675
$15,248		$4,040.74 plus 35%	–$15,248

TABLE 3 – SEMIMONTHLY Payroll Period

(a) SINGLE person (including head of household)–
If the amount of wages (after subtracting withholding allowances) is: The amount of income tax to withhold is:

Not over $90 . . . $0

Over–	But not over		of excess over–
$90	–$452	10%	–$90
$452	–$1,563	$36.20 plus 15%	–$452
$1,563	–$3,658	$202.85 plus 25%	–$1,563
$3,658	–$7,533	$726.60 plus 28%	–$3,658
$7,533	–$16,271	$1,811.60 plus 33%	–$7,533
$16,271		$4,695.14 plus 35%	–$16,271

(b) MARRIED person (including head of household)–
If the amount of wages (after subtracting withholding allowances) is: The amount of income tax to withhold is:

Not over $338 . . . $0

Over–	But not over		of excess over–
$338	–$1,063	10%	–$338
$1,063	–$3,283	$72.50 plus 15%	–$1,063
$3,283	–$6,283	$405.50 plus 25%	–$3,283
$6,283	–$9,398	$1,155.50 plus 28%	–$6,283
$9,398	–$16,519	$2,027.70 plus 33%	–$9,398
$16,519		$4,377.63 plus 35%	–$16,519

TABLE 4 – MONTHLY Payroll Period

(a) SINGLE person (including head of household)–
If the amount of wages (after subtracting withholding allowances) is: The amount of income tax to withhold is:

Not over $179 . . . $0

Over–	But not over		of excess over–
$179	–$904	10%	–$179
$904	–$3,125	$72.50 plus 15%	–$904
$3,125	–$7,317	$405.65 plus 25%	–$3,125
$7,317	–$15,067	$1,453.65 plus 28%	–$7,317
$15,067	–$32,542	$3,623.65 plus 33%	–$15,067
$32,542		$9,390.40 plus 35%	–$32,542

(b) MARRIED person (including head of household)–
If the amount of wages (after subtracting withholding allowances) is: The amount of income tax to withhold is:

Not over $675 . . . $0

Over–	But not over		of excess over–
$675	–$2,125	10%	–$675
$2,125	–$6,567	$145.00 plus 15%	–$2,125
$6,567	–$12,567	$811.30 plus 25%	–$6,567
$12,567	–$18,796	$2,311.30 plus 28%	–$12,567
$18,796	–$33,038	$4,055.42 plus 33%	–$18,796
$33,038		$8,755.28 plus 35%	–$33,038

Tables for Percentage Method of State Withholding
(For Wages Paid in 2012)

TABLE 1 – WEEKLY Payroll Period

(a) SINGLE person (including head of household)–
If the amount of wages (after subtracting withholding allowances) is: Not over $58 . . . The amount of income tax to withhold is: $0

Over–	But not over		of excess over–
$58	–$346 . .	$0.00 plus 3.50%	–$58
$346	–$635 . .	$10.10 plus 6.25%	–$346
$635	. . . . . .	$28.13 plus 6.45%	–$635

(a) MARRIED person–
If the amount of wages (after subtracting withholding allowances) is: Not over $115 . . . The amount of income tax to withhold is: $0

Over–	But not over		of excess over–
$115	–$692 . .	$0.00 plus 3.50%	–$115
$692	–$1,269 . .	$20.19 plus 6.25%	–$692
$1,269	. . . . . .	$56.25 plus 6.45%	–$1,269

TABLE 2 – BIWEEKLY Payroll Period

(a) SINGLE person (including head of household)–
If the amount of wages (after subtracting withholding allowances) is: Not over $115 . . . The amount of income tax to withhold is: $0

Over–	But not over		of excess over–
$115	–$692 . .	$0.00 plus 3.50%	–$115
$692	–$1,269 . .	$20.19 plus 6.25%	–$692
$1,269	. . . . . .	$56.25 plus 6.45%	–$1,269

(b) MARRIED person–
If the amount of wages (after subtracting withholding allowances) is: Not over $231 . . . The amount of income tax to withhold is: $0

Over–	But not over		of excess over–
$231	–$1,385 . .	$0.00 plus 3.50%	–$231
$1,385	–$2,538 . .	$40.38 plus 6.25%	–$1,385
$2,538	. . . . . .	$112.50 plus 6.45%	–$2,538

TABLE 3 – SEMIMONTHLY Payroll Period

(a) SINGLE person (including head of household)–
If the amount of wages (after subtracting withholding allowances) is: Not over $125 . . . The amount of income tax to withhold is: $0

Over–	But not over		of excess over–
$125	–$750 . .	$0.00 plus 3.50%	–$125
$750	–$1,375 . .	$21.88 plus 6.25%	–$750
$1,375	. . . . . .	$60.94 plus 6.45%	–$1,375

(b) MARRIED person–
If the amount of wages (after subtracting withholding allowances) is: Not over $250 . . . The amount of income tax to withhold is: $0

Over–	But not over		of excess over–
$250	–$1,500 . .	$0.00 plus 3.50%	–$250
$1,500	–$2,750 . .	$43.75 plus 6.25%	–$1,500
$2,750	. . . . . .	$121.88 plus 6.45%	–$2,750

TABLE 4 – MONTHLY Payroll Period

(a) SINGLE person (including head of household)–
If the amount of wages (after subtracting withholding allowances) is: Not over $250 . . . The amount of income tax to withhold is: $0

Over–	But not over		of excess over–
$250	–$1,500 . .	$0.00 plus 3.50%	–$250
$1,500	–$2,750 . .	$43.75 plus 6.25%	–$1,500
$2,750	. . . . . .	$121.88 plus 6.45%	–$2,750

(b) MARRIED person–
If the amount of wages (after subtracting withholding allowances) is: Not over $500 . . . The amount of income tax to withhold is: $0

Over–	But not over		of excess over–
$500	–$3,000 . .	$0.00 plus 3.50%	–$500
$3,000	–$5,500 . .	$87.50 plus 6.25%	–$3,000
$5,500	. . . . . .	$243.75 plus 6.45%	–$5,500

Table of Days

Day	Jan	Feb	Mar	Apr	May	Jun	Jul	Aug	Sep	Oct	Nov	Dec	Day
1	1	32	60	91	121	152	182	213	244	274	305	335	1
2	2	33	61	92	122	153	183	214	245	275	306	336	2
3	3	34	62	93	123	154	184	215	246	276	307	337	3
4	4	35	63	94	124	155	185	216	247	277	308	338	4
5	5	36	64	95	125	156	186	217	248	278	309	339	5
6	6	37	65	96	126	157	187	218	249	279	310	340	6
7	7	38	66	97	127	158	188	219	250	280	311	341	7
8	8	39	67	98	128	159	189	220	251	281	312	342	8
9	9	40	68	99	129	160	190	221	252	282	313	343	9
10	10	41	69	100	130	161	191	222	253	283	314	344	10
11	11	42	70	101	131	162	192	223	254	284	315	345	11
12	12	43	71	102	132	163	193	224	255	285	316	346	12
13	13	44	72	103	133	164	194	225	256	286	317	347	13
14	14	45	73	104	134	165	195	226	257	287	318	348	14
15	15	46	74	105	135	166	196	227	258	288	319	349	15
16	16	47	75	106	136	167	197	228	259	289	320	350	16
17	17	48	76	107	137	168	198	229	260	290	321	351	17
18	18	49	77	108	138	169	199	230	261	291	322	352	18
19	19	50	78	109	139	170	200	231	262	292	323	353	19
20	20	51	79	110	140	171	201	232	263	293	324	354	20
21	21	52	80	111	141	172	202	233	264	294	325	355	21
22	22	53	81	112	142	173	203	234	265	295	326	356	22
23	23	54	82	113	143	174	204	235	266	296	327	357	23
24	24	55	83	114	144	175	205	236	267	297	328	358	24
25	25	56	84	115	145	176	206	237	268	298	329	359	25
26	26	57	85	116	146	177	207	238	269	299	330	360	26
27	27	58	86	117	147	178	208	239	270	300	331	361	27
28	28	59	87	118	148	179	209	240	271	301	332	362	28
29	29		88	119	149	180	210	241	272	302	333	363	29
30	30		89	120	150	181	211	242	273	303	334	364	30
31	31		90		151		212	243		304		365	31
Day	Jan	Feb	Mar	Apr	May	Jun	Jul	Aug	Sep	Oct	Nov	Dec	Day

During leap years (2012, 2016, 2020, 2024, etc.), February 29 is day 60, and 1 should be added to each day number after that date.

Formulas for Compound Interest and Annuities

For those who wish or need to program a calculator or computer (or for those who are curious about the computations occurring behind the calculator window), we present the algebraic formulas. The standard sign convention is used in these formulas. Basically, this means that deposits and present values are positive numbers, but withdrawals and future values are negative numbers. The variables used in the formulas have the following definitions:

A = future value
N = number of periods
I = periodic interest rate
P = present value
M = periodic payment
k = 0 for an ordinary annuity, 1 for an annuity due
(Either value of k can be used for a lump sum deposit.)

For lump sum deposit problems (when the payment is zero), the algebraic formulas are:

$$A = P(1+i)^N \qquad N = \frac{\log\left(\frac{A}{P}\right)}{\log(1+i)}$$

$$P = \frac{A}{(1+i)^N} \qquad i = \left(\frac{A}{P}\right)^{\frac{1}{N}} - 1$$

For annuity problems (with non-zero payments), the formulas are:

$$A = \left[P + \frac{M(1+ki)}{i}\right][1-(1+i)^N] - P \qquad M = \frac{1}{1+ki}\left[\frac{i(A+P)}{1-(1+i)^N} - iP\right]$$

$$P = \left[A - \frac{M(1+ki)}{i}\right]\left[1 - \frac{1}{(1+i)^N}\right] - A \qquad N = \frac{\log\left[\frac{M(1+ki)-iA}{M(1+ki)+iP}\right]}{\log(1+i)}$$

The lump sum deposit formulas are actually special cases of the annuity formulas.

The solution of an annuity problem for the interest rate involves the following large degree polynomial equation:

$$[P + Mk](1+i)^{N+1} + [M - Mk - P](1+i)^N + [A - Mk](1+i) + [Mk - M - A] = 0$$

In order to solve this equation for I, an approximation method must be used, since no exact algebraic method exists. The following algorithm is an application of Newton's Method.

Let $B = 1$

Let $C = 1.1$

While $|B - C| \geq 0.00001$

Let $B = C$

Let $D = [P + Mk]B^{N+1} + [M - Mk - P]B^N + [A - Mk]B + [Mk - M - A]$

Let $E = [N+1][P + Mk]B^N + N[M - Mk - P]B^{N-1} + [A - Mk]$

Let $C = B - \frac{D}{E}$

End While

Let $I = C - 1$

If you do not have a financial calculator then you will need to make use of these formulas.

If your calculator has an equation solver, you will need to store only the first annuity equation in your calculator's memory. The calculator will then be able to solve that equation for any of the variables.

If your calculator is programmable, but does not have an equation solver, you will need to obtain or write a program using all the formulas and the algorithm for finding the interest rate.

If your calculator is not programmable and does not have an equation solver, then you will need to know and use the formulas in your computations.

Answers to Selected Exercises

Exercises 1.1

1. 5
3. 6
5. 0.5
7. 700,000
9. $\frac{8}{11}$
11. $\frac{6}{13}$
13. 275,384.65
15. 275,384.6
17. $\frac{147}{50}, 2\frac{47}{50}$
19. $2.125, 2\frac{1}{8}$
21. $7.8, \frac{39}{5}$

Exercises 1.2

1. $\frac{5}{2}$
3. $\frac{1}{4}$
5. $\frac{25}{73}$
7. $\frac{2}{5}$
9. $\frac{8}{21}$
11. $\frac{143}{10}$
13. $\frac{64}{105}$
15. $\frac{2}{3}$
17. $\frac{34}{35}$
19. $\frac{8}{7}$
21. 19.723
23. 4.65117
25. 6
27. 4
29. probably 4
31. 150,000
33. 0.03
35. 20
37. 10,800
39. 12

Exercises 1.3

1. CA: \$43,000, KS: \$40,000
3. CT, \$56,000
5. 3,000
7. 24,000,000
9. Vertical scale begins at 15,000,000
11. 90%

Exercises 1.4

1. mean = 28, median = 28, mode = 28
3. mean 63.625, median 63, modes 57,83
5. 230 thousand metric tons
7. 230–240 and 240–250 thousand metric tons
9. 12th grade
11. 2.5 persons
13. 2 persons

Exercises 1.5

1. 20
3. 2.22
5. 1.22
7. 41.225
9. 108 quarts
11. 23 lbs. 7 oz.
13. 153 sq. ft.
15. 14.8 lbs.
17. 548.89 pounds
19. 26,397 rupees
21. \$268.94
23. \$236.52

Chapter 1 Review

1. 200,000, 0.4, 0.0009
2. probably 6
3. $\frac{2}{7}$
4. $\frac{51}{25}, 2\frac{1}{25}$
5. 0.375
6. $\frac{55}{16}, 3.4375$
7. $\frac{3}{10}$
8. $\frac{27}{28}$
9. $\frac{187}{12}$
10. $\frac{3}{2}$
11. $\frac{29}{24}$
12. 15.2143
13. 0.2252634
14. 340,344.8
15. 240,000
16. 38
17. 25%
18. mean = 32.4, median = 27, mode = 27
19. 16.8

Exercises 2.1

1. adults
3. factory retail price
5. Out of every 100 convicted bank robbers, there were 20 repeat offenders.
7. For every 100 units of current tailpipe emissions, new cars will produce an average of 80 units less.
9. Out of every 100 units of nitrogen oxide pollution, autos were the cause of about 22 units.
11. Out of every 100 businesses, 90 are small or mid-sized; and out of every $100 of value produced nationally, $50 of value was produced by small or mid-sized businesses.
13. For every $100 of previous salary and benefits, almost $6 in increases were provided.
15. For every $100 in previous profits, there is an increase in $55.40 in new profits.

Exercises 2.2

1. 0.46
3. 1.72
5. 0.0729
7. 0.0275
9. $\frac{37}{100}$
11. 7
13. $\frac{249}{1000}$
15. $\frac{19}{250}$
17. 68%
19. 0.34%
21. 1260%
23. 40%
25. $58\frac{1}{3}\%$
27. 355%

Exercises 2.3

1. 20.7
3. 24%
5. 123.37
7. 4.21%
9. 15,500 people
11. $12,500
13. $2,467.50
15. $63,636.36

Exercises 2.4

1. 100%, 114%, $756, $6156
3. 100%, 131%, $212.31, $65.82
5. 100%, 43%, $147.54, $63.44
7. 100%, 25%, $17.38, $86.88
9. 100%, 151%, $67.06, $101.27
11. 100%, 54%, $1435.19, $660.19
13. 100%, 27.78%, 127.78%, $46
15. 100%, 16.67%, 83.33%, $65
17. 100%, 27.59%, 72.41%, $16
19. $36,842.40
21. $23.96
23. $284.29
25. 44.96%
27. 6.45%
29. no

Exercises 2.5

1. 29.92% increase 3. 2.96% increase 5. 88% decrease 7. 43.6528% decrease 9. 59.51% decrease 11. 6.54% increase 13. 9.62% decrease 15. 44% 17. 27.1% 19. 14.29%

Chapter 2 Review

1. Of every 100 trucks on the road, 46 have poorly adjusted brakes.
2. $0.2307, \frac{2307}{10000}$
3. 8.6%
4. 62.5%
5. 2187.5
6. 763.64%
7. 495.36
8. 100%, 95.2%, $154.73, $7.43
9. 154.22 million
10. $45,370.37
11. $173,000
12. 16.41%
13. 17.65%

Exercises 3.1

1. $3,250 3. $1,059.62 5. $874.62 7. $1,175 9. $35,620 11. $3,141.67 13. $1,121.25 15. $877 17. $856.15 19. $36,792 21. $230.10 23. $336.90 25. $368.08 27. $373.94 29. $340.00 31. $429.44 33. $655 per week 35. $438.55 37. $650.00 39. no 41. no

Exercises 3.2

1. $23,968 3. $1,280 5. $2,029.23 7. $721.68 9. $1,152 11. $1,102.50 13. $32,571 15. $555 17. $1,569.25 19. $1,230.67 21. $557.28 23. $37.98 25. $204.75 27. $166.75

Exercises 3.3

1. $15.05, $5.20 3. $51.46, $17.77 5. $0, $36.74 7. $4.78, $17.17 9. $46.64, $22.31 11. $52.35, $18.07 13. $0.24, $32.78 15. $0, $7.69 17. $50.65, $23.04 19. $87.99, $30.38 21. $9.83, $19.36 23. $105.74 25. $22.72, $9.50 27. $60.35, $47.24 29. $2.74, $46.54 31. $6.41, $57.30 33. $8.60, $103.76

Exercises 3.4

1. $17.50, $25.81 3. $88.39, $29.04 5. $95.67, $39.98 7. $1,337.79, $386.56 9. $138.23, $56.03 11. $694.23, $228.85 13. $1,748.13, $486.27 15. $36.99, $20.24 17. $61.27, $45.65 19. $127.48, $49.65

Exercises 3.5

1a. $1,451.13 1b. 14.64% 1c. $1,918.45 1d. 75.64%
3a. $1,049.85 3b. 22.23% 3c. $1,453.28 3d. 72.24%

Chapter 3 Review

1. $596.31 2. $409.33 3. $2,439.70 4. $140
5. $138.04, $59.68 6. $3.13, $22.72 7. $2,583.95 8. $29.34, $130.07
9. $1,415.97, 26.46% 10. $3,019.47

Exercises 4.1

1.

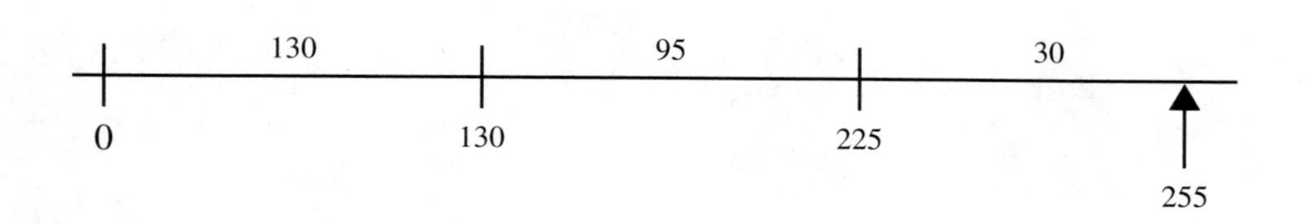

3.

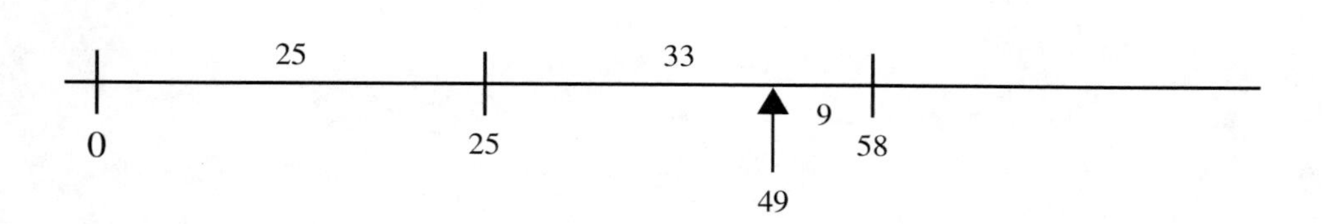

5. $119, $137 7. $107, $315 9. $148, $431 11. $13, $2.50
13. $352, $33 15. $296, $960 17. $438, $699 19. $295, $45
21. $712, $323, $90 23. $180, $898, $678 25. $364, $0, $785 27. $795000, $55000
29. 28¢, 88¢ 31. $125.40, $345.40, $49.60
33. $18, $63, $4 35. $19.60, $44.10, $25.10, $5.50

Exercises 4.2

1. $68.75 3. $171.23 5. 43.3% 7. $336
9. $9.55 11. 46% discount, 54% cost
13. 37% discount, 63% cost 15. 32.3125% discount, 67.6875% cost
17. $48 19. $17.50 21. 60.40% 23. $7.16
25. $271.43 27. second supplier 29. 10%, 46% 31. 6.12%, 43.67%
33. no

Exercises 4.3

1. Nov. 8
3. May 12, 2012
5. March 15, 2014
7. May 15, 2016
9. Apr. 24, May 14
11. June 13, June 28
13. Oct. 21 and Oct. 31 for discounts, Nov. 10 for net
15. Feb. 10, Mar. 2
17. Oct. 10, Oct. 30
19. Jan. 10, Jan. 30
21. Sep. 14, Oct. 4
23. Mar. 31, Apr. 20
25. yes
27. no
29. $21,380
31. $11,642.40
33. $3,552.50
35. Feb. 10: $970.58
    Feb. 20: $979.98
    Mar. 7: $989.37
37. 5 days after goods received: $1,095.87
    25 days after goods received: $1106.43

Exercises 4.4

1. $425
3. $800
5. $134.55
7. $441.82
9. 86.33%
11. 51.27%
13. $27
15. $341.43
17. $21.62
19. $2.24
21. 76.92%
23. 54.91%
25. 35% on cost

Exercises 4.5

1. $87.63, $2.63
3. $5.38, $0.43
5. $3.61
7. $1.24
9. $103.09
11. $74.12
13. $0.37

Exercises 4.6

1. $371.25
3. $500
5. 27.45%
7. $30.39
9. $1,046.50
11. 16.67%
13. $162.48
15. $20.45, 43.77%
17. 20.91%
19. 17.71%

Exercises 4.7

1. $2.06, $41.33
3. $179.53, $13.02
5. $296.19, $308.63
7. 5.99%, $40.51
9. 3.52%, $0.44
11. $9.88, 5.47%
13. $147.01
15. $2.41
17. 7.23%
19. $3.226

Exercises 4.8

1. net profit $77,863
3. cost of goods sold: 37.84%
   gross profit: 62.16%
   operating expenses: 60.12%
   net profit: 2.05%
5. 37.84%
7. 62.16%
9. net sales: 4.02%, cost of goods sold: 5.80%, operating expenses: 4.80%, net profit: (31.92%)

Chapter 4 Review

1. $793.50
2. $165
3. 38.8%
4. 44.625%
5. July 13
6. June 30
7. 70%, 100%, $50.63, $21.70
8. $270.32
9. $146.15
10. 30% on selling price
11. 96¢
12. $21.96
13. $65.26 loss
14. 40.60%
15. $89.21
16. net profit: $9991, 2.11%

Exercises 5.1

1. total assets: $151,646
   owner's equity: $75,816
3. current assets: 29.51%
   fixed assets: 70.49%
   current liabilities: 20.15%
   long-term liabilities: 34.81%
   owner's equity: 45.04%
5. total assets: 3.30%
   total liabilities: (2.62%)
   owner's equity: 11.58%

Exercises 5.2

1. $1,015
3. $1,175
5. $1,095
7. $1,264
9. $1,332
11. $1,253.03
13. $2,400
15. $2,041
17. $2,279.55
19. $2,953
21. $2,416

Exercises 5.3

1. $3,133
3. $7,500
5. $9,789
7. $4,928
9. $19,050
11. $10,938

Exercises 5.4

1. $30,880
3. $12,600
5. $7,500
7. $6,125

Exercises 5.5

1. 3.23, 1.46
3. 5.85%, 54.70%
5. 5.19, 70 days
7. 0.35
9. 18.01%
11. 1.06
13. 2.05%
15. 3.96
17. 5.28%
19. 0.60
21. 0.29%
23. 5.51
25. 2.53, 144 days

Chapter 5 Review

1. total assets: 7.86%, total liabilities: (4.32%), owner's equity: 23.71%
2. $92.76
3. $85.41
4. $89.01
5. $1,700
6. $24,600
11. current ratio: 2.23, inventory turnover ratio: 2.02, return on equity: 8.84%

Exercises 6.1

1. 149 days
3. 402 days
5. 1,352 days
7. $23.60
9. $221,693.13
11. $931.18
13. $90.75
15. $5.18
17. $365.76
19. $7.59
21. $11.82
23. $107.57
25. $18.75
27. $1,575
29. $3.86
31. $4.68
33. $290
35. $1.41
37. $474.30
39. $0.51

Exercises 6.2

1. $2,708.33
3. $16,911.29
5. $600
7. 7%
9. 4.25%
11. 9 years
13. 37 days
15. $2,536.23
17. $1,821.43
19. 11.79%
21. 3.19%
23. 7.4 years
25. 259 days
27. 28.6 years

Exercises 6.3

1. $7,438.20, $32,738.20
3. $47,329.28, $47,503.75
5. 14.20%, $933.89
7. 150 days, $512.02
9. 9%, $13,320
11. 5 years, $11,573.10
13. $95,405.33, 36 days
15. $2,400, 6%
17. $310.10, $334.90
19. $2,191.97, $160.44
21. $1,710
23. $689.63
25. Nov. 13, $104.17, $2,500, $2,604.17
27. Apr. 19, $1,800, $45,000, $46,800
29. Feb. 28, $400, $15,000, $15,400
31. $3,300
33. $5,950

Exercises 6.4

1. $166.36, $19,233.64
3. $8,042.49, $7,768.04
5. 19.12%, $806.95
7. 86 days, $848.98
9. 17.85%, $2,320
11. 9 months, $971.67
13. $65,722.45, 52 days
15. $3,884, 5.87%
17. $660.82, $19.82
19. $2,559.66, $187.35
21. $24,770.83
23. $3,277.85
25. Apr. 14, $682, $7,843, $8,525
27. $9,908.75
29. $4,565
31. $165.20, $7,578.55
33. $542.21, $15,957.79
35a. $566.04, $15,108.96
37a. $14,000, $14,026.13, $14,074.13
37b. 34.06%
37c. 31.23%

Exercises 6.5

1. 12.5%
3. 9.41%
5. 9.32%
7. 13.18%
9. 15.23%
11. 9.00%
13. 18.43%
15. 17.01%
17. 21.72%

Exercises 6.6

1. $4,369.28 payment on June 15
3. $6,410.40 payment on May 7
5. $14,468.91 payment on Aug. 24
7. $5,164.25 payment on July 15
9. $8,263.26 payment on May 17
11. $2,698.45
13. $5,358.66
15. $4,168.02
17. $2,609.49
19. $9,659.04

Chapter 6 Review

1. $1,120
2. $105.42
3. $15.04
4. 3.97 years
5. 279 days
6. 3.74%
7. $21,212.12
8. July 28, $36, $2,400, $2,436, 6.08%
9. Mar. 15, $203.42, $5,296.58, $5,500, 9.35%
10. $3,431.37
11. $1,851.43
12. 12.81%
13. $39.09, $2809.24
14. $3,328.89
15. $1,694.52

Exercises 7.1

1. $562.43
3. $378.67
5. $6,367.20
7. $905.97
9. $4,977.99
11. $443.11
13. PV = 1200
15. N = 6, P/Y = 1
17. I/Y = 2.4, P/Y = 12
19. PV = 2000
21. FV = 0
23. PMT = –80
25. N = 4, I/Y = 3, P/Y = 1, PV = 400, PMT = 0, FV = ???
27. N = 36, I/Y = 4, P/Y = 2, PV = ???, PMT = 0, FV = 100
29. N = 20, I/Y = ???, P/Y = 4, PV = 1592, PMT = 0, FV = 1844
31. N = 45, I/Y = 2.5, P/Y = 52, PV = 0, PMT = 10, FV = ???
33. N = 96, I/Y = 11, P/Y = 12, PV = 124000, PMT = –1180.89, FV = ???

Exercises 7.2

1. $1,352.19
3. $21,519.77
5. 23.19 years
7. 3.71%
9. $103.55
11. $5,204.59
13. 6.59 years
15. 83.90%
17. $1,025.26
19. $1,073.24
21. $2,127.59, $66.81
23. 13.95 years

Exercises 7.3

1. $23,252
3. $35,493.39
5. $1,808.77
7. $189.55
9. 18.9 years
11. 9.58%
13. $2,531.47
15. $13,325.77
17. $16,469.87
19. $91,523.93
21. $883.52
23. 11.25%
25. 11.95 years
27. $5,680.17
29. $12,109.60
31. $1,335,300.62
33. 5.43 years

Exercises 7.4

1. $23,566.20
3. $5,128.20
5. $434,285.68
7. 12.54 years
9. 8.44%
11. $2,920.02
13. 29.93 years
15. $4,685.00
17. $79,873.81
19. 29.58 years
21. forever
23. 25.11 years

Exercises 7.5

1. $1,014.21
3. $969.64
5. $27,595.82
7. $19,774.25
9. $11,882.60
11. 15.89 years
13. 7.60%
15. $1,086.20
17. $55,486.29
19. $367.02
21. $1,751.28
23. $135,866.75
25. 11.81%
27. 14.55 years
29. $61,373.40
31. $13,317.93
33. $163,658.24

Chapter 7 Review

1. $457.10
2. $4,768.90
3. 14.26 years
4. 7.58%
5. $4,855.21
6. $375,358.87
7. 12.9 years
8. $3,598.07
9. $47,510.43
10. $31,567.90
11. $261.51
12. 15.55 years
13. $1,394.04
14. 16.86%

Exercises 8.1

1. $4,000
3. $11,859.12
5. $4,880
7. $3,520
9. $3,000
11. $2,017.60
13. $152,556
15. $1,059.68
17. $55,906.99
19. $688,573.60
21. $174,053.20
23. $22.16

Exercises 8.2

1. 6.29%
3. 6.96%
5. 13.84%
7. 40.30%
9. 31 payments, $19.06
11. 40.58%

Exercises 8.3

1. 20%
3. 7.4%
5. 22.65%
7. 106.74%
9. 2.52%
11. 5.44%
13. 16.36%
15. 5.42%
17. 2.96%
19. 4.82%
21. 6%, 50.36%
23. 10.73%, 50.33%
25. 112.23%
27. 5.41%
29. 4.88%
31. 4.72%
33. 33.82%
35. no

Exercises 8.4

1. $26,520.48
3. $114,880.95
5. $10,183.28
7. $20,668.30
9. $9,711.94
11. $5,883.65
13. $2,556.16
15. $62,811.35
17. $21,159.37
19. $9,877.02

Exercises 8.5

1. $886.47
3. $22,306.68
5. 23.45 years
7. 14.87%
9. $36,265.62
11. 7.93%
13. $8.77
15. $1.30
17. $30,695.66
19. 5.84%

Chapter 8 Review

1. $6,723.47
2. $1,919.04
3. 9.19%
4. 16.12%
5. 7.17%
6. 5.12%
7. $29,583.91
8. $850,274.92
9. $70,556.98

Index